Amenability of Discrete Groups by Examples

Mathematical
Surveys
and
Monographs

Volume 266

Amenability of Discrete Groups by Examples

Kate Juschenko

AMERICAN
MATHEMATICAL
SOCIETY
Providence, Rhode Island

2020 *Mathematics Subject Classification.* Primary 20-03, 20L99, 22-02.

For additional information and updates on this book, visit
www.ams.org/bookpages/surv-266

Library of Congress Cataloging-in-Publication Data

Cataloging-in-Publication Data has been applied for by the AMS.
See http://www.loc.gov/publish/cip/.
DOI: https://doi.org/10.1090/surv/266

Contents

Preface

This book aims to treat all currently known examples of amenable groups and techniques behind proving amenability. We do not elaborate on any examples of non-amenable groups in detail (except free groups); rather, we list all known examples of non-amenable groups which do not contain free groups in the Introduction.

The subject of amenability has its roots in measure theory. In 1904, Lebesgue asked whether a finitely additive translation-invariant measure defined on all Lebesgue measurable sets is necessarily the Lebesgue measure. This question was answered negatively by Banach. The core of his proof is the Hahn-Banach theorem and a connection between finitely additive measures and means. This essentially led to a first example of an amenable group: the group of real numbers.

The next step in the development of amenability was the Hausdorff paradox. It states that the unit sphere can be decomposed into finitely many pieces in a way that rotating these pieces around one can obtain two spheres. Hausdorff showed that the non-abelian free group on two generators (which is now considered a canonical example of a non-amenable group) is a subgroup of the group of rotations. It is easy to make a paradoxical decomposition of the free group itself. Having this decomposition in hand, Hausdorff pushed it to the action of the rotation group on the sphere, which implied his famous paradox.

Considering a unit ball and projecting each point of the ball (except the center) onto the sphere, one obtains a paradoxical decomposition of the ball without a center. Notably, the entire ball admits a paradoxical decomposition if one allows use of rotations and translations in the rearranging of the sets. This counterintuitive paradox was proved by Banach and Tarski in 1929. A strong version of the Banach-Tarski paradox claims that any bounded set with non-empty interior can be decomposed and rearranged to any other bounded set with non-empty interior. This is striking, as it implies that a tiny pea that can be decomposed to the sun.

In 1929, von Neumann extracted an essential property of the group that forbids paradoxical decomposition: the existence of an invariant mean. He coined a German name "meßbar", which translates to English as "measurable". Studying the properties of meßbar groups, he showed that this class is closed under taking natural group operations: subgroups, extensions, quotients, and direct limits. Moreover, it contains all finite and abelian groups. This immediately explained why the Banach-Tarski paradox is impossible in the two dimensional case, where the rotation group is solvable.

In 1957, Day gave an English term "amenable" as analog of von Neumann's "meßbar" groups. He defined the class of elementary amenable groups as the smallest class of groups containing all finite groups and abelian groups, and closed under taking subgroups, extensions, quotients, and direct limits. No substantial progress in understanding this class was made until the '80s, when Chou showed that all

elementary amenable groups have either polynomial or exponential growth, and
Grigorchuk gave an example of a group with intermediate growth. Grigorchuk's
group served as a starting point in developing the theory of groups with intermediate growth, all of them being non-elementary amenable (it is easy to show that
all non-amenable groups have exponential growth).

The class of non-elementary amenable groups of exponential growth challenged
many mathematicians. One of the primary difficulties is that the amenability for
these groups does not come for free, as it does for the subexponential growth groups.
Additionally, proving that these groups are not elementary amenable can be alge-
braically difficult for a given group. An important class of groups containing many
non-elementary amenable groups of exponential growth is the class of automata
groups. The first example of a non-elementary amenable group with exponential growth is the Basilica group introduced by Grigorchuk and Zuk. Furthermore, amenability of the Basilica group is a technically difficult problem solved by
Bartholdi and Virág in 2005. In 2009, Bartholdi, Nekrashevych, and Kaimanovich
demonstrated the amenability of the group of bounded automata of finite state,
which as a consequence gives another proof of amenability of the Basilica group. In
2010, this result was extended to automata of linear activity by Amir, Angel, and
Virág. In 2012, Monod and the author showed that the topological full group of
a Cantor minimal system is amenable. By results of Matui in 2006, these groups
have a simple and finitely generated commutator subgroup; in particular, it is not
elementary amenable, giving the first examples of simple finitely generated infinite
and amenable groups. In 2013, Nekrashevych, de la Salle, and the author produced
a unified proof of amenability of all known examples of amenable groups. This
approach further covers amenability of automata groups of quadratic activity. In
2016, Nekrashevych [117] found subgroups of topological full groups which give
examples of simple Burnside groups of intermediate growth.

*   *   *

The purpose of this monograph is to give an introduction to amenability of
discrete groups and provide a self-contained presentation of all currently known
amenable groups. The techniques that are used for proving amenability in this
book are largely based on the recent work of my collaborators and myself, which
is mainly a combination of analytic and probabilistic tools with geometric group
theory. In this book, I do not cover all available material related to topological
groups; instead, I concentrate on treating examples of finitely generated amenable
groups and their properties.

The monograph was developed from a sequence of lectures on amenability that
I gave on different occasions in 2013–2017. This includes a winter school in CIRM at
Luminy; three graduate courses at Northwestern University in Evanston; a winter
school in Santiago de Chili; a summer school at Bernoulli Center in Lausanne; a
winter school in RIMS, Kyoto; a YMCA summer school; and an Israeli Women in
Mathematics meeting. Many open problems in the end of the book were discussed
during a workshop on amenability at American Institute of Mathematics in 2016.

I am grateful to many people who provided me with numerous comments on
the early drafts. I am thankful to Narutaka Ozawa and Stefaan Vaes for allowing
me to reproduce their unpublished proofs: lemma on recurrency implies extensive
amenability, and a group-theoretical reproof of the main result of [88]. I am very
grateful to Yves de Cornulier, Max Chorniy, Tsachik Gelander, Yair Glasner, Pierre

de la Harpe, Rostislav Grigorchuk, Rostyslav Kravchenko, Nicolas Monod, Vasco Schiavo, Emmanuel Rauzy, Anatoliy Vershik, and Tom Ward for providing useful remarks on all stages of the book. Nico Matte Bon, Nicolas Monod, and Mikael de la Salle had numerous discussions on the topic of extensive amenability with me, and I am truly grateful for opportunity to learn from them and their contribution to my understanding of the subject A very elegant proof of the growth dichotomy for elementary amenable groups was kindly provided by Phillip Wesolek and Pierre-Emmanuel Caprace. I thank to them for the opportunity to include it in the book. I thank to Volodia Nekrashevych for numerous discussions on the structure of the book, and support during the writing process.

CHAPTER 1

Introduction

The roots of the subject of amenability lie in measure theory. The notion of measure originated with Lebesgue in 1904, who defined a measure on the set of real numbers which is positive, countably additive and translation invariant. Lebesgue realized that the measure he defined is the unique such measure that satisfies the monotone convergence theorem. Recall that the monotone convergence theorem is equivalent to stating that the measure is countably additive. Thus the question of Lebesgue 1904, [**100**], can be formulated as:

Is it true that every finitely additive translation invariant measure, defined on all Lebesgue-measurable sets is necessarily the Lebesgue measure?

The question can be viewed as the first historical germ of amenability. Essentially this question is the same as the Ruziewicz problem for $\mathbb{R}$, posed by Banach in 1923, [**8**], where he answered it negatively. Using the Hahn-Banach theorem, he constructed a translation invariant, finitely additive measure on all subsets of the real numbers with a set of measure 1, whose Lebesgue measure is equal to zero, showing in particular that it is not the Lebesgue measure. In fact, this was one of the first applications of the Hahn-Banach theorem. Historically, the real numbers became the first example of what we would now call an amenable group. Of course at that time it was not phrased in terms of groups, but rather in terms of invariant under translation means.

The next development in amenability was the Hausdorff and Banach-Tarski paradoxes. Since not all bounded subsets of $\mathbb{R}^n$ are Lebesgue measurable, in 1914 Hausdorff asked the following question:

For a fixed $E \subseteq \mathbb{R}^n$, does there exist a finitely additive measure on $\mathbb{R}^n$ defined on all bounded subsets of $\mathbb{R}^n$, invariant under the action of the group of isometries giving the full weight to the set E.

This question was answered positively by Stefan Banach in 1923, [**8**], for the case when $n = 1, 2$ and E is an interval and unit square respectively. Hausdorff solved the question negatively for $n \geq 3$ by producing a paradoxical decomposition of the unit sphere, [**80**]. Namely, he showed the following:

The unit sphere can be decomposed into finitely many pieces, such that rotating those pieces we can obtain two unit spheres.

By projecting points of the unit ball except its center onto the sphere, this immediately implies the same paradox for the unit ball without its center. In 1929,

Banach and Tarski, [9], showed that there exists a decomposition of a ball into finitely many pieces such that by rotating and shifting each piece, we can obtain two balls of the same size as the original ball. The pieces are not solid in the usual sense, but rather are sets of points and some of the pieces are necessarily not Lebesgue measurable. Their work is based on Hausdorff's paradoxical decomposition and on an earlier work of Giuseppe Vitali, [153], who constructed the first example of non-Lebesgue measurable set. Vital's and Hausdorff's results are dependent on Zermelo's axiom of choice, which is also crucial for the Banach-Tarski paradox.

A stronger version of Banach-Tarski says that any bounded set with non-empty interior can be decomposed and rearranged into any other bounded set with non-empty interior. This paradox is also called the pea-to-Sun paradox:

We can obtain the Sun by cutting and moving around finitely many pieces of a tiny pea.

As it was shown by Banach in 1923, [8], the Banach-Tarski paradox fails in dimensions one and two. The difference between dimensions was conceptually explained by von Neumann: unlike the group of rotations of the 3-dimensional space, the groups of isometries of $\mathbb{R}$ and $\mathbb{R}^2$ are solvable and thus amenable. This was a crucial step in the further development of amenability. In 1929 von Neumann coined a German name "meßbar" which translates to English as "measurable", satisfying the following definition:

DEFINITION 1.1. A group G is amenable if there exists a finitely additive measure μ on all subsets of G with $\mu(G) = 1$ and satisfying

$$\mu(gE) = \mu(E)$$

for every $E \subseteq G$ and $g \in G$.

von Neumann showed that finite and abelian groups are amenable. Moreover, von Neumann showed that the class of amenable groups is closed under taking subgroups, quotients, extensions and direct limits. For a long time the only known examples of amenable and non-amenable groups were those that were introduced by von Neumann.

The monograph of Banach 1932, [6] (with English translation [7]), made an important correspondence between finitely additive measures and means. This served as one of the key tools for von Neumann, who primarily used the existence of translation invariant means on spaces of functions associated with a group as the definition of amenability. This dramatically changed the entire approach to amenability by shifting the subject to functional analysis.

The underlying idea of the Hausdorff and Banach-Tarski paradoxes is the presence of the free group on two generators in the group of rotations of the 3-dimensional Euclidean space. Tarski, in [147], showed that the groups satisfying Definition 1.1 are exactly those groups that do not admit a paradoxical decomposition.

As it was pointed out recently by Grigorchuk and de la Harpe, [72], that there are possible other independent origins of amenability due to Bogolyubov, [24] and [25], who was not aware of the work of von Neumann.

Day coined an English term "amenable" as an analog of von Neumann's "meßbar" and extended the notion to semigroups, [44]. He explicitly defined the class of elementary amenable groups to be the smallest class of groups that contain finite and abelian groups and which is closed under taking subgroups, quotients, extensions and direct limits. This is the largest class of groups whose amenability was known to von Neumann. Wondering whether there are other amenable groups, Day posed a problem in [**44**]:

Does there exists an amenable group which is not elementary amenable?

Because of the essential contribution of von Neumann, this problem is called von Neumann-Day problem. The large part of the work to understand the class of elementary amenable groups was done by Chou, [**37**], Milnor, [**110**], and Wolf, [**156**]. Chou shows, building on the works of Milnor and Wolf that every elementary amenable group has either polynomial or exponential growth. He further shows that the operations of taking subgroups and quotients are redundant in the definition of elementary amenability. The first example of group which is not of polynomial nor exponential growth (intermediate growth) was constructed by Grigorchuk in 1985, [**69**]. The group is automatically amenable, since all non-amenable groups have exponential growth. One of the consequences of Chou's result is that each infinite finitely generated simple group is not elementary amenable. The proof of amenability for groups that are not elementary amenable is always challenging. Currently available sources of such groups are:

- Groups of intermediate growth;
- Certain subgroups of automorphism group of rooted trees;
- Topological full groups of Cantor minimal systems.

There are several other non-elementary amenable groups, that are essentially build up from the listed class of groups. In [**70**], the finitely presented non-elementary amenable group is presented. It is an amenable HNN-extention of the first Grigorchuk group.

At the time of defining the notion of amenability, von Neumann noticed in [**126**], that the free group on two generators is not amenable. Since amenability passes to subgroups he posed the following problem, in 1929:

Does there exists a non-amenable group without free non-abelian subgroups?

The historically first candidate to provide the negative answer to this question was a group introduced by Thompson in 1965, which is today called the Thompson group F. While the question of its amenability is still an open problem, there are many examples with all imaginable properties showing the question has an affirmative answer. The very first such example is due to Ol'shanskii 1980, [**129**],. He produced a non-amenable group all of whose proper subgroups are cyclic. In 1983, Adyan showed that the free Burnside group $B(n, m)$ is not amenable for $m \geq 2$ and n odd with $n \geq 665$. None of these examples are finitely presented. In 2013, Ol'shanskii and Sapir, [**130**], produced a finitely presented non-amenable group without free non-abelian subgroups. A geometric method for constructing finitely generated non-amenable periodic groups was described by Gromov in [**76**].

Golod-Shafarevich groups were introduced in connection with the class field tower problem, which is a famous question of Furtwängler, posed in 1925, it remained open for 40 years. This problem asks whether the class field tower of any number field is finite. It was solved negatively by Golod and Shafarevich in 1964, [**63**]. Later Golod-Shafarevich groups found many applications in topology and group theory. Using these groups, Lubotzky, [**103**], solved a major open conjecture of Serre, which states that arithmetic lattices in $SL_2(\mathbb{C})$ fail to have the congruence subgroup property. Golod-Shafarevich groups gave the first counterexamples to the general Burnside problem, posed by Burnside in 1902, it asks whether a finitely generated group in which every element has finite order must necessarily be a finite group. Obviously, these groups do not contain non-abelian free groups. Ershov, [**54**], proved that Golod-Shafarevych groups have property (T), which infinite amenable groups can not have. This gives one more counterexample to the von Neumann problem. We refer to the detailed survey of Ershov, [**55**], for more on this subject.

In [**132**], Osin constructed a group without free subgroups, which has positive first l_2-Betti number. In particular, this implies that it is non-amenable.

Ghys and Carrière, [**60**], showed the equivalence relations generated by the action of $PSL_2(\mathbb{R})$ on the circle is not amenable. Using this, Monod showed that for a dense subring A of $\mathbb{R}$ the group of $PSL_2(A)$-piecewise homeomorphisms of the projective line which stabilizes infinity, denote by H, is not amenable, see [**114**]. The group H contains Thompson group F, however the action of Thompson's group F on $\mathbb{R}$ is amenable, which is one of the reasons why the problem of amenability of Thompson's group F is so challenging. The fact that Thompson's group F does not contain free groups can be generalized to the group H itself. While the group H is not finitely presented, it contains a non-amenable finitely presented subgroup, which contains Thompson group F in its turn, see [**102**].

This book does not intend to cover the entire field of amenability with it's numerous applications in mathematics. We also refer the reader to other sources on amenable groups, for example: [**59**], [**64**], [**133**], [**134**], [**138**], [**154**].

CHAPTER 2

The first germs of amenability:
Paradoxical decompositions

In this Chapter we discuss classical paradoxical decompositions: Hausdorff, Banach-Tarski and strong Banach-Tarski paradoxes. We refer to the book of Wagon, [154], for more on paradoxes. We refer the reader to the lecture notes of Gelander, [59], for a similar introduction to amenability that we give in the first chapters.

The starting point in the developments of paradoxical decompositions of group actions was the famous paradoxical decomposition of the sphere due to Hausdorff, [80]. He showed that the unit sphere can be decomposed into finitely many pieces in a way that rotating these pieces around one can obtain two unit spheres. The main reason why this paradox exists is the presence of the free group on two generators $\mathbb{F}_2$ in the group of rotations. Remarkably, Hausdorff was the first to find two rotations that generate $\mathbb{F}_2$. It is easy to see that $\mathbb{F}_2$ has a paradoxical decomposition while acting on itself. Moreover, if a group acts freely on a set and the left action of this group on itself is paradoxical, then the action is also paradoxical. Consider $\mathbb{F}_2$ as a subgroup of the group of rotations. The complement of the set of fixed points of the action of $\mathbb{F}_2$ on the sphere is free, therefore it can be paradoxically decomposed. Moreover, we will show that the complement of any countable set on the sphere can be decomposed into finitely many pieces which we can rotate and obtain the whole sphere. This outlines Hausdorff's proof.

Paradoxical decompositions constitute an essential step in the development of amenability. A group is called paradoxical if its left action on itself is paradoxical. In the later chapter we will prove a famous theorem of Tarski: a group is paradoxical if and only if it is not amenable.

Having Hausdorff's paradox in hand, one can project points of the unit ball onto the sphere and immediately obtain paradoxical decomposition of the unit ball without its center. Banach and Tarski, [9], showed that there exists a decomposition of a ball into finitely many pieces such that rotating and translating each piece we can obtain two balls of the size of the original ball. Certainly, the group of translations is also needed, since one needs to take care of the center of the ball.

The pieces from Banach-Tarski paradox are not solid in the usual sense, but rather sets of points, and some of the pieces are non-Lebesgue measurable. Therefore, the paradox can not have physical implications.

The work of Banach and Tarski is based on Hausdorff paradox and on an earlier work of Giuseppe Vitali, [153], who constructed the first example of a non-Lebesgue measurable set. Vitali's and Hausdorff's results are dependent on Zermelo's axiom of choice, which is also crucial for Banach-Tarski paradox. We will state precisely the parts of the proof that involve the axiom of choice.

A stronger version of Banach-Tarski says that any bounded set with non-empty interior can be decomposed and rearranged into any other bounded set with non-empty interior. This paradox is also called pea-to-Sun paradox: one can obtain the Sun by cutting and moving around the pieces of a tiny pea.

We continue the chapter by introducing basic definitions of amenable groups, and giving first examples based on these definitions. A basic tool in functional analysis is the correspondence between means and finitely additive measures on a set. This correspondence was firstly introduced by Banach as one of the first applications of the Hahn-Banach theorem, see Appendix A.

John von Neumann in 1920's realized the importance of paradoxical actions, and started a classification of groups that do not admit any. He extracted a proper notion which forbids paradoxes: the existence of probability measure which is invariant under the action of the ambient group. He coined the German name "meßbar" with English translation "measurable", and showed that finite and abelian groups are amenable. Moreover, he showed that the class of amenable groups is closed under taking subgroups, quotients, extensions and direct limits. This explains why the Banach-Tarski paradox fails in dimensions one and two: the Euclidean group of $\mathbb{R}^2$ is solvable, and therefore, it is amenable.

Mahlon Day coined the American term "amenable" as analog of von Neumann's "meßbar" and extended the notion to semigroups, [**44**]. He defined the class of elementary amenable groups: the smallest class of groups that contain finite and abelian groups and which is closed under taking subgroups, quotients, extensions and direct limits. This is the largest class of groups amenability of which was known to John von Neumann.

The chapter is aimed to give the very first definition of amenability: the existence of invariant means and measures, approximately invariant means, and the Følner condition. We will show that the class of amenable groups is closed under taking extensions, quotients, subgroups and direct limits. The final section of the chapter explains why amenable groups do not admit paradoxical actions.

1. Paradoxical actions

We start this section with classical definitions.

DEFINITION 2.1. Let G be a group acting on a set X. A subset $E \subset X$ is **paradoxical** if there exist pairwise disjoint subsets $A_1, \ldots, A_n, B_1, \ldots, B_m$ in E and group elements $g_1, \ldots, g_n, h_1, \ldots, h_m$ in G such that

$$E = \bigcup_{i=1}^{n} g_i A_i = \bigcup_{j=1}^{m} h_j B_j.$$

Note that we do not assume that $g_i A_i \cap g_j A_j = \emptyset$, this can be arranged by Lemma A.14. An action of a group G on a set X is paradoxical if X is paradoxical. The group G is called paradoxical if the action of G on itself by left multiplication is paradoxical. Later on we will show a famous theorem of Tarski which states that the group is paradoxical if and only if it is non-amenable. The very first example and the only known explicit construction of a paradoxical decomposition is provided by the free group on two generators $\mathbb{F}_2$. Let $a, b \in \mathbb{F}_2$ be free generators of $\mathbb{F}_2$. Given $x \in \{a, b, a^{-1}, b^{-1}\}$ denote by $\omega(x)$ the set of all reduced words in $\mathbb{F}_2$ that start with x. Thus the group can be decomposed into pairwise disjoint sets as follows

$$\mathbb{F}_2 = \{e\} \cup \omega(a) \cup \omega(a^{-1}) \cup \omega(b) \cup \omega(b^{-1}).$$

Since $\mathbb{F}_2 \backslash \omega(x) = x\omega(x^{-1})$ for all x in $\{a, a^{-1}, b, b^{-1}\}$ we have a paradoxical decomposition:

$$\mathbb{F}_2 = \omega(a) \cup a\omega(a^{-1}) = \omega(b) \cup b\omega(b^{-1}).$$

In fact, with few additional assumptions one can push a paradoxical decomposition of a group onto the set on which it acts. This is exactly the place where the axiom of choice is needed.

THEOREM 2.2. *If a group G is paradoxical, then any free action of G on a set X is paradoxical.*

PROOF. Let

$$G = \bigcup_{i=1}^{n} g_i A_i = \bigcup_{j=1}^{m} h_j B_j$$

be a paradoxical decomposition of G. By the axiom of choice we can select a subset M of X which contains exactly one element from each orbit of G. Then $\bigcup_{g \in G} gM$ is a disjoint partition of X. Indeed, if $gx = hy$ for some $g, h \in G$ and $x, y \in M$, then $x = y$ by the choice of M. Since the action is free, we have $g = h$. Define now

$$\widehat{A}_i = \bigcup_{g \in A_i} gM \text{ and } \widehat{B}_j = \bigcup_{g \in B_j} gM.$$

Obviously these sets remain disjoint, and we have

$$X = \bigcup_{i=1}^{n} g_i \widehat{A}_i = \bigcup_{j=1}^{m} h_j \widehat{B}_j.$$

Thus, the action of G on X is paradoxical. □

This theorem implies, in particular, that all free actions of $\mathbb{F}_2$ admit paradoxical decompositions. Note that, if the action of G on X is transitive, we don't need the axiom of choice.

THEOREM 2.3. *Suppose that G acts on sets X and Y and that $f : Y \to X$ is a G-equivariant map. Then if the action of G on X is paradoxical, this implies that the action of G on Y is paradoxical. In particular, if G has a paradoxical action, then G is a paradoxical group.*

PROOF. It suffices to notice that if $A_1, \ldots, A_n, B_1, \ldots, B_m \subset X$ give a paradoxical decomposition of X then their preimages under f give a paradoxical decomposition of Y.

Now, if the action of G on X is paradoxical, take any $x \in X$ and consider the map $g \mapsto gx$. This map is G-equivariant. Therefore by above G is paradoxical. □

We remark, that this theorem is a general statement of the converse to Theorem 2.2. Indeed, assume that the action of G on a set X is paradoxical, then by the definition of paradoxical actions the restriction of the action of G on each orbit $Orb_G(x)$ is also paradoxical. Now we can apply the theorem to the orbital map $f : G \to Orb_G(x)$, defined by $f(g) = gx$, obtain that G itself is paradoxical.

2. Hausdorff paradox

In this section we will present Hausdorff's paradox, which is historically the first paradox of sets in 3-dimensional Euclidean space.

THEOREM 2.4 (Hausdorff Paradox). *The 3-dimensional sphere S^2 is paradoxical under the action of the group of rotations $SO(3)$.*

One of the main ingredients of the Hausdorff paradox is the presence of the free group on two generators as a subgroup of $SO(3)$. There are many non-constructive proofs of this fact. For example, one can invoke Tits alternative to show it. In fact, a stronger statement is true. If we consider $SO(3) \times SO(3)$ with product topology, then the set of all pairs that generate $\mathbb{F}_2$ is dense in $SO(3) \times SO(3)$.

For our future purposes it is sufficient to specify only one copy of $\mathbb{F}_2$ is $SO(3)$. The first explicit construction of such is due to Hausdorff, [**80**]. Here we give a simplified construction of Świerczkowski, [**146**].

THEOREM 2.5. *The free group on two generators is a subgroup of the group of rotations $SO(3)$.*

PROOF. We define two rotations explicitly by matrices

$$
T^{\pm 1} = \begin{pmatrix} \frac{1}{3} & \mp\frac{2\sqrt{2}}{3} & 0 \\ \pm\frac{2\sqrt{2}}{3} & \frac{1}{3} & 0 \\ 0 & 0 & 1 \end{pmatrix}; \quad R^{\pm 1} = \begin{pmatrix} 1 & 0 & 0 \\ 0 & \frac{1}{3} & \mp\frac{2\sqrt{2}}{3} \\ 0 & \pm\frac{2\sqrt{2}}{3} & \frac{1}{3} \end{pmatrix}.
$$

These are rotations by the angle $\arccos(\frac{1}{3})$ around the z-axis and x-axis respectively. Let us show that these rotations generate $\mathbb{F}_2$. Let ω be a non-trivial reduced word in the free group on two generators. We will show that $q(\omega)$ is a non-trivial rotation, where q is a homomorphism of $\mathbb{F}_2 = \langle a, b \rangle$ that sends generators to T and R respectively. To simplify notations we will denote $q(\omega)$ again by ω. Conjugating ω by T, we may assume that ω ends by $T^{\pm 1}$ on the right. To prove the theorem it would suffice to show that

$$
\omega \begin{pmatrix} 1 \\ 0 \\ 0 \end{pmatrix} = \frac{1}{3^k} \begin{pmatrix} a \\ b\sqrt{2} \\ c \end{pmatrix},
$$

where a, b, c are integers, b is not divisible by 3, and k is the length of ω.

In order to show this we will proceed by induction on the length of ω. If $|\omega| = 1$, then $\omega = T^{\pm 1}$ and

$$
\omega \begin{pmatrix} 1 \\ 0 \\ 0 \end{pmatrix} = \frac{1}{3} \begin{pmatrix} 1 \\ \pm 2\sqrt{2} \\ 0 \end{pmatrix}.
$$

Now let ω be equal to $T^{\pm 1}\omega'$ or $R^{\pm 1}\omega'$, where ω' satisfies

$$
\omega' \begin{pmatrix} 1 \\ 0 \\ 0 \end{pmatrix} = \frac{1}{3^{k-1}} \begin{pmatrix} a' \\ b'\sqrt{2} \\ c' \end{pmatrix},
$$

where a', b', c' are integers, b' is not divisible by 3, and $k - 1$ is the length of ω.

Applying matrices we see that either $a = a' \mp 4b'$, $b = b' \pm 2a'$ and $c = 3c'$ or $a = 3a'$, $b = b' \mp 2c'$ and $c = c' \pm 4b'$. Thus a, b and c are integers. It is left to show that b is not divisible by 3. Now ω can be written as $T^{\pm 1}R^{\pm 1}v$, $R^{\pm 1}T^{\pm 1}v$,

$T^{\pm 1}T^{\pm 1}v$ or $R^{\pm 1}R^{\pm 1}v$, for some possibly empty word v. Thus we have 4 cases to consider:

(1) $\omega = T^{\pm 1}R^{\pm 1}v$. In this case $b = b' \mp 2a'$ and a' is divisible by 3. By assumption, b' is not divisible by 3, and thus b is not divisible by 3 either.

(2) $\omega = R^{\pm 1}T^{\pm 1}v$. In this case $b = b' \mp 2c'$ and c' is divisible by 3. But b' is not divisible by 3, thus b is not divisible by 3 either.

(3) $\omega = T^{\pm 1}T^{\pm 1}v$. By assumption, $v(1,0,0) = \frac{1}{3^{k-2}}(a'', \sqrt{2}b'', c'')$. It follows that $b = b' \pm 2a' = b \pm 2(a'' \mp 4b'') = b' + b'' \pm 2a'' - 9b'' = 2b' - 9b''$. Therefore, b is not divisible by 3.

(4) $\omega = R^{\pm 1}R^{\pm 1}v$. This case is similar to the previous one.

Thus, in all possible cases b is not divisible by 3, which implies the statement of the theorem. $\qquad\square$

We can summarize our current constructions as follows.

THEOREM 2.6. *There exists a countable subset in the unit sphere S^2 such that its complement in S^2 is $SO(3)$-paradoxical.*

PROOF. Consider a copy of $\mathbb{F}_2$ in $SO(3)$, and let

$$M = \{x \in S^2 : \text{there exists } g \in \mathbb{F}_2 \text{ such that } gx = x, g \neq 1\}.$$

Obviously, M is countable and $S^2 \backslash M$ is invariant under the action of our free group. Thus, by Theorem 2.2 the statement follows. $\qquad\square$

Let us introduce a notations for the simplification of further discussion of the Hausdorff paradox.

DEFINITION 2.7. *Let G be a group acting on a set X. Two subsets $A, B \subset X$ are equidecomposable (or G-equidecomposable), if there exist pairwise disjoint subsets $A_1, \ldots, A_n \subset A$, pairwise disjoint subsets $B_1, \ldots, B_n \subset B$ and $g_1, \ldots, g_n$ in G such that*

$$A = \bigcup_{i=1}^{n} A_i, \qquad B = \bigcup_{j=1}^{n} B_j$$

and $g_i(A_i) = B_i$ for all $1 \leq i \leq n$.

It is straightforward to check that equidecomposibility is an equivalence relation. We denote it by $A \sim_G B$ or by $A \sim B$ when the ambient group is clear.

PROPOSITION 2.8. *Let G be a group that acts on a set X. If $F \subseteq X$ is paradoxical and F is equidecomposable to $E \subseteq X$, then E is paradoxical.*

PROOF. Let

$$F = \bigcup_{i=1}^{n} g_i A_i = \bigcup_{j=1}^{m} h_j B_j$$

be a paradoxical decomposition of F. By transitivity, E is equidecomposable to both $\bigcup_{i=1}^{n} A_i$ and $\bigcup_{j=1}^{m} B_j$. This implies that E is paradoxical. $\qquad\square$

Now we are ready to show the last piece of the proof of the Hausdorff paradox.

PROPOSITION 2.9. *Let D be a countable subset of S^2. Then S^2 and $S^2 \backslash D$ are $SO(3)$-equidecomposable.*

PROOF. Since D is countable we can find a line L containing the origin which does not intersect D. Let Λ be the collection of all $\alpha \in [0, 2\pi]$ for which there exist a natural number n and a point x in D such that both x and $\rho(x)$ are in D, where ρ is the rotation around L by an angle $n\alpha$. Obviously, Λ is countable and we can find $\theta \in [0, 2\pi) \backslash \Lambda$. Let ρ be the rotation by θ around L, then $\rho^n(D) \cap \rho^k(D) = \emptyset$ for all natural numbers $k \neq n$. Thus for $D' = \bigcup_{n \geq 0} \rho^n(D)$ we have

$$S^2 = D' \cup (S^2 \backslash D') \sim \rho(D') \cup (S^2 \backslash D') = S^2 \backslash D,$$

which proves the claim.   □

The Hausdorff paradox, Theorem 2.4, is a direct consequence of this proposition and Theorem 2.6.

3. Banach-Tarski paradox

The classical Banach-Tarski paradox amounts to a decomposition of the unit ball into finitely many pieces, and rearranging these pieces into two unit balls. Since the center of the ball is invariant under the action of the group of rotations, the ball is not $SO(3)$-paradoxical. In order to have paradoxical decompositions we will consider the group of Eucledean transformations of $\mathbb{R}^3$, i.e., the group generated by all rotations and translations.

Now we are ready to state and prove Banach-Tarski paradox, [9]. Denote by $E(3)$ the group of all Euclidean transformations of $\mathbb{R}^3$, that is the group generated by all rotations and translations.

THEOREM 2.10 (Banach-Tarski Paradox). *Every ball in $\mathbb{R}^3$ is $E(3)$-paradoxical.*

PROOF. Without loss of generality we can assume that the ball has its center in the origin. We prove the statement for the ball of radius 1, the general case is a straightforward adaption of the proof. Let B be the unit ball around the origin. By Theorem 2.4, we can find pairwise disjoint sets $A_1, \ldots, A_n, B_1, \ldots, B_n \subset S^2$ and $g_1, \ldots, g_n, h_1, \ldots, h_m \in SO(3)$ such that

$$S^2 = \bigcup_{i=1}^{n} g_i A_i = \bigcup_{j=1}^{m} h_j B_j.$$

Now, define

$$\widehat{A}_i = \{tx : t \in (0,1], x \in A_i\} \text{ and } \widehat{B}_j = \{tx : t \in (0,1], x \in B_j\}.$$

We have $\widehat{A}_1, \ldots, \widehat{A}_n, \widehat{B}_1, \ldots, \widehat{B}_n \subset B_1 \backslash \{0\}$ are pairwise disjoint and $B = \bigcup_{1 \leq j \leq n} g_i \widehat{A}_i = \bigcup_{1 \leq j \leq m} h_j \widehat{A}_j$. Thus $B_1 \backslash \{0\}$ is paradoxical. We will show that it is equidecomposable to B_1.

Let $x = (0, 0, \frac{1}{2})$. Let L be a line which does not contain origin and with $x \in L$. Let ρ be any rotation of infinite order around this line. Define $D = \{\rho^n(0) : n \geq 0\}$. Since $0 \notin \rho(D)$ and $\rho(D) \subset D$, we have

$$B_1 = D \cup (B_1 \backslash D) \sim \rho(D) \cup (B_1 \backslash D) = B_1 \backslash \{0\}.$$

Thus by Proposition 2.8 we have the statement.   □

4. Pea to Sun paradox

In this section we present a stronger version of Banach-Tarski paradox, which says that every two bounded sets with non-empty interior are equidecomposable with respect to the action of $E(3)$. This paradox is called *Pea to Sun Paradox*, since even a small pea can be decomposed and rearranged to form the Sun.

Consider a group G acting on a set X, and let A, B be two subsets of X. We will write $A \preceq_G B$ is there exists a subset in B, which is G-equidecomposable with A.

It is trivial to check that if two sets A and B are G-equidecomposable, then there exists a bijection $\phi : A \to B$ such that every $C \subset A$ is G-equidecomposable with $\phi(C)$.

LEMMA 2.11 (Banach-Schröder-Bernstein). Let G be a group that acts on a set X and let A, B be two subsets of X. If $A \preceq_G B$ and $B \preceq_G A$, then $A \sim_G B$.

PROOF. Let $A' \subseteq A$ and $B' \subseteq B$ be such that $A' \sim_G B$ and $B' \sim_G A$. Let $\phi : A \to B'$ be a bijection with the property that every $C \subset A$ is G-equidecomposable with $\phi(C)$. Similarly, let $\psi : B \to A'$ be a bijection with the property that every $D \subset B$ is G-equidecomposable with $\psi(D)$.

Define $C_0 = A \backslash A'$, and $C_{n+1} = \psi(\phi(C_n))$, and let $C = \bigcup_{n=0}^{\infty} C_n$. We have $\psi^{-1}(A \backslash C) = B \backslash \phi(C)$. This implies that the sets $A \backslash C$ and $B \backslash \phi(C)$ are G-equidecomposable. Similarly, $C \sim_G \phi(C)$. Hence, we have

$$A = (A \backslash C) \cup C \sim_G (B \backslash \phi(C)) \cup \phi(C) = B.$$

$\square$

The following theorem is not a direct consequence of Banach-Tarski paradox as we don't require the sets $g_1 A_1, \ldots, g_n A_n, h_1 B_1, \ldots, h_m B_m$ to be pairwise disjoint in the definition of paradoxical decomposition.

THEOREM 2.12. Let $B, B_1, \ldots, B_n$ be a sequence of balls in $\mathbb{R}^3$ of the same radius, such that $B_1, \ldots, B_n$ are pairwise disjoint. Then $\bigcup_i B_i \sim_{E(3)} B$.

PROOF. Obviously, we have $B \preceq_{E(3)} \bigcup_i B_i$. By Lemma 2.11, it suffices to show that $\bigcup_i B_i \preceq_{E(3)} B$.

Let us show that $B_1 \cup B_2 \preceq_{E(3)} B$. So let us take pairwise disjoint $A_1, \ldots, A_s$, $C_1, \ldots, C_k \subset B$ and $g_1, \ldots, g_s, h_1, \ldots, h_k \in E(3)$ such that

$$B = \bigcup_i g_i A_i = \bigcup_j h_j C_j.$$

Then

$$B_1 \sim_{E(3)} B = \bigcup_i g_i A_i \preceq_{E(3)} \bigcup_i A_i,$$

$$B_2 \sim_{E(3)} B = \bigcup_j h_j C_j \preceq_{E(3)} \bigcup_j C_j.$$

Therefore, $B_1 \cup B_2 \preceq_{E(3)} B$. By induction, it is easy to see that the general case $\cup_i B_i \preceq_{E(3)} B$ is also true.

$\square$

Now we have all pieces to give a proof of a strong version of the Banach-Tarski paradox.

THEOREM 2.13 (Pea to Sun Paradox). Let A and B be bounded subsets of $\mathbb{R}^3$ with non-empty interior. Then A and B are $E(3)$-equidecomposable.

PROOF. By Lemma 2.11 it is sufficient to prove that $A \preceq B$. Since A is bounded we can find $r > 0$ such that $A \subset B_r(0)$. Let x be an interior point of B. Then there is $\varepsilon > 0$, such that $B_\varepsilon(x) \subset B$. Let $g_1, \ldots, g_n$ be translations of $\mathbb{R}^3$ such that

$$B_r(0) \subset g_1 B_\varepsilon(x) \cup \ldots \cup g_n B_\varepsilon(x).$$

Choose translations $h_1, \ldots, h_n$ of $\mathbb{R}^3$, which satisfy

$$h_i B_\varepsilon(x) \cap h_j B_\varepsilon(x) = \emptyset, \text{ for all } i \neq j.$$

Consider the set

$$Y = \bigcup_j h_j B_\varepsilon(x).$$

By Theorem 2.12, we have $Y \preceq B_\varepsilon(x)$. Hence,

$$A \subset B_r(0) \subset g_1 B_\varepsilon(x) \cup \ldots \cup g_n B_\varepsilon(x) \preceq Y \preceq B_\varepsilon(x) \subset B,$$

which implies the statement. $\qquad\square$

5. First definitions: invariant mean, Følner condition

We start with one of the classical definitions of amenability due to von Neumann.

DEFINITION 2.14. A group G is amenable if there exists a finitely additive measure μ on all subsets of G into $[0, 1]$ with $\mu(G) = 1$ and satisfying

$$\mu(gE) = \mu(E)$$

for every $E \subseteq G$ and $g \in G$.

Let G be a group acting and X be a set. We use the notation $G \curvearrowright X$ to specify that the group G acts on X. If $f : X \to \mathbb{C}$ is a function on X, then for every $g \in G$ we define a function $g.f$ on X by $(g.f)(x) = f(g^{-1}x)$ for every $x \in X$. This defines an action on many classical function spaces. For example, the space $l^p(G)$ of p-summable functions on G is invariant under this action.

Recall, a mean on G is a linear functional μ on $l^\infty(G)$ with the properties that $\mu(\chi_G) = 1$, and $\mu(f) \geq 0$ for every $f \geq 0$, $f \in l^\infty(G)$. The set of all means on G is denoted by $M(G)$. A mean μ is called G-invariant, if $\mu(t.f) = \mu(f)$ for all $f \in l^\infty(G)$ and $t \in G$. Note that, one can also consider the right action of G on itself, and thus, on $l^\infty(G)$. This action is defined by $(gf)(t) = f(tg)$. It is easy to check that the existence of right G-invariant means on G is equivalent to the existence of the left G-invariant means. For topological groups, the situation is completely different and these two notions are not the same. This is discussed in the book of Cornulier and de la Harpe, Chapter 4 [42].

We denote the set of probability measures on G by

$$Prob(G) = \{\mu \in l^1(G) : \|\mu\|_1 = 1 \text{ and } \mu \geq 0\}.$$

A subset $S \subset G$ is called symmetric if $S = S^{-1} = \{s^{-1} : s \in S\}$.

Theorem A.4 implies that there is one-to-one correspondence between means and finitely additive probability measures. Moreover, it is straightforward to check that every G-invariant finitely additive measure this correspondence associates G-invariant mean. Thus we immediately obtain the following equivalent definition of amenability.

DEFINITION 2.15. A group G is amenable if it admits a G-invariant mean.

As our tools will develop we will present more and more sophisticated definitions of amenability. The following is the first set of equivalent definitions. Note that one can give an alternative proof of the theorem below by using paradoxical decompositions and Tarski's theorem, see Chapter A, where we collect other equivalent definitions and facts.

THEOREM 2.16. For a discrete group G the following are equivalent:

(1) G is amenable.
(2) *Reiter's condition (or approximate mean condition).* For any finite subset $E \subset G$ there exists $\mu \in Prob(G)$ such that $\|s.\mu - \mu\|_1 \leq \varepsilon$ for all $s \in E$.
(3) *Følner's condition.* For any finite subset $E \subset G$ and $\varepsilon > 0$, there exists a finite subset $F \subset G$ such that

$$|gF\Delta F| \leq \varepsilon|F| \text{ for all } g \in E.$$

PROOF. (1) $\implies$ (2). Let E be a finite subset of G and $\mu \in l^\infty(G)^*$ be a G-invariant mean. Since $l^1(G)$ is weak*-dense in $l^\infty(G)^* = l^1(G)^{**}$, let $\mu_i \in Prob(G)$ be a sequence which weak*-converges to μ. This implies that $s.\mu_i - \mu_i$ converges to zero in weak*-topology. Moreover, $s.\mu_i - \mu_i$ converges weakly to 0 in $l^1(G)$ for all $s \in G$. Consider the weak closure of the convex set

$$\{\bigoplus_{s \in E} s.\mu - \mu : \mu \in Prob(G)\} \subseteq \bigoplus_E l^1(G).$$

This closure contains zero. By the Hahn-Banach Separation theorem, it is also norm closed. Thus (2) follows.

(2) $\implies$ (3). Given $E \subset G$ and $\varepsilon > 0$, let μ satisfy (2). Let $f \in l^1(G)$ and $r \geq 0$. Define $F(f, r) = \{t \in G : f(t) > r\}$.

For positive functions f, h in $l^1(G)$ with $\|f\|_1 = \|h\|_1 = 1$, we have $|\chi_{F(f,r)}(t) - \chi_{F(h,r)}(t)| = 1$ if and only if $f(t) \leq r \leq h(t)$ or $h(t) \leq r \leq f(t)$. Hence for two functions bounded above by 1 we have

$$|f(t) - h(t)| = \int_0^1 |\chi_{F(f,r)}(t) - \chi_{F(h,r)}(t)|dr.$$

Thus we can apply this to $\mu(t)$ and $s.\mu(t)$:

$$\|s.\mu - \mu\|_1 = \sum_{t \in G} |s.\mu(t) - \mu(t)|$$

$$= \sum_{t \in G} \int_0^1 |\chi_{F(s.\mu,r)}(t) - \chi_{F(\mu,r)}(t)|dr$$

$$= \int_0^1 \left(\sum_{t \in G} |\chi_{s.F(\mu,r)}(t) - \chi_{F(\mu,r)}(t)|\right) dr$$

$$= \int_0^1 |s.F(\mu,r)\Delta F(\mu,r)|dr$$

Since $\|f\|_1 = 1$ and μ satisfies (2), it follows that

$$\int_0^1 \sum_{s \in E} |s.F(\mu, r) \Delta F(\mu, r)| dr \leq \varepsilon |E|$$

$$= \varepsilon |E| \sum_{t \in G} \mu(t)$$

$$= \varepsilon |E| \sum_{t \in G} \int_0^{\mu(t)} dr$$

$$= \varepsilon |E| \int_0^1 |\{t \in G : \mu(t) > r\}| dr$$

$$= \varepsilon |E| \int_0^1 |F(\mu, r)| dr.$$

Thus, there exists r such that

$$\sum_{s \in E} |s.F(\mu, r) \Delta F(\mu, r)| \leq \varepsilon |E| |F(\mu, r)|.$$

(3) $\implies$ (1). Let E_i be an increasing and exhausting sequence of finite subsets and let ε_i coverge to zero. By (3), we can find F_i that satisfy

$$|gF_i \Delta F_i| \leq \varepsilon_i |F_i| \text{ for all } g \in E_i.$$

Denote by $\mu_i = \frac{1}{|F_i|} \chi_{F_i} \in Prob(G)$, then

$$\|g.\mu_i - \mu_i\|_1 = \frac{1}{|F_i|} |gF_i \Delta F_i|.$$

Let $\mu \in l^\infty(G)^*$ be a cluster point in the weak*-topology of the sequence μ_i, then μ is an invariant mean. $\qquad \square$

We remark that the proof of the implication (2) $\implies$ (3) is due to Namioka, [**116**], and the implication (1) $\implies$ (2) is due to Day, [**44**].

Suppose G is a group generated by a finite set S. A sequence $\{F_i\}_{i \in \mathbb{N}}$ is called a *Følner sequence*, if there exists a sequence $\{\varepsilon_i\}_{i \in \mathbb{N}}$ that converges to zero that

$$|gF_i \Delta F_i| \leq \varepsilon_i |F_i| \text{ for all } g \in S \text{ and all } i \in \mathbb{N}.$$

Let $s, h \in G$ and F be a finite subset of G, then

$$|shF \Delta F| = |(shF \Delta sF) \Delta (sF \Delta F)| \leq |hF \Delta F| + |sF \Delta F|.$$

Since any finite set is contained in a ball of a large enough radius of the Cayley graph, by the inequality above we have the following.

PROPOSITION 2.17. A finitely generated group is amenable if and only if it admits a Følner sequence for some generating set.

This implies that amenability is a local property, i.e. in order to verify it one needs to verify the property on all finite subsets of the group. We will use the proposition above without a quote from now on.

6. First examples

In this section we present examples of amenable and non-amenable groups based on the definitions that we already developed.

Finite groups. Finite groups are amenable. If G is finite, then $F_i = G$ is a Følner sequence.

Groups of subexponential growth. A group G has *subexponential growth* if
$$\limsup_n |B_n(S)|^{1/n} = 1$$
for any finite subset $S \subset G$, where $B_n(S) = S^n = \{s_1 \cdots s_n : s_1, \ldots, s_n \in S\}$. Since for a finitely generated group it is sufficient to verify the condition above on a symmetric generating set.

Let us prove that groups of subexponential growth are amenable. Let S be a symmetric generating set of G containing identity. The sequence $B_n = B_n(S)$ is an increasing sequence of sets. By the definition of subexponential growth we have that for every $\varepsilon > 0$ there exists $k \in \mathbb{N}$ such that
$$|B_{k+1}|/|B_k| \le (1 + \varepsilon).$$
Indeed, to reach a contradiction assume that for there exists $\varepsilon > 0$ such that for all k
$$|B_{k+1}| > (1 + \varepsilon)|B_k|.$$
Hence $|B_{k+1}| > (1 + \varepsilon)^k |B_1|$ and therefore $\limsup_k |B_k|^{1/k} \ge 1 + \varepsilon$, which is a contradiction.

Now for every $\varepsilon > 0$ there is a natural number k such that for every $g \in S$ we have
$$\frac{|gB_k \setminus B_k|}{|B_k|} \le \frac{|B_{k+1}| - |B_k|}{|B_k|} \le \varepsilon.$$
This implies that G is amenable.

Abelian groups. There are many ways to see that Abelian groups are amenable. One of them is to notice that finitely generated Abelian groups are of subexponential growth.

Free groups. The free group $\mathbb{F}_2$ of rank 2 is the typical example of a non-amenable group. Let $a, b \in \mathbb{F}_2$ be the free generators of $\mathbb{F}_2$. Denote by $\omega(x)$ the set of all reduced words in $\mathbb{F}_2$ that start with x. Thus the group can be decomposed as follows
$$\mathbb{F}_2 = \{e\} \cup \omega(a) \cup \omega(a^{-1}) \cup \omega(b) \cup \omega(b^{-1}).$$
To reach a contradiction assume that $\mathbb{F}_2$ admits a finitely additive measure μ. Since the group is infinite and μ is invariant we have $\mu(\{t\}) = 0$ for all $t \in \mathbb{F}_2$. Moreover, applying the fact that $\omega(x) = x(\mathbb{F}_2 \setminus \omega(x^{-1}))$ for $x \in \{a, b, a^{-1}, b^1\}$ we obtain:
$$
\begin{aligned}
1 = \mu(\mathbb{F}_2) &= \mu(\{e\}) + \mu(\omega(a)) \\
&+ \mu(\omega(a^{-1})) + \mu(\omega(b)) + \mu(\omega(b^{-1})) \\
&= \mu(\{e\}) + \left[1 - \mu(\omega(a^{-1}))\right] + \left[1 - \mu(\omega(a))\right] \\
&+ \left[1 - \mu(\omega(b^{-1}))\right] + \left[1 - \mu(\omega(b))\right] = 2,
\end{aligned}
$$
which is a contradiction.

7. Operations that preserve amenability

In this section we list basic operations that preserve amenability.

Subgroups. Amenability passes to subgroups. Indeed, let H be a subgroup of an amenable group G and $\mathcal{R}$ be a complete set of representatives of the right cosets of H.

Given $\varepsilon > 0$ and a finite set $F \subset H$, let $\mu \in Prob(G)$ be an approximately invariant mean that satisfies $\|s.\mu - \mu\|_1 \leq \varepsilon$ for all $s \in F$. Define $\tilde{\mu} \in Prob(H)$ by

$$\tilde{\mu}(h) = \sum_{r \in \mathcal{R}} \mu(hr).$$

Since for all $s \in F$ we have

$$\|s.\tilde{\mu} - \tilde{\mu}\|_1 = \sum_{h \in H} |s.\tilde{\mu}(h) - \tilde{\mu}(h)|$$

$$= \sum_{h \in H} |\sum_{r \in \mathcal{R}} s.\mu(hr) - \mu(hr)|$$

$$\leq \|s.\mu - \mu\|_1 \leq \varepsilon,$$

it follows that $\tilde{\mu}$ is an approximate mean for F, thus H is amenable.

Summarizing above, we have that amenability is a local property of groups: a group G is amenable if and only if all its finitely generated subgroups are amenable.

Quotients. Let G be an amenable group with normal subgroup H, then G/H is amenable. Indeed, consider a G-invariant finitely additive probability measure $\mu : \mathcal{P}(G) \to [0,1]$ on G. Let $q : G \to G/H$ be the canonical quotient map. We will show that the map $\overline{\mu} : \mathcal{P}(G/H) \to [0,1]$ defined by

$$\overline{\mu}(A) = \mu(q^{-1}(A)), \text{ for all } A \in \mathcal{P}(G/H),$$

is a finitely additive G/H-invariant probability measure of G/H.

Clearly we have

$$\overline{\mu}(G/H) = \mu(q^{-1}(G/H)) = \mu(G) = 1,$$

and for every pair of disjoint sets A and B in G/H we have

$$\overline{\mu}(A \cap B) = \mu(q^{-1}(A \cap B)) = \mu(q^{-1}(A) \cap q^{-1}(B)) = \mu(q^{-1}(A)) + \mu(q^{-1}(B)).$$

Now if $g \in G$ and $A \subset G/H$ then

$$\overline{\mu}(q(g)A) = \mu(q^{-1}(q(g)A)) = \mu(gq^{-1}(A)) = \mu(q^{-1}(A)) = \overline{\mu}(A).$$

Thus $\overline{\mu}$ is finitely additive G/H-invariant probability measure of G/H.

Extensions. Let G be a group with normal subgroup H such that both H and G/H are amenable, then G is amenable.

Let μ_H and $\mu_{G/H}$ be invariant means of H and G/H correspondingly. For $\phi \in l^{\infty}(G)$, let $\phi_\mu \in l^{\infty}(G/H)$ be defined by

$$\phi_\mu(gH) = \mu_H((g^{-1}.\phi)|_H).$$

This map is well-defined. Indeed, for $g_1, g_2 \in G$ such that $g_2 = g_1 h$ for some $h \in H$ we have

$$\mu_H((g_2^{-1}.\phi)|_H) = \mu_H((h^{-1}g_1^{-1}.\phi)|_H) = \mu_H((g_1^{-1}.\phi)|_H).$$

Moreover, $\|\phi_\mu\| \leq \|\phi\|_\infty$.

Define a functional $\overline{\mu} \in l^{\infty}(G)^*$ by setting:

$$\overline{\mu}(\phi) = \mu_{G/H}(\phi_\mu), \text{ for every } \phi \in l^{\infty}(G).$$

Obviously, $\overline{\mu}$ is a mean. We will show that it is G-invariant. Let $g \in G$, $\phi \in l^\infty(G)$. Then for every $g' \in G$, we have

$$(g\phi)_\mu(g'H) = \mu_H((g'^{-1}g\phi)|_H) = \mu_H((g^{-1}g')^{-1}\phi|_H) = \phi_\mu(g^{-1}g'H) = \overline{g}\phi_\mu(g'H),$$

where $\overline{g} = gH$. This implies that $(g\phi)_\mu = \overline{g}\phi_\mu$. Since $\mu_{G/H}$ is G/H-invariant, we obtain

$$\overline{\mu}(g\phi) = \mu_{G/H}((g\phi)_\mu) = \mu_{G/H}(\overline{g}\phi_\mu) = \mu_{G/H}(\phi_\mu) = \overline{\mu}(\phi),$$

which implies that $\overline{\mu}$ is G-invariant.

Direct limits. The direct limit of groups $G = \lim_\to G_i$ has the property that for each finite set in the limit group G, the group generated by this set belongs to one of the G_i. Therefore, we can apply Følner's condition to conclude that G is also amenable.

8. Amenable actions: first definitions

In this section we study amenable actions. Recall, a discrete group G acts on a set X, denoted by $G \curvearrowright X$, that is there is a map $(g, x) \mapsto gx$ from $G \times X$ to X such that $(gh)x = g(h(x))$ for all g, h in G. Then we can induce action on the space of functions on X by $g.f(x) = f(g^{-1}x)$. A mean on X is a linear functional $m \in l^\infty(X)^*$ which satisfies $m(\chi_X) = 1$, and $m(f) \geq 0$ for all $f \geq 0$ in $l^\infty(X)$, where $\chi_X(x) = 1$ for all x in X. This automatically implies $\|m\| = 1$. Denote the set of all means on X by $M(X)$. The group G acts on $M(X)$, by $(g.m)(f) = m(g.f)$. A fixed point of this action (if is exists) is called a G-invariant mean.

We recall that there is one-to-one correspondence between means on X and finitely additive probability measures on X, Section 1.

DEFINITION 2.18. An action of a discrete group G on a set X is amenable if there exists a G-invariant mean on X.

We will identity the set $\{0, 1\}^X$ of all sequences indexed by X with values in $\{0, 1\}$ with the set of all subsets of X. The proof of the theorem is exactly the same as the proof of Theorem 2.16.

THEOREM 2.19. Let a discrete group G act on a set X. Then the following are equivalent:

(i) An action of G on X is amenable;
(ii) There exists a finitely additive G-invariant measure on X;
(iii) *Følner condition.* For every finite set $E \subset G$ and for every $\varepsilon > 0$ there exists a finite set $F \subseteq X$ such that for every $g \in E$ we have:
$$|gF \Delta F| \leq \varepsilon \cdot |F|$$
(iv) *Reiter's condition (or approximate mean condition).* For every finite set $S \subset G$ and for every $\varepsilon > 0$ there exists a non-negative function $\phi \in l^1(X)$ such that $\|\phi\| = 1$ and $\|g.\phi - \phi\|_1 \leq \varepsilon$ for all $g \in S$.

We observe that in order for the action to be amenable it is sufficient that its restriction to one of the orbits is amenable.

The following theorem is an almost direct consequence of the existence of Følner sequence for amenable groups. The proof is reminiscent to the proof of the implication (3) $\implies$ (1) of Theorem 2.16.

THEOREM 2.20. If G is amenable, then every action of G is amenable.

PROOF. let E_i be an increasing and exhausting to G sequence of finite subsets and $\{\varepsilon_i\}_{i \in \mathbb{N}}$ be a converging to zero positive sequence. By (3) we can find F_i that satisfy

$$|gF_i \Delta F_i| \leq \varepsilon_i |F_i|, \text{ for all } g \in E_i.$$

Fix a point p in X and denote $\mu_i = \frac{1}{|F_i|} \sum_{g \in F_i} \delta_{gp} \in Prob(X)$, then

$$\|g.\mu_i - \mu_i\|_1 = \frac{1}{|F_i|}|gF_i \Delta F_i|.$$

Let $\mu \in l^\infty(X)^*$ be a cluster point in the weak*-topology of the sequence μ_i, then μ is an invariant mean on X. $\qquad \square$

The converse of the theorem is not true. Indeed, the free group on two generators a and b acts on $\mathbb{Z}$ amenably: $a(i) = i+1$ and $b(i) = i$. As it is discussed below, an additional requirement on the action will imply amenability of the group.

Let X, Y be sets on which a group G acts, and let $\Phi : X \to Y$ be a map. Then we have a canonical map $\overline{\Phi} : l^\infty(Y) \to l^\infty(X)$ defined by $\overline{\Phi}(f) = f \circ \Phi$ for all $f \in l^\infty(Y)$. Consider the dual $\overline{\Phi}^* : l^\infty(X)^* \to l^\infty(Y)^*$ of $\overline{\Phi}$. **The push-forward** of a mean $\mu \in l^\infty(X)^*$ with respect to Φ is the mean $\overline{\Phi}^*(\mu)$, we will denote it by $\Phi_*\mu$. It is straightforward that if Φ is a G-map ($\Phi(gx) = g\Phi(x)$ for all x and g) then the push-forward of a G-invariant mean is G-invariant.

Let $m \in M(M(X))$ be a mean on the space of means. The **barycenter** of m is the mean $\overline{m} \in M(X)$ defined by $\overline{m}(f) = m(\mu \mapsto \mu(f))$ for all $f \in l^\infty(X)$. It is easy to check that if m is G-invariant then $\overline{m}$ is also G-invariant.

THEOREM 2.21. *If G acts amenably on a set X and the stabilizer of each point of X is amenable, then G is amenable.*

PROOF. Let μ be a G-invariant mean on X. Define a G-map $\Phi : X \to M(G)$ as follows. For each point $x \in X$, the stabilizer of it acts amenably on $M(G)$, thus it has a fixed point μ_x. Let Y be a set of orbit representatives and $X = \bigcup_{x \in Y} Orb(x, G)$ be a decomposition of X into the (disjoint) orbits of G. Then if $x \in Y$ we define $\Phi(x) = \mu_x$ and if $y = gx$ for $x \in Y$ we define $\Phi(y) = g.\mu_x$. In other words, Φ is the orbital map. It is straightforward to check that Φ is a G-map.

Let $\Phi_*\mu \in M(M(G))$ be the push-forward of μ. Then its barycenter is an invariant mean on G. $\qquad \square$

Let G be a finitely generated group acting on a set X. Let S be a generating set of G. By a graph of the action we mean a graph such that X is a set of vertices, and there is an edge between x and y labeled by $s \in S$ if and only if $y = sx$. If the action $G \curvearrowright X$ is transitive, then this graph coincides with the Schreier graph of the coset space by the stabilizer of a point in X. More precisely, let $x \in X$ and $H = Stab_G(x)$, then the vertex set X of the graph of the action can be identified with the coset space $\{gH : g \in G\}$ and the action of G on it is the action of left multiplication. We say that the action $G \curvearrowright X$ is of subexponential growth if there is x in X such that

$$\limsup_n B(n, x)^{1/n} = 1,$$

where $B(n, x)$ is the ball of radius n around x. Similarly to the proof of amenability of groups of subexponential growth one can show the following lemma.

LEMMA 2.22. *Let G be a finitely generated group acting on a set X. If the graph of the action $G \curvearrowright X$ has subexponential growth, then this action is amenable.*

9. Paradoxical decompositions and amenable actions

In this section we prove that paradoxical actions are not amenable. This, in particular, implies that amenable groups can not admit paradoxical actions. Recall from Section 1, that an action $G \curvearrowright X$ is paradoxical if there exist pairwise disjoint subsets $A_1, \ldots, A_n, B_1, \ldots, B_m$ in X and group elements $g_1, \ldots, g_n, h_1, \ldots, h_m$ in G such that

$$X = \bigcup_{i=1}^{n} g_i A_i = \bigcup_{j=1}^{m} h_j B_j.$$

THEOREM 2.23. Assume that an action of a group G on a set X is amenable, then it is not paradoxical.

PROOF. From the definition of amenable actions there exists a finitely additive G-invariant finitely additive probability measure μ on X. To reach a contradiction assume that the action is paradoxical and there exist a pairwise disjoint subsets $A_1, \ldots, A_n, B_1, \ldots, B_m$ in X and group elements $g_1, \ldots, g_n, h_1, \ldots, h_m$ in G such that

$$X = \bigcup_{i=1}^{n} g_i A_i = \bigcup_{j=1}^{m} h_j B_j.$$

By Lemma A.14 we can assume that $g_i A_i \cap g_j A_j = \emptyset$ for all $i \neq j$. Taking the measure the subsets involved and using G-invariance of μ we obtain:

$$1 = \mu(X) \geq \mu(\bigcup_{i=1}^{n} A_i) + \mu(\bigcup_{j=1}^{m} B_j)$$

$$= \sum_{i=1}^{n} \mu(A_i) + \sum_{j=1}^{m} \mu(B_j)$$

$$= \sum_{i=1}^{n} \mu(g_i A_i) + \sum_{j=1}^{m} \mu(h_j B_j)$$

$$\geq \mu(\bigcup_{i=1}^{n} g_i A_i) + \mu(\bigcup_{j=1}^{m} h_j B_j)$$

$$= 2.$$

Thus, the action is not paradoxical.   □

A famous theorem of Tarski, see Appendix A.15, shows that the opposite direction is also true for the action of G on itself.

10. Faithful amenable actions of non-amenable groups

It is natural to ask if there is a non-amenable group which can act faithfully and amenably on a set. In this section we give examples of such actions and elaborate more on this question.

A basic example of this section is the class of *wobbling groups* constructed from a metric space. This class of groups is relatively new. It is expected that there is a strong connection between the group structure of $W(X)$ and the metric space X. They were also used to prove non-amenability results in [**75**, Remark 0.5 C_1'''], [**46**], [**52**].

Let (X, d) be a metric space. We define *the wobbling group* $W(X)$ as the group of all bijections g of X satisfying

$$|g|_w = \sup\{d(g(x), x) : x \in X\} < \infty.$$

A more general definition of this group appears in [35] and [46]. Wobbling groups will be important in one of the proofs of amenability of *topological full groups* in later sections.

Usually we will be interested in metric spaces coming from graphs. In the case when all connected components of X are of finite cardinality, the group $W(X)$ is locally finite. However, this is the only case when a wobbling group can be amenable.

An infinite path in a metric space X is a sequence $x_0, x_1 \ldots \in X$ such that $x_i \neq x_j$ for all $i \neq j$ and $d(x_i, x_{i+1}) < C$ for some constant C.

PROPOSITION 2.24. *If X contains an infinite path then $W(X)$ contains $\mathbb{F}_2$.*

PROOF. We will show that the group

$$\Gamma = \mathbb{Z}/2\mathbb{Z} * \mathbb{Z}/2\mathbb{Z} * \mathbb{Z}/2\mathbb{Z} = \langle a, b, c : a^2 = b^2 = c^2 \rangle$$

is a subgroup of $W(X)$. Moreover, this subgroup will be supported on an infinite path $x_0, x_1 \ldots \in X$.

Let w be a reduced word in Γ of length n. We enumerate w from the right to the left. Define an action of Γ on $\{1, \ldots, n + 1\}$ as follows. Let $g \in \{a, b, c\}$ be a generator. Then $g(i) = i + 1$ and $g(i + 1) = i$ if g is the i-th element of w, and $g(i) = i$ on the rest of the points. Consecutively, we have $w(1) = n + 1$. For example, let $w = abac$, then we can define an action of Γ on $\{1, .., 5\}$ by defining $c(1) = 2$, $c(2) = 1$; $a(2) = 3$, $a(3) = 2$, $a(4) = 5$, $a(5) = 4$; $b(3) = 4$, $b(4) = 3$, and fixing the rest of the points to complete the action of a, b and c. Thus, $abac(1) = 5$. This construction implies that for every reduced word w we can find a interval in $\mathbb{N}$ and an action of Γ on it where w does not act trivially.

Since the set of reduced words is countable we can associate a set of pairwise disjoint intervals in $\mathbb{N}$ with the sizes that correspond to the lengths of the reduced words plus one. Now we let the group Γ to act on every interval that corresponds to a reduced word by the action defined above. In particular, the generating sets has infinite support under this action. Moreover, every reduced word w acts non-trivially. Since we can identify an infinite path with $\mathbb{N}$ and $\mathbb{F}_2 < \Gamma$ the statement follows.   □

This fact have been used by Elek and Monod, [52], to construct topological full group of minimal $\mathbb{Z}^2$-actions with a free non-abelian subgroup, which will be discussed in the later chapters. The proof originates from Schreier, [144], who used it to show that $\mathbb{F}_2$ is residually finite.

Properties of wobbling groups. It is an interesting question to extract properties of the group $W(X)$ using the properties of the underlying metric space. Along these lines we show amenability of the action of $W(X)$ on X provided that X is an *amenable graph* and absence of infinite *Kazhdan's property (T)* subgroups in $W(X)$ for X of subexponential growth.

A graph (V, E) is amenable if for every $\varepsilon > 0$ there exists a finite set of vertices V_ε such that

$$|\partial_E(V_\varepsilon)| \leq \varepsilon |V_\epsilon|,$$

here $\partial_E(V_\varepsilon)$ stands for the number of edges connecting V_ε and its complement.

It follows from Theorem 2.19 that a group acts on a set amenably if and only if the Schreier graph of this action is amenable. Assuming that the graph (V, E) is homogeneous and amenable it is easy to check that the Schreier graph of any finitely generated subgroup of $W(V)$ is amenable. Thus we have the following lemma.

LEMMA 2.25. If X is an amenable graph, then the action of $W(X)$ on X is amenable.

A group G has Kazhdan's Property (T) if there exists $\varepsilon > 0$, such that for every unitary action of G on a Hilbert space H without a fixed point we have

$$(1) \qquad \max_{g \in S} \|g \cdot \xi - \xi\|^2 \geq \varepsilon \|\xi\|^2$$

for every $\xi \in H$.

Below we prove that $W(X)$ cannot contain property (T) groups when X is of subexponential growth. A very similar observation, attributed to Kazhdan, was made by Gromov ([**75**] Remark 0.5.F): a discrete property (T) group G cannot contain a subgroup G' such that G/G' has subexponential growth unless G/G' is finite.

THEOREM 2.26. Let X be a metric space with uniform subexponential growth:

$$(2) \qquad \lim_n \log(\sup_{x \in X} |B(x, n)|)/n = 0.$$

Then $W(X)$ does not contain an infinite countable property (T) group.

PROOF. Assume $G < W(X)$ is a finitely generated property (T) group, with a finite symmetric generating set S. We will prove that G is finite. To do so we prove that the G-orbits on X are finite, with a uniform bound. Assume that $1 \in S$. If $m = max\{|g|_w : g \in S\}$, then $S^n x \subset B(x, mn)$ for every $x \in X$, so that by assumption, the growth of $S^n x$ is subexponential. We will show that the expanding properties for actions of (T) groups will imply that the orbit of x is finite with size uniformly bounded in x. The later implies that G is finite.

Let Y be a G-orbit of x. Since the Schreier graph of the action of G on Y has subexponential growth, by Lemma 2.22 we have that this action is amenable. By Kazhdan's Property (T) we have that there exists $\varepsilon > 0$, such that for every unitary action of G on a Hilbert space H without invariant vectors we have

$$(3) \qquad \max_{g \in S} \|g \cdot \xi - \xi\|^2 \geq \varepsilon \|\xi\|^2$$

for every $\xi \in H$.

Assume that Y is infinite and consider the Hilbert space $l^2(Y)$. Let F be a finite subset of Y. Applying the inequality above to the normalized indicator function $\chi_F/\|\chi_F\|_2$ we obtain

$$\max_{g \in S} |gF \Delta F| \geq \varepsilon \cdot \|\chi_F\|^2 = \varepsilon |F|,$$

which implies that the action of G on Y is not amenable, thus Y is finite.

Assuming that Y is finite, we will estimate it's size uniformly on x. Consider a Hilbert space $l_0^2(Y) = \{\xi \in l^2(Y) : \sum_{y \in Y} \xi(y) = 0\}$ with vector

$$\xi = \chi_F - (|F|/|F^c| \cdot \chi_{F^c}),$$

where F is any finite subset of Y such that $2|F| \leq |Y|$. Then $\|\xi\|_2^2 = 2|F|$ and

$$\|g\xi - \xi\|_2^2 = \|(1 + |F|/|F^c|)(\chi_{gF} - \chi_F)\|_2^2$$
$$= (1 + |F|/|F^c|)^2 |gF \Delta F|$$
$$\leq 4|gF \Delta F|.$$

Applying the inequality (3) we obtain

$$\max_{g \in S} |gF \Delta F| \geq \frac{1}{4} \max_{g \in S} \|g\xi - \xi\|_2^2 \geq \frac{\varepsilon}{4} \|\xi\|_2^2 = \frac{\varepsilon}{2}|F|.$$

Thus as soon as $2|F| \leq |Y|$ we have $\max_{s \in S} |gF \Delta F| \geq \frac{\varepsilon}{2}|F|$. Now assume that

$$2|S^n x| \leq |Y|$$

for some n and x. Then there exists $g \in S$ such that

$$|gS^n x \Delta S^n x| \geq \frac{\varepsilon}{2}|S^n x|.$$

Note that $|S^n x \backslash g S^n x| = |g^{-1} S^n x \backslash S^n x|$, thus

$$|gS^n x \Delta S^n x| = |gS^n x \backslash S^n x| + |g^{-1} S^n x \backslash S^n x|$$
$$\leq 2 \max_{h \in \{g, g^{-1}\}} |hS^n x \backslash S^n x|$$
$$\leq 2|S^{n+1} x \backslash S^n x|.$$

Thus $2|S^{n+1} x - S^n x| \geq \frac{\varepsilon}{2}|S^n x|$ which implies

$$|S^{n+1} x| \geq \left(1 + \frac{\varepsilon}{4}\right)|S^n x|.$$

Since $2|S^n x| \leq |Y|$ implies $2|S^m x| \leq |Y|$ for all $m \leq n$ and $|S^0 x| = 1$ we have

$$|S^{n+1} x| \geq \left(1 + \frac{\varepsilon}{4}\right)^{n+1}$$

provided $2|S^n x| \leq |Y|$. Suppose that there exists a sequence of orbits Y_k of arbitrarily large size. Hence we can find a divergent sequence n_k and $x_k \in Y_k$ such that

$$2|S^{n_k} x_k| \leq |Y_k|,$$

thus

$$\frac{\log |S^{n_k+1} x_k|}{n_k + 1} \geq 1 + \frac{\varepsilon}{4},$$

which contradicts (2).   □

We will show that it is possible to construct amenable spaces X such that $W(X)$ contains property (T) groups. We first remark that the groups $W(X)$ behave well with respect to coarse embeddings. A map $q : (X, d_X) \to (Y, d_Y)$ between metric spaces is *a coarse embedding* if there exist nondecreasing functions $\varphi_+, \varphi_- : [0, \infty[\to \mathbb{R}$ such that $\lim_{t \to \infty} \varphi_-(t) = \infty$ and

$$\varphi_-(d_X(x, x')) \leq d_Y(q(x), q(x')) \leq \varphi_+(d_X(x, x'))$$

for every $x, x' \in X$.

LEMMA 2.27. Let $q : (X, d_X) \to (Y, d_Y)$ be a map such that there is an increasing function $\varphi_+ : \mathbb{R}^+ \to \mathbb{R}^+$ such that $d_Y(qx, qy) \leq \varphi_+(d_X(x, y))$, and such that the preimage $q^{-1}(y)$ of every $y \in Y$ has cardinality less than some constant K (e.g. q is a coarse embedding and X has bounded geometry). Let F be a finite metric space of cardinality K. Then $W(X)$ is isomorphic to a subgroup of $W(Y \times F)$.

PROOF. In this statement $Y \times F$ is equipped with the distance

$$d((y, f), (y', f')) = d_Y(y, y') + d_F(f, f').$$

Since F is bigger than $q^{-1}(y)$ for all y, there is a map $f : X \to F$ such that the map

$$\widetilde{q} : x \in X \mapsto (q(x), f(x)) \in Y \times F$$

is injective. We can therefore define an action of $W(X)$ on $Y \times F$ by setting $g(\widetilde{q}(x)) = \widetilde{q}(gx)$ and $g(y, f) = (y, f)$ if $(y, f) \notin \widetilde{q}(X)$. The existence of φ_+ guarantees that this action is wobbling, i.e., that it defines an embedding of $W(X)$ into $W(Y \times F)$. $\square$

CHAPTER 3

Elementary amenable groups

In the previous chapter, we showed that all finite groups and all abelian groups are amenable, and that the class of amenable groups is closed under *elementary operations*: taking subgroups, quotients, extensions, direct unions. This was originally proved by [**126**]. In [**44**], Day defined the following class of groups.

DEFINITION 3.1. *The class of elementary amenable groups* EG is the smallest class of groups that contains all finite groups and all abelian groups, and which is closed under taking elementary operations.

This chapter is dedicated to the systematic treatment of the class of elementary amenable groups.

The following is a classical example of elementary amenable groups.

THEOREM 3.2. Every solvable group is in EG. In particular, every nilpotent group is in EG.

PROOF. Let Γ be a solvable group. By definition, it admits a composition series

$$\{1\} = \Gamma_0 \trianglelefteq \Gamma_1 \trianglelefteq \ldots \trianglelefteq \Gamma_k = \Gamma,$$

such that Γ_i/Γ_{i-1} is an abelian group, for $i = 1, \ldots, k$. Since Γ can be constructed inductively using extensions and abelian groups, we have that Γ is in EG.

One of the definitions of nilpotent group Γ is the existence of upper central series that terminates at it:

$$\{1\} = Z_0 \trianglelefteq Z_1 \trianglelefteq \ldots \trianglelefteq Z_k = \Gamma,$$

where $Z_{i+1} = \{x \in \Gamma : \forall y \in \Gamma : [x, y] \in Z_i\}$. In particular, Z_{i+1}/Z_i is the center of Γ/Z_i, which implies that Γ is solvable. $\square$

Essentially, the class of elementary amenable groups is the largest class of amenable groups which was known to von Neumann. For this reason von Neumann's is popularly attached to the following problem.

PROBLEM 3.3 (Day-von Neumann). Does there exist an amenable group which is not-elementary amenable?

This problem remained open for several decades, after it was posed in [**44**]. Let us discuss the history of this problem in full details.

Let G be a group generated by a finite set S. We say that a non-decreasing function f dominates a non-decreasing function h, if there exist constants α and $C > 0$ such that for for all $n > 1$ we have

$$h(n) \le Cf(\alpha n)$$

Functions f and h are equivalent, $f \sim h$, if we have both $h \preceq f$ and $f \preceq h$.

A non-decreasing function $\gamma_G^S : \mathbb{N} \to \mathbb{N}$ is called *the growth function* of G is defined to be the size of the ball of radius n in the Cayley graph with respect to the generating set S:

$$\gamma_G^S = |B_n(S)|.$$

It is easy to check that if S' is another generating set then $\gamma_G^S \sim \gamma_G^{S'}$. Thus we can omit the subscript that corresponds to the generating set and write γ_G instead.

The growth function γ is *polynomial* is $\gamma(n) \preceq n^\beta$ for some $\beta > 0$. It is *exponential* if $\gamma \succeq e^n$. If a growth function γ is neither polynomial nor exponential, we say that γ is of *intermediate growth*. The growth function is *subexponential* if $\lim_{n \to \infty} \gamma^{1/n}(n) = 1$. Milnor, [**111**], was the first to notice that the $\lim_{n \to \infty} \gamma^{1/n}(n)$ exists. In particular, this result implies that every finitely generated group has either exponential or subexponential growth.

By Gromov's theorem, [**77**], every group of polynomial growth is virtually nilpotent. Thus, by Theorem 3.2, it is elementary amenable. A technical result of Milnor, [**110**] and Wolf, [**156**], shows that there is dichotomy of growth for solvable groups. Namely, every finitely generated solvable group has either exponential or polynomial growth. In [**37**], Chou extended this result to the class of elementary amenable groups. In [**66**], Grigorchuk gave a first example of a group of intermediate growth, thus, solving several longstanding problems: Milnor's problem, and von Neumann-Day problem on existence of a non-elementary amenable group. This ingenious group have received a lot of attention and have been used to answer many other open problems in geometric group theory. Currently, there are many known groups of intermediate growth. We give a review of them in Section 5 of this chapter.

By Chou's result all groups of intermediate growth are not elementary amenable. In all of the known cases it is easier to give an algebraic proof of this fact without relying on their growth. We will give more direct proofs as well as a proof of Chou's result in this chapter.

In [**37**], Chou also proved that the operations of taking subgroups and quotients are redundant in the definition of elementary amenable groups. In particular, this implies that simple infinite, finitely generated groups are not elementary amenable. Currently, the source of all known non-elementary amenable groups is either subgroups of automorphisms of trees or simple finitely generated infinite amenable groups. The only known source of simple finitely generated amenable groups at this time is the class of topological full groups of actions of abelian groups on the Cantor set and their subgroups. The first examples that come from $\mathbb{Z}$-actions have been produced by a combination of results of Matui, Monod and the author. We refer the reader to Chapter 4 for a detailed account on these classes of groups as well as for a detailed proof of their simplicity, finite generation and several proofs of amenability.

1. Simplification of the class of elementary amenable groups

The main goal of this section is to simplify the set of operations needed to define elementary amenable groups: originally this have been done by Chou in [**37**]. Note that we will be giving simplified proofs for the most of the case without following the original proofs of Chou. We will show that the EG class is the smallest class containing finite groups and abelian groups, and closed under taking direct unions and extensions by finite groups or abelian groups.

Let EG_0 be the class of all finite groups and abelian groups. Assume that α is an ordinal such that for all ordinals $\beta < \alpha$ we have already constructed the class EG_β. If α is a limit ordinal we set

$$EG_\alpha = \bigcup_{\beta < \alpha} EG_\beta.$$

If α is a successor, we set EG_α as the class of all groups which can be obtained from $EG_{\alpha-1}$ by taking one time (and one time only!) either a direct union or an extension of a group from $EG_{\alpha-1}$ by either finite group or abelian group.

This allows us to define a rank on the class of elementary amenable groups. For $G \in EG$, the **construction rank** of G is

$$\mathrm{rk}(G) := \min\{\alpha \mid G \in EG_\alpha\}.$$

The construction rank is always either a successor ordinal or zero.

LEMMA 3.4. For every ordinal α the class EG_α is closed under taking subgroups and quotients.

PROOF. The statement of the lemma is trivial for EG_0. Assume that $\alpha > 0$ and for all $\beta < \alpha$ the class EG_β is closed under taking subgroups and quotients. Let $G \in EG_\alpha$, K be a subgroup of G and H be a normal subgroup of G with canonical quotient map $q : G \to G/H$. We have to show that both G/H and K are in EG_α.

If α is a limit ordinal then by the definition $G \in EG_\beta$ for some $\beta < \alpha$, then G/H and K are in EG_β ad there for in EG_α.

If $\alpha - 1$ is a successor ordinal then we have two possible cases: either G is an extension of a group in $EG_{\alpha-1}$ by a finite group or abelian group, or G is a direct union of groups from $EG_{\alpha-1}$.

In the first case we have a short exact sequence $e \to F \to G \to E \to e$ for some groups $F \in EG_{\alpha-1}$ and $E \in EG_0$. Then K is the extension of $F \cap K$ by a subgroup of E. Thus K is in EG_α. In turn G/H is in EG_α, since it is the extension of $q(F)$ and $q(E)$.

Now assume that G is the direct union of $\{G_i\}_{i \in I}$ for some index set I. Then K is the direct union of $\{G_i \cap K\}_{i \in I}$ and G/H is the direct union of $\{q(G_i)\}_{i \in I}$. By assumption, $G_i \cap K$ and $q(G_i)$ are in $EG_{\alpha-1}$, therefore K and G/H are in EG_α. By transfinite induction, we obtain the statement of the lemma. $\square$

Now we are ready to simplify the class of elementary amenable groups.

THEOREM 3.5. The class of elementary amenable groups is the smallest class, which contains all finite groups and all abelian groups and which is closed under taking direct unions and extensions by finite groups or abelian groups.

PROOF. We will show that

$$EG = \bigcup \{EG_\alpha : \alpha \text{ is an ordinal}\},$$

which concludes the statement.

Obviously, $\bigcup_\alpha EG_\alpha$ is closed under taking extensions and, by the previous lemma, it is also closed under taking subgroups and quotients. To see that it is also closed under taking direct limits, let G be a direct union of $\{G_i\}$ for $G_i \in \bigcup_\alpha EG_\alpha$. Thus for each G_i there exists an ordinal α_i such that $G_i \in EG_{\alpha_i}$. Then for $\alpha = \sup_i \alpha_i$ we have $G \in EG_{\alpha+1}$. Therefore, $\bigcup_\alpha EG_\alpha$ coincides with the class of elementary amenable groups. $\square$

As a consequence of the previous theorem we have:

COROLLARY 3.6. *Every finitely generated simple elementary amenable is finite.*

PROOF. Let G be a finitely generated simple group in EG. Let α be the smallest ordinal such that $G \in \text{EG}_\alpha$. Clearly, α is not a limit ordinal. If $\alpha > 0$ then since G is simple it must be a direct union of groups $\{G_i\}$ in $\text{EG}_{\alpha-1}$. Since G is finitely generated it belongs to one of the G_i, which contradicts minimality of α. Thus $\alpha = 0$ which implies that G is finite. $\qquad\square$

2. Elementary classes of amenable groups

Aiming for a classification of amenable groups it is natural to consider the smallest class of groups that contains a given class $\mathcal{B}$ of amenable groups and is closed under taking subgroups, quotients, extensions and direct unions. This class of groups was developed by Osin, [**131**], who called it elementary closure of the class $\mathcal{B}$, and denoted it by $\text{EG}(\mathcal{B})$. As an analog with elementary amenable groups $\text{EG}(\mathcal{B})$ can be defined using ordinals as follows:

Let $\text{EG}_0(\mathcal{B})$ be the base class $\mathcal{B}$. Assume that α is an ordinal such that for all ordinals $\beta < \alpha$ we have already constructed the class $\text{EG}_\beta(\mathcal{B})$. If α is a limit ordinal we set

$$\text{EG}_\alpha(\mathcal{B}) = \bigcup_{\beta < \alpha} \text{EG}_\beta(\mathcal{B}).$$

If α is a successor, we set $\text{EG}_\alpha(\mathcal{B})$ as the class of all groups which can be obtained from $\text{EG}_{\alpha-1}(\mathcal{B})$ by taking one time either a direct union or extension of a group from $\text{EG}_{\alpha-1}(\mathcal{B})$ by a group from the base class $\mathcal{B}$. Define

$$\text{EG}(\mathcal{B}) = \bigcup_{\alpha \text{ is an ordinal}} \text{EG}_\alpha(\mathcal{B}).$$

The proof of the following theorem is completely analogous to the proof of the same statements for elementary amenable groups.

THEOREM 3.7. *Let $\mathcal{B}$ be a class of groups which is closed under taking subgroups and quotients. Then for every ordinal α the class $\text{EG}_\alpha(\mathcal{B})$ is closed under taking subgroups and quotients. Moreover, the elementary closure of $\mathcal{B}$ is the smallest class which contains $\mathcal{B}$ and is closed under taking direct unions or extensions by $\mathcal{B}$.*

In complete analogy with Corollary 3.6 we have

COROLLARY 3.8. *Let $\mathcal{B}$ be a class of groups which is closed under taking subgroups and quotients. Then every finitely generated simple group in $\text{EG}(\mathcal{B})$ is in $\mathcal{B}$.*

In general, it seems to be a rather technical task to separate an elementary closure of one class from another. In particular, as we already mentioned, it was a long standing problem of Day and von Neumann to find an amenable group which is not elementary amenable. We list here natural base classes:

- amenable groups;
- groups of subexponential growth;
- abelian groups;
- finite groups.

The elementary closure of the class of all groups of subexponential growth is called elementary subexponentially amenable groups. Later we will show that there are amenable groups which are not in this closure.

3. Torsion groups

In this section we will show a theorem which will help us to construct non-elementary amenable groups. This is almost a direct consequence of Theorem 3.5.

THEOREM 3.9. *Every torsion elementary amenable group is locally finite.*

PROOF. The class EG_0 clearly satisfies the statement. Assume that $\alpha > 0$ is an ordinal and that EG_β satisfies the statement for every $\beta < \alpha$. Let $G \in EG_\alpha$ be a torsion group. If α is a limit ordinal then G is in EG_β for some $\beta < \alpha$, thus it is locally finite by the induction hypothesis. If α is not a limit ordinal, then G is either a direct union $\bigcup_i G_i$ of groups in $EG_{\alpha-1}$ or an extension

$$e \to K \to G \to Q \to e$$

where $H \in EG_{\alpha-1}$ and $K \in EG_0$.

In the first case, we have that every finitely generated subgroup of G will be in one of G_i, thus finite. In the second case, any finitely generated subgroup H of G will have a finite image in the quotient Q, so the kernel $H \cap K$ is of finite index in H and therefore will be a finitely generated subgroup of K, which implies that H is finite.

Therefore by Theorem 3.5 we have that G is locally finite.   □

4. Dichotomy of the growth of elementary amenable groups

The combination of the results of Milnor, [**110**], and Wolf, [**156**], gives the following theorem.

THEOREM 3.10 (Milnor-Wolf). *Every solvable group has either exponential or polynomial growth.*

The proof of Chou, [**37**], of the following theorem relies heavily on the original proof of Milnor and Wolf.

THEOREM 3.11 (Chou). *Every elementary amenable group has either polynomial or exponential growth.*

Since every solvable group is elementary amenable, we have that Milnor-Wolf theorem is a corollary of Chou's theorem. We begin the proof of Chou's theorem with several lemmas from linear algebra. Recall, that by identifying the standard basis for $\mathbb{Z}^n$ with the standard bases for $\mathbb{Q}^n$ and $\mathbb{C}^n$, we have $GL_n(\mathbb{Z}) \leq GL_n(\mathbb{Q})$ and $GL_n(\mathbb{Z}) \leq GL_n(\mathbb{C})$. We will often implicitly use these embeddings.

LEMMA 3.12 (Tits, [**151**, Lemma 3]). *For $g \in GL_n(\mathbb{Z})$, the following hold*
  (1) *If g is semisimple and all eigenvalues have absolute value 1, then $|g| < \infty$.*
  (2) *If g has an eigenvalue with absolute value at least 2, then there is $a \in A$ so that for each $m \geq 0$ the elements*

$$\sum_{i=0}^{m} \epsilon_i g^i(a)$$

where the ϵ_i vary over $\{0, 1\}$ are pairwise distinct.

PROOF. Suppose first g is semisimple and all eigenvalues have absolute value 1. Taking the basis for $\mathbb{C}^n$ of eigenvectors for g, we see the orbits of g on $\mathbb{C}^n$ are compact. Returning to the standard basis, the orbits of g on $\mathbb{Z}^n$ must be finite, and it follows that $|g| < \infty$.

Suppose that g has an eigenvalue λ with $|\lambda| \geq 2$ and let $v \in \mathbb{C}^n$ be an eigenvector for λ. Let $\beta : \mathbb{C}^n \to \mathbb{C}$ be the projection onto the subspace spanned by v. It now follows that $\beta \circ g = \lambda\beta$, and the composition $\gamma : \mathbb{Z}^n \to \mathbb{C}^n \to \mathbb{C}$ is a non-trivial homomorphism with $\gamma \circ g = \lambda\gamma$.

Taking $a \in \mathbb{Z}^n$ so that $\gamma(a)$ is non-trivial and fixing $m \geq 0$, we compute

$$\gamma\left(\sum_{i=0}^{m} \epsilon_i g^i(a)\right) = \left(\sum_{i=0}^{m} \epsilon_i \lambda^i\right)\gamma(a).$$

Since $|\lambda| \geq 2$, an easy calculation verifies that the sums are distinct for all distinct choices of the ϵ_i. We conclude the elements $\sum_{i=0}^{m} \epsilon_i g^i(a)$, as $\epsilon_i \in \{0,1\}$ varies, are pairwise distinct. $\square$

For a finitely generated group G, we let $d(G)$ be the minimal number of generators of G.

LEMMA 3.13. For $g \in GL_n(\mathbb{Z})$, one of the following holds:

(1) g is semisimple; or
(2) there is a non-trivial g-invariant $A \leq \mathbb{Z}^n$ with $d(A) < n$.

PROOF. We suppose g is not semisimple and show that (2) holds.

Since g is not semisimple, the unipotent part g_u of the Jordan decomposition $g = g_u g_s$ is non-trivial. By classical results, $g_u, g_s \in GL_n(\mathbb{Q})$, so there is a non-trivial maximal $\mathbb{Q}$-vector space $W \leq \mathbb{Q}^n$ so that g_u acts trivially on W. The elements g_u and g_s commute, whereby W is indeed invariant under the action of g. The group $A := W \cap \mathbb{Z}^n$ is then a non-trivial g-invariant subgroup of $\mathbb{Z}^n$. Furthermore, $d(A) < n$, since otherwise $W = \mathbb{Q}^n$ implying $g_u = id$. $\square$

We now prove two group-theoretic lemmas.

LEMMA 3.14 (Milnor, [**110**]). Let $\{1\} \to K \to G \xrightarrow{\psi} A \to 0$ be a short exact sequence of groups with G finitely generated and A abelian. If G has subexponential growth, then K is finitely generated. In particular, $[G, G]$ is finitely generated for any subexponential growth group G.

PROOF. By induction, it suffices to consider the case of $A = \mathbb{Z}$.

Let $g \in G$ be so that $\psi(g) = 1$, find $e_1, \ldots, e_n \in K$ so that $\langle g, e_1, \ldots, e_n \rangle = G$, and put

$$g_{m,i} := g^m e_i g^{-m}$$

for $m \in \mathbb{Z}$ and $1 \leq i \leq n$.

We now argue that $K = \langle g_{m,i} \mid m \in \mathbb{Z} \text{ and } 1 \leq i \leq n \rangle$ by induction on the word length in $\{g^{\pm 1}, e_1^{\pm 1}, \ldots, e_n^{\pm 1}\}$ of $k \in K$. As the base case is immediate, suppose $k \in K$ has length $n + 1$. Since k cannot be a power of g, there is some $l \in \mathbb{Z}$ with $|l|$ least so that $k = he_i^{\pm 1}g^l$ with $|h| \leq n - l$. We now see that $k = hg^l g_{-l,i}^{\pm 1}$, so $kg_{-l,i}^{\mp 1} = hg^l$ and $|hg^l|$ has length at most n. The induction hypothesis thus implies that $kg_{-l,i}^{\mp 1} \in \langle g_{m,i} \mid m \in \mathbb{Z} \text{ and } 1 \leq i \leq n \rangle$. We conclude that $k \in \langle g_{m,i} \mid m \in \mathbb{Z} \text{ and } 1 \leq i \leq n \rangle$, completing the induction.

Fix i and for $m > 0$ consider the words of the form

$$g_{0,i}^{\epsilon_0} \cdots g_{m,i}^{\epsilon_m}$$

where $\epsilon_j \in \{0, 1\}$. There are 2^{m+1} such words. On the other hand, as an easy calculation shows all such words have length at most $3(m + 1)$ in G. Since G has subexponential growth, there is $m > 0$ so that

$$g_{0,i}^{\epsilon_0} \cdots g_{m,i}^{\epsilon_m} = g_{0,i}^{\delta_0} \cdots g_{m,i}^{\delta_m}$$

and $\epsilon_m \neq \delta_m$. We thus deduce that $g_{m,i} \in \langle g_{0,1}, \ldots, g_{m-1,i} \rangle$. It now follows that $g_{k,i} \in \langle g_{0,1}, \ldots, g_{m-1,i} \rangle$ for all $k \geq 0$. The same argument gives the result for $m < 0$. For each i, we thus find $m > 0$, so that

$$g_{k,i} \in \langle g_{j,i} \mid |j| \leq m \rangle$$

for all $k \in \mathbb{Z}$. Since there are only finitely many i, we deduce that K is finitely generated. $\qquad\square$

LEMMA 3.15 (Tits, [**151**, Lemma 2]). Let $\{1\} \to K \to G \xrightarrow{\psi} A \to 0$ be a short exact sequence of groups with G finitely generated and A abelian. If G has subexponential growth and K is virtually nilpotent, then G is virtually nilpotent.

PROOF. We may plainly reduce to the case that A is a free abelian group. Let $g_1, \ldots, g_n$ be so that $\psi(g_1), \ldots, \psi(g_n)$ are free generators for A. By Lemma 3.14, K is finitely generated, so $\langle K, g_1 \rangle$ is finitely generated and has subexponential growth. Furthermore, $\langle K, g_1 \rangle / K = \mathbb{Z}$. We now see that if the lemma holds for $A = \mathbb{Z}$, then the obvious induction argument gives the lemma. We thus assume $A = \mathbb{Z}$ and let $g \in G$ be so that $\psi(g)$ generates A. We also fix a finite symmetric generating set for G which contains g.

Take $L \trianglelefteq K$ a maximal nilpotent subgroup and observe that L is a finite index characteristic subgroup of K. The subgroup $\langle g, L \rangle$ is therefore a finite index subgroup of G, has subexponential growth, and $G/L \simeq \mathbb{Z}$. It thus further suffices to assume that K is nilpotent.

Let $\{1\} = K_0 < K_1 < \cdots < K_n = K$ be a central series for K. We may refine this series so that each factor K_i/K_{i-1} is either finite or finitely generated free abelian. This series can be refined further so that each infinite factor K_i/K_{i-1} admits no non-trivial g-invariant $A \leq K_i/K_{i-1}$ so that $d(A) < d(K_i/K_{i-1})$. Since the original series is central, our refinement remains a normal series of K.

On each factor K_i/K_{i-1}, the element g acts as an automorphism; call this automorphism g_i. When $A_i := K_i/K_{i-1}$ is infinite abelian, we have that $g_i \in GL_n(\mathbb{Z})$ for some n, and by our choice of the series, Lemma 3.13 ensures the g_i is semisimple.

In order to reach a contradiction suppose that there is some i so that A_i is infinite abelian and g_i has an eigenvalue with absolute value different from 1. By passing to G/K_{i-1}, we may assume $i - 1 = 0$, so $A_i = K_1$. Taking the inverse of g and powers, if necessary, we may assume g_1 has an eigenvalue with absolute value greater than 2. Lemma 3.12 then implies that there is $a \in K_1$ so that the sums

$$\sum_{i=0}^{m} \epsilon_i g_1^i(a) = \sum_{i=1}^{m} \epsilon_i g^i a g^{-i}$$

where ϵ_i vary over $\{0, 1\}$ are pairwise distinct. On the other hand, the word length of any such sum is at most $3m|a|$. This, however, contradicts that G has subexponential growth.

For each i so that A_i is infinite, $g_i \in GL_n(\mathbb{Z})$ thus has all eigenvalues equal to one, so Lemma 3.12 thus implies g_i is torsion. It now follows that there is $N \geq 1$ so that g^N acts trivially on each factor K_i/K_{i-1}. As an easy exercise, one verifies that $\langle g^N, K \rangle$ is nilpotent, hence G is virtually nilpotent.   □

Now we are ready to prove Chou's theorem.

PROOF OF THEOREM 3.11. Assume that G is a finitely generated elementary amenable group. Since all virtually nilpotent groups have polynomial growth, we will show that G is either virtually nilpotent or has exponential growth. We argue by induction on the construction rank of G. As the base case is clear, suppose the theorem holds for all finitely generated groups with rank at most α and let $\mathrm{rk}(G) = \alpha + 1$. If G has exponential growth, we are done, so we assume G has subexponential growth.

Since G is finitely generated, the rank is given by a group extension. That is to say, there is $L \trianglelefteq G$ so that $\mathrm{rk}(L) \leq \alpha$ and G/L is either finite or abelian. Applying Lemma 3.14, we further have that L is finitely generated. Plainly, L cannot have exponential growth, so the induction hypothesis implies that L is virtually nilpotent.

If G/L is finite, the inductive claim obviously holds. On the other hand, if G/L is abelian, Lemma 3.15 implies that G is virtually nilpotent. The induction is now finished.   □

5. Groups of intermediate growth

The growth of finitely generated groups is one of the central subjects in geometric group theory. It started with remarkable works of Gromov and Grigorchuk, which play a central role in the current state of the subject. In 1980, Gromov characterized groups of polynomial growth, they all are nilpotent-by-finite. It is easy to produce examples of such groups, as well as examples of groups of exponential growth. The problem whether there are groups that do not have neither polynomial nor exponential growth is due to Milnor, dated 1968, [**112**]. Such type of growth is called intermediate. A seminal example of a group with intermediate growth was constructed by Grigorchuk in [**66**]. His work was a starting point for many future developments in geometric group theory.

In this section we list all currently known groups of intermediate growth. They are the basic examples of non-elementary amenable groups. As far as one can prove that a group has subexponential growth, one can easily deduce that the group is amenable, see Section 6 for the proof. By Theorem 3.11 of Chou every group of intermediate growth is not elementary amenable. In fact, sometimes it is possible to give more straightforward proof of non-elementary amenability, especially for groups acting on rooted trees, see Section 7. In the later chapters we will also see how to prove amenability of these groups without relying on their growth. The main motivation for this is that the proof of intermediate growth varies from one example to another, while the proof of amenability will be unique for all these cases.

It's not a surprise, that some groups of intermediate growth appeared in the history before Grigorchuk's group. However the breakthrough in the field was made exactly by the proof that the first Grigorchuk's group is of intermediate growth.

In fact, there are still many groups, the growth of which we don't know. We list groups of intermediate growth in the chronological order they appeared.

- Sushchanski's p-groups, [145]. The idea of the proof of intermediate growth was outlined by Grigorchuk in [69], a detailed proof was done in [29].
- The first Grigorchuk's group, defined in [66], [108], and will be discussed in Section 8.
- The class of p-groups G_ω, where ω is an infinite sequence on 3 letters, such that at least 2 letters appear in ω infinitely many times. The class was introduced by Grigorchuk in [69].
- The class of groups constructed by Bartholdi and Erschler in [10], which gave the first examples of groups for which the growth function is known. This remarkable class of groups was a starting point for the future developments of the gap conjecture, which asks to produce a group with a given growth function. The torsion groups are constructed recursively starting from the group $K_0 = C_2$ and defining K_{r+1} as a wreath product of K_r with the first Grigorchuk group. The class of torsion free groups are constructed by taking the torsion free Grigorchuk group H as a base group H_1 and making an induction by taking H_{r+1} as a wreath product of H and H_{r+1}.
- A remarkable class of groups constructed by Kassabov and Pak in [93] produces, in particular, a group with growth function oscillating between e^{n^α} and any prescribed function that grows as rapidly as desired. Each group from this class projects onto a Grigorchuk's group of intermediate growth with a projection having a locally finite kernel, thus, it can be constructed using elementary operations out of Grigorchuk's group and finite groups.
- Simple Burnside groups of intermediate growth by Nekrashevych, [117].

The intermediate growth is preserved by taking a product and finite extension of groups, the other known examples are constructed in this way. We will show directly that Grigorchuk's group is not elementary amenable. In particular, this implies that Bartholdi-Erschler groups are also non-elementary amenable.

In the first section we describe historically the first group of intermediate growth constructed by Grigorchuk in [66].

6. Groups acting on rooted trees

Let $\Omega = (E_1, E_2, \ldots)$ be a sequence of finite sets. Define $\Omega_n = E_1 \times E_2 \times \cdots \times E_n$, where Ω_0 is a singleton. The disjoint union $\Omega^* = \bigsqcup_{n \geq 0} \Omega_n$ can be naturally identified with set of vertices of a rooted tree. The sets Ω_n are its levels, i.e., we will consider them as the sets of vertices on the n-th level of the rooted tree. Vertices $v_1 \in \Omega_n$ and $v_2 \in \Omega_{n+1}$ are connected by an edge if and only if v_2 is a continuation of v_1, namely $v_2 = v_1 e$ for some $e \in E_{n+1}$.

Denote by $\mathrm{Aut}(\Omega^*)$ the automorphism group of the rooted tree Ω^*. The group $\mathrm{Aut}(\Omega^*)$ acts transitively on each of the levels Ω_n. Denote by $_m\Omega^*$ the tree of finite paths of the "truncated" diagram defined by the sequence

$$_m\Omega = (E_{m+1}, E_{m+2}, \ldots).$$

For every $g \in \mathrm{Aut}(\Omega^*)$ and $v \in \Omega_n$ there exists an automorphism $g|_v \in \mathrm{Aut}(_m\Omega^*)$ such that

$$g(vw) = g(v)g|_v(w)$$

for all $w \in {}_m\Omega^*$. The automorphism $g|_v$ is called the *section* of g at v.

We list obvious properties of sections. For all $g_1, g_2, g \in \mathrm{Aut}(\Omega^*)$, $v \in \Omega^*$, $v_2 \in {}_n\Omega^*$ and $v_1 \in \Omega_n$ we have

$$(g_1 g_2)|_v = g_1|_{g_2(v)} g_2|_v, \qquad g|_{v_1 v_2} = g|_{v_1}|_{v_2}.$$

An automorphism $g \in \mathrm{Aut}\,\Omega^*$ is said to be *finitary* of *depth* at most n if all sections $g|_v$ for $v \in \Omega_n$ are trivial.

Let $g \in \mathrm{Aut}\,\Omega^*$. Denote by $\alpha_n(g)$ the number of paths $v \in \Omega_n$ such that $g|_v$ is non-trivial. We say that $g \in \mathrm{Aut}\,\Omega^*$ is *bounded (or of bounded type)* if the sequence $\alpha_n(g)$ is bounded.

If $g \in \mathrm{Aut}\,\Omega^*$ is bounded, then there exists a finite set $P \subset \Omega$ of infinite paths such that $g|_v$ is non-finitary only if v is a beginning of some element of P. Consequently, bounded automorphisms of Ω^* act on Ω by homeomorphisms of bounded type.

Suppose that the sequence $\Omega = (E_1, E_2, \ldots) = (X, X, \ldots)$ is constant, so that $_m\Omega^*$ does not depend on m, and $X = \{x_1, \ldots, x_d\}$. In this case, we will denote Ω^* by X^*. An automorphism $g \in \mathrm{Aut}\,\Omega^*$ is said to be *finite-state* if the set $\{g|_v : v \in \Omega^*\} \subset \mathrm{Aut}\,\Omega^*$ is finite.

Let $Aut(X^*)^X$ be the direct product of d copies of $Aut(X^*)$. Consider the wreath product

$$Aut(X^*) \wr S_d = Aut(X^*)^X \rtimes S_d,$$

where the multiplication is given by

$$(a_1, \ldots, a_d)\varepsilon \cdot (b_1, \ldots, b_d)\nu = (a_1 b_{\varepsilon^{-1}(1)}, \ldots, a_d b_{\varepsilon^{-1}(d)})\varepsilon\nu,$$

for every $(a_1, \ldots, a_d)\varepsilon, (b_1, \ldots, b_d)\nu \in Aut(X^*)^X \rtimes S_d$. Note that there exists a homomorphism from $Aut(X^*)$ into $Aut(X^*) \wr S_d$, given by

$$g \mapsto (g|_{x_1}, g|_{x_2}, \ldots, g|_{x_d})\sigma_g,$$

where σ_g is the permutation that g induces on the first level of the tree. In the later sections, we will identify g with its image under this map.

Assume that $g \in Aut(\Omega^*)$ fixes a vertex v of the tree, then we can define a projection of g on the subtree that grows from v by $p_v(g) = g|_v$.

We will use the following notations. The stabilizer of a vertex v of the tree will be denoted by $Stab_G(v)$. The stabilizer of the n-th level is denoted by $Stab_G(n)$. *The rigid stabilizer* of a vertex $v \in \Omega_n$ is defined by

$$rist_G(v) = \{g \in G : g \in Stab_G(n), \text{ if } w \neq v, w \in \Omega_n \text{ then } g|_w = id\}.$$

The rigid stabilizer of the n-th level, $rist_G(n)$, is defined as the group generated by all $rist_G(v)$ with $v \in \Omega_n$. In other words,

$$rist_G(n) = \prod_{v \in \Omega} rist_G(v).$$

7. Non-elemetary amenable groups acting on rooted trees

In the following theorem we give a condition on a finitely generated group of automorphisms of a tree that insures its non-elementary amenability. We will show that this condition is satisfied for Grigorchuk's group, Basilica group and any finitely generated branch group. We will discuss amenability of these groups in later chapters.

THEOREM 3.16. Let $\mathcal{A}$ be the class of finitely generated, non-abelian, infinite groups acting on locally finite rooted trees. Assume that for every G in $\mathcal{A}$, for every vertex v the rigid stabilizer $rist_G(v)$ contains a subgroup admitting a homomorphic image in $\mathcal{A}$. Then every group of $\mathcal{A}$ is not elementary amenable. Moreover, if all groups of $\mathcal{A}$ are of exponential growth, then the groups of $\mathcal{A}$ are not elementary subexponentially amenable.

PROOF. We start the proof with the following claim.

CLAIM 3.17. Let $G \in \mathcal{A}$. For every normal subgroup H of G, there exists a vertex v, a subgroup H_0 of H and a homomorphism $\pi : H_0 \to H_1$ onto a group H_1 which contains $K = rist_G(v)$ as a subgroup.

Firstly, we will deduce the statement from the claim. Assume α is the minimal ordinal among all α with $EG_\alpha \cap \mathcal{A} \neq \emptyset$. Denote by G the group that belongs to $EG_\alpha \cap \mathcal{A}$.

Since G is infinite and non-abelian, it is not in the class EG_0. Clearly, α is not a limit ordinal. Thus G is obtained from the class $EG_{\alpha-1}$ by taking either extension or a direct union. It can not be obtained as a direct union, since finite generacy of G would imply $G \in EG_{\alpha-1}$ contradicting minimality of α. Hence G is obtained as an extension of groups from the class $EG_{\alpha-1}$. Therefore we can find a normal subgroup H of G, which is in the class $EG_{\alpha-1}$. Then H_0, H_1 and K, are in $EG_{\alpha-1}$. Since K contains a subgroup (again in $EG_{\alpha-1}$) admitting a homomorphic image in $\mathcal{A}$, which implies that there exists a group in $\mathcal{A} \cap EG_{\alpha-1}$. This contradicts minimality of α. Since the class of subexponetially amenable groups is closed under taking subgroups and quotients, exactly the same considerations imply that if G is of exponential growth then it is not subexponetially elementary amenable.

To prove the claim we will consider the wreath product presentation of G. Let g be a non-trivial element in H. The group H_0 from the claim is the normal closure of g. Let n be the level of the tree which is fixed by g and the next level is not fixed by g. Then, for some d and $1 \leq k \leq d$, g has the form

$$g = (g_1, \ldots, g_{k-1}, \overline{g}, g_{k+1}, \ldots, g_d)$$

where $\overline{g}$ is an automorphism of the tree which does not fix the first level. In other words,

$$\overline{g} = (\overline{g}_1, \overline{g}_2, .., \overline{g}_{d'})s,$$

for some automorphisms $g_1, g_2, .., g_{d'}$ of the of corresponding trees and a non-trivial permutation $s \in Sym(d')$. Let $m \in \{1, \ldots, d'\}$ be such that $s(m) \neq m$. Let us substitute $\overline{g}$ to g:

$$g = (g_1, \ldots, g_{k-1}, (\overline{g}_1, \overline{g}_2, .., \overline{g}_{d'})s, g_{k+1}, \ldots, g_d).$$

Let $\overline{h} = (1, \ldots, 1, w, 1, \ldots, 1)$, where the automorphism w is placed at the m-th entry. Now, we place $\overline{h}$ at the k-th entry in h:

$$h = (1 \ldots, 1, \overline{h}, 1, \ldots, 1) = (1 \ldots, 1, (1, \ldots, 1, w, 1, \ldots, 1), 1, \ldots, 1).$$

Clearly h belongs to the rigid stabilizer $rist_G(v)$ for some vertex v. Moreover, any element of $rist_G(v)$ can be expressed in the form of h for corresponding w. Let us now compute

$$[g, h] = g^{-1}h^{-1}gh$$
$$= (g_1^{-1}, \ldots, g_{k-1}^{-1}, (\overline{g}_{s(1)}^{-1}, \overline{g}_{s(2)}^{-1}, \ldots, \overline{g}_{s(d')}^{-1})s^{-1}, g_{k+1}^{-1}, \ldots, g_d^{-1})$$
$$\cdot (1 \ldots, 1, (1, \ldots, 1, w^{-1}, 1, \ldots, 1), 1, \ldots, 1)$$
$$\cdot (g_1, \ldots, g_{k-1}, (\overline{g}_1, \overline{g}_2, \ldots, \overline{g}_{d'})s, g_{k+1}, \ldots, g_d)$$
$$\cdot (1 \ldots, 1, (1, \ldots, 1, w, 1, \ldots, 1), 1, \ldots, 1)$$
$$= (g_1^{-1}, \ldots, g_{k-1}^{-1}, (\overline{g}_{s(1)}^{-1}, \ldots, \overline{g}_{s(m-1)}^{-1},$$
$$\overline{g}_{s(m)}^{-1}w^{-1}, \overline{g}_{s(m+1)}^{-1}, \ldots, \overline{g}_{s(d')}^{-1})s^{-1}, g_{k+1}^{-1}, \ldots, g_d^{-1})$$
$$\cdot (g_1, \ldots, g_{k-1}, (\overline{g}_1, \ldots, \overline{g}_{s(m)-1}, \overline{g}_{s(m)}w, \overline{g}_{s(m)+1}, \ldots, \overline{g}_{d'})s, g_{k+1}, \ldots, g_d)$$
$$= (1 \ldots, 1, (y_1, \ldots, y_{m-1}, w, y_{m+1}, \ldots, y_{d'}), 1, \ldots, 1),$$

where w is placed on the m-th entry and $y_1, \ldots, y_{d'}$ are all but one trivial automorphisms of the tree. This implies that $p_v([g, h]) = w$, thus there is a homomorphism from H_0 onto the rigid stabilizer $rist_G(v)$, which completes the proof of the claim. $\square$

The statement of the next corollary follows follows from assumption $\mathcal{A} = \{G\}$.

COROLLARY 3.18. Let G be a finitely generated, non-abelian, infinite group of automorphisms of a d-homogeneous tree $\mathcal{T}$. If there exists a subgroup $K < G$ such that the following holds:

(i) $K \times K \times \ldots \times K < K$, where the product is taken d times,
(ii) for some vertex v on the tree, $p_v(Stab_K(v))$ contains G.

Then G is not elementary amenable. Moreover, if G is of exponential growth, then G is not subexponentially elementary amenable.

8. The first Grigorchuk's group

In this section we describe historically the first group of intermediate growth constructed by Grigorchuk in 1980, [66]. The existence of such group was an open problem of Milnor, dated 1968, [112]. We refer the reader to the paper [2] producing an example of a group which contains Grigorchuk's group as a finite index subgroup, this implies that this group is also of intermediate growth.

The Grigorchuk's group is generated by 4 automorphisms of the binary tree $\mathcal{T}$, for a finite word v in $\{0, 1\}$, they are defined recursively

$$
\begin{aligned}
a(0v) &= 1v, & a(1v) &= 0v; \\
b(00v) &= 01v, & b(01v) &= 00v, & b(1v) &= 1c(v); \\
c(00v) &= (01v), & c(01v) &= (00v), & c(1v) &= 1d(v); \\
d(0v) &= 0v, & d(1v) &= 1b(v).
\end{aligned}
$$

It has the following wreath product presentation:

$$a = (1, 1)\varepsilon, \quad b = (a, c), \quad c = (a, d), \quad d = (1, b),$$

where ε is the non-trivial element of the group $\mathbb{Z}/2\mathbb{Z}$.

COROLLARY 3.19. Grigorchuk's group is not elementary amenable.

PROOF. Let K be the normal subgroup generated by $(ab)^2$. It is well known, see for example [**79**], that $K \times K < K$. We will prove this here for completeness. Note that $a^2 = b^2 = c^2 = d^2 = 1$, $b = cd$ and b, c, d generate a finite abelian group. It is easy to check that both $p_0(St_G(1))$ and $p_1(St_G(1))$ contain G. Since $(abad)^2 = (ab)^2 d^{-1}(ab)^{-2}d$, we have $(abad)^2$ is in K. It follows

$$(abad)^2 = (1, abab) \in K.$$

Moreover, $a(abad)^2 a^{-1} = (abab, 1) \in K$. Therefore, we have $K \times K < K$.

Now we will show that there exists a vertex v such that $p_1(St_K(v))$ contains G. Note that

$$(ab)^2 = (ca, ac) \in K.$$

Therefore, $p_1(St_K(1))$ contains ca and, thus, it contains $H = \langle ca \rangle^G$. We claim that ac, ad, b are in $H' = p_1(St_H(1))$. This implies that $\langle ad, b \rangle^G$ is a subgroup in H'. From this it follows that the elements $b = (a, c)$, $b^a = (c, a)$, $(ad)b(ad) = (d, ab)$ are in H', and $p_1(St_{H'}(1))$ contains G (because it contains a, c and d), which implies the statement.

Our claim follow from the following computations:

$$ca = (a, d)\varepsilon,$$
$$(ca)^2 = (ad, da) \in H,$$
$$ac(ca)^d = (d, a)\varepsilon(ab, bd)\varepsilon = (b, b) \in H.$$

$\square$

9. Basilica group

In this section, we will only consider the wreath product presentation of Basilica group, which was introduced in [**74**]:

$$a = (1, b) \text{ and } b = (1, a)\varepsilon,$$

where ε is a non-trivial element of the group $\mathbb{Z}/2\mathbb{Z}$. The proof of the following becomes almost straightforward.

COROLLARY 3.20. The Basilica group is not elementary subexponentially amenable. In particular, it is not elementary amenable.

PROOF. Let G be the Basilica group. Firstly we note that, by Lemma 3.21, G contains a free semigroup and, thus, it is of exponential growth. We will apply Theorem 3.18 with $K = G'$.

CLAIM. $G' \geq G' \times G'$. We start by showing that the projections onto both coordinates of $St_G(1)$ coincide with G. Direct computations show

$$a^b = (a^{-1}, 1)\varepsilon(1, b)(1, a)\varepsilon - (a^{-1}ba, 1) = (b^a, 1) \in St_G(1)$$
$$b^2 = (a, a) \in St_G(1),$$

and moreover $a = (1, b) \in St_G(1)$. Thus, $p_1(St_G(1)) = p_2(St_G(1)) = G$.

Note that

$$[a, b^2] = (1, b^{-1})(a^{-1}, a^{-1})(1, b)(a, a) = (1, b^{-1}a^{-1}ba) = (1, [b, a]).$$

Summarizing above, we obtain

$$G' \geq \langle [a, b^2] \rangle^G \geq \{e\} \times \langle [b, a] \rangle^G = \{e\} \times G'.$$

Moreover, $(\{e\} \times G')^b = G' \times \{e\}$, therefore the claim follows.

Since we have the following expressions

$$b^{-1}, a] = (b^{-1}, b) \text{ and } [a, b^2] = (1, b^{-1}a^{-1}ba)$$

we obtain that $b, b^{-1}a^{-1}ba \in p_2(G')$. But

$$b^2 = (a, a) \text{ and } b^{-1}a^{-1}ba = (a^{-1}b^{-1}a, b).$$

Thus $p_2(p_2(G'))$ contains G. In [**74**], it was shown that G is of exponential growth, we add the proof of this in the Lemma 3.21 for completeness. Applying Theorem 3.18 we obtain the statement. $\qquad\square$

LEMMA 3.21 (Grigorchuk-Żuk, [**74**]). The semigroup generated by a and b is isomorphic to the free non-abelian semigroup.

PROOF. To reach a contradiction consider two different words V and W that represent the same element in G and such that $\rho = |V| + |W|$ is minimal. It is easy to check that ρ can not be 0 or 1. From the wreath product representation of G we see that the parity of occurrences of b in V and in W should be the same. Both words V and W are products of the elements of the form

$$a^n = (1, b^n), \quad n \geq 0$$

or of the form

$$ba^m b = (1, a)\varepsilon(1, b^m)(1, a)\varepsilon = (b^m a, a), \quad m \geq 0.$$

Assume that one of the words does not contain b, say $W = a^n$. Then, since a is of infinite order, V must contain b. Projecting V to the first coordinate we obtain a word which is equal to identity. Moreover the length of this word is strictly less ρ, which gives a contradiction. Thus we can assume that both words contain b.

Suppose that the number of b's in W and V is one, then by minimality these words should have the form ba^n and $a^m b$. But $ba^n = (b^n, a)\varepsilon$ and $a^m b = (1, b^m a)\varepsilon$, which represent two different words.

Multiplying by b both words V and W, we can assume that b appears an even number of times. This can increase the length of V and W by at most 1. Suppose that in both words b appears twice.

Thus either both words contain two b's and $|V| + |W| = \rho$ or one of them contains at least four b's, in which case we have $|V| + |W| \leq \rho + 2$. In the first case, taking the projection of the words onto the second coordinate we see that ρ decreases by 2 for these projections, which contradicts minimality. Similarly, in the second case ρ decreases by 3 which again contradicts minimality. Hence, the statement follows. $\qquad\square$

10. Finitely generated branch groups

Suppose that $m = \{m_i \mid i \geq 0\}$ is a sequence of natural numbers. We denote by T_m the rooted tree, such that that any vertex at level i has m_i children. Such trees are called spherically homogeneous.

For a vertex v of T_m denote T_v the subtree of T_m which lies under v. Let $|v|$ be the distance from the root to v.

A group G acting on a spherically homogeneous tree is called *branch group* if the following conditions are satisfied:

(1) All rigid stabilizers are of finite index in G, i.e., $|G : rist_G(n)| < \infty$ for every $n \in \mathbb{N}$;

(2) G acts transitively on each level.

We remark that branch groups can not be of polynomial growth. We start with analyzing rigid stabilizers.

DEFINITION 3.22. Let G be a group of automorphisms on T_m, and let v be a vertex of T_m. Denote by $st_G(v)$ the subgroup of G that fixes v. For $g \in st_G(v)$ denote $g_{|v} = \pi_v(g)$ the automorphism of the subtree T_v, obtained by restricting g to T_v.

If G is a branch group, we are going to show that every $rist_G(v)$ has a homomorphic image that is also branch. To construct it, we will choose a subgraph of T_v where $rist_G(v)$ acts transitively, and restrict $rist_G(v)$ to that subgraph.

We start with a lemma. Let Y be a subset of vertices of level n of the tree T_m. Denote by T_Y the union of subtrees T_v, $v \in Y$. If g fixes each element of Y, denote by $g_{|Y}$ the restriction of g to T_Y.

LEMMA 3.23. Let G be a branch group. Then $\prod_{v \in Y} rist_G(v)$ is of finite index in $st_G(n)_{|Y}$.

PROOF. Since G is branch, $\prod_{v:|v|=n} rist_G(v)$ is of finite index in $st_G(n)$. Restricting to Y, we have that $(\prod_{v:|v|=n} rist_G(v))_{|Y}$ is of finite index in $st_G(n)_{|Y}$. It is left to notice that restricting to Y kills every $rist_G(v)$ for $v \notin Y$, and so $(\prod_{v:|v|=n} rist_G(v))_{|Y} = \prod_{v \in Y} rist_G(v)$ □

We have the following corollary.

COROLLARY 3.24. For every v, $rist_G(v)$ is of finite index in $st_G(v)_{|v}$.

PROOF. To derive it from the lemma, take $Y = \{v\}$.   □

We also need the following general lemma

LEMMA 3.25. Suppose G acts transitively on a set X, and $H < G$ is of index at most k. Then the number of H-orbits in X is at most k.

PROOF. Let $G = \cup_{i=1}^k H g_i$. Then $X = Gx = \cup_{i=1}^k H g_i x$, where each $H g_i x$ is an H-orbit.   □

LEMMA 3.26. If G is a branch group, for every vertex v, $rist_G(v)$ has a homomorphic image that is also branch.

PROOF. Since G is transitive on levels of the tree, it follows that $st_G(v)$ is transitive on levels of the subtree T_v. The group $rist_G(v)$ may not be transitive on levels of T_v, but the number of orbits on each level is uniformly bounded, since $rist_G(v)$ is of finite index in $st_G(v)_{|v}$ by Lemma 3.23.

Let O_n be the set of orbits of $rist_G(v)$ on the n-th level of T_v. If $Y \in O_n$ is an orbit, define $e(Y) \in O_{n-1}$ as the orbit of (some) parent of a vertex in Y. Since $rist_G(v)$ consists of tree automorphisms, the map $e : O_n \to O_{n-1}$ is well-defined (i.e. does not depend on the choice of a vertex in Y). We should actually use e_n, but we suppress the dependence on n to ease the notation.

Now note that e is surjective for all n, since each vertex has children. It follows that the number of elements in O_n cannot decrease. Since it is uniformly bounded, it must become constant after some n, and after that the map $e : O_n \to O_{n-1}$ is a bijection, since it is a surjective map between sets of equal size.

It follows that for some n_0 there are orbits $Y_n \in O_n$ for $n \geq n_0$, such that $e^{-1}(Y_n) = Y_{n+1}$, that is, all children of vertices in Y_n lie in Y_{n+1}. Let Γ be the graph which is the union of subtrees T_w, $w \in Y_{n_0}$. Then Γ is invariant with respect to $rist_G(v)$. Note that Y_n is the union of level sets of T_w, $w \in Y_{n_0}$, and recall that $rist_G(v)$ acts transitively on Y_n for each $n \geq n_0$.

By Lemma 3.23, the subgroup $\prod_{w \in Y_n} rist_G(w)$ is of finite index in $rist_G(v)_{|\Gamma}$.

It is left to note that by connecting all vertices in Y_{n_0} to a new vertex (root), we turn Γ into a tree on which $rist_G(v)$ acts. By above this action is transitive on levels, and the rigid stabilizers of the levels are of finite index. Thus $rist_G(v)_{|\Gamma}$ is a branch group.   □

COROLLARY 3.27. *Finitely generated branch groups are not elementary amenable.*

PROOF. Let $\mathcal{A}$ be the class of all finitely generated branch groups. Then for every vertex v there exist a group from $\mathcal{A}$ on which $rist_G(v)$ projects. Indeed, for a given group G in $\mathcal{A}$, we have that the rigid stabilizer of each level is finitely generated. Since the later is a product of rigid stabilizers of the vertices on the n-th level, we have that all rigid stabilizers of any vertex are finitely generated. By Lemma 3.26, we have that each rigid stabilizer projects onto a branch group, thus, a group from $\mathcal{A}$. Therefore Theorem 3.18 implies the statement.   □

CHAPTER 4

The topological full group
of a Cantor minimal system

In this chapter we introduce topological full groups of Cantor minimal dynamical systems. These groups are sources of non-elementary amenable groups. In 2006, Matui showed that the commutator subgroups of topological full groups of Cantor minimal *subshifts* are finitely generated and simple. In 2012, Monod and the author showed that they are amenable. Moreover, by a combination of results of Giordano-Putnam-Skau and Boyle one can deduce that there are uncountably many of such groups. The aim of this chapter is to give the full proof the result of Matui, and the fact that there are uncountably many pairwise non-isomorphic subshifts.

In the first sections we give basic notions and properties of homeomorphisms of the Cantor space. We introduce the notion of a Kakutani-Rokhlin partition used to construct elements of topological full groups with given properties.

Let T be a homeomorphism of a Cantor space $\mathbf{C}$, such that there is no T-invariant proper closed subset in $\mathbf{C}$. The topological full group of T, denoted by $[[T]]$, is the group of all piecewise powers of T homeomorphisms of $\mathbf{C}$, i.e., for every element g in $[[T]]$ there is a finite clopen partition of $\mathbf{C}$ such that on each piece of this partition g acts as a constant power of T.

A central role in the proof of simplicity of $[[T]]'$ is played by the space $\mathcal{M}(T)$ of all T-invariant Borel probability measures on the Cantor space. The key step for proving simplicity of the commutator subgroup is a construction of Glasner and Weiss: given two clopen subsets $A, B \subset \mathbf{C}$ related by $\mu(A) < \mu(B)$ for every $\mu \in \mathcal{M}(T)$, there exists an involution g in $[[T]]$ with $g(A) \subset B$.

One of the realizations of Cantor spaces is the space of all sequences indexed by integers $\mathbb{Z}$ with values in a finite set A. The topology is given by the product topology on $A^{\mathbb{Z}}$. *The shift* on $A^{\mathbb{Z}}$ is the homeomorphism S which shifts a sequence, i.e., $S[(a_i)_{i \in \mathbb{Z}}] = (a_{i-1})_{i \in \mathbb{Z}}$. A *subshift* is a closed subset of $A^{\mathbb{Z}}$ such that the restriction of S is minimal on it.

In order to prove simplicity of $[[T]]'$ we do not impose any restrictions on T except minimality. On the other hand, to prove finite generation of $[[T]]'$, in addition to minimality, we require T to be a subshift.

The idea of finite generation is simple, it is based on several reductions of generating sets, however the proof itself is rather technical. The main idea is as follows. Let U be a clopen set in $\mathbf{C}$, such that U, $T(U)$ and $T^{-1}(U)$ are pairwise disjoint. Define

$$f_U(x) = \begin{cases} T(x), & x \in T^{-1}(U) \cup U \\ T^{-2}(x), & x \in T(U) \\ x, & \text{otherwise.} \end{cases}$$

One can show that $f_U \in [[T]]'$ and make the first reduction to the generating set by proving that $\mathcal{U} = \{f_U : U$ is clopen set and $U, T(U), T^{-1}(U)$ are pairwise disjoint$\}$ generates $[[T]]'$. If T is a subshift, it is possible to reduce this generating set to the set where U is a cylinder, i.e., a subset of $A^{\mathbb{Z}}$ of the type

$$\langle\langle a_{-m} \ldots a_{-1} \underline{a_0} a_1 \ldots a_n \rangle\rangle = \{x \in A^{\mathbb{Z}} : x(i) = a_i, -m \le i \le n\},$$

where $a_{-m}, \ldots, a_n$ are fixed and the underlining of a_0 means that a_0 is in the 0's position of $\mathbb{Z}$-enumeration. Using this reduction and finiteness of A it is almost straightforward to conclude that this set can be further reduced to a finite generating set.

A famous result of Giordano, Putnam and Skau states that every isomorphism of a topological full group is necessarily spatial, i.e., it is given by a homeomorphism of the underlining Cantor space. This result was extended by Bezuglyi and Medynets to the commutator subgroups. Namely, every isomorphism of commutator subgroups is nessesarily spatial. Moreover, by Boyle's conjugacy theorem any spatial isomorphism of two topological groups $[[T_1]]$ and $[[T_2]]$ is given by flip conjugation: there exists a homeomorphism S of $\mathbf{C}$ such that $T_1 = S^{-1}T_2 S$ or $T_1 = S^{-1}T_2^{-1}S$.

Thus, in order to deduce that there are uncountably many pairwise non-isomorphic commutator subgroups of topological full groups of minimal subshifts one needs to construct uncountably many subshifts which are not flip conjugate. This can be done by considering rotations of the circle, and building from the circle a Cantor set. Namely, for an irrational number α and the rotation $r_\alpha : z \mapsto z + \alpha$ on the circle $\mathbb{R}/\mathbb{Z}$, we can define a Cantor set set X_α by replacing each $x \in \alpha\mathbb{Z}$ on the circle $\mathbb{R}/\mathbb{Z}$ with the pair of points denoted by $\{x_-, x_+\}$. Let $R_\alpha : X_\alpha \to X_\alpha$ be defined by $R_\alpha(x) = x + \alpha$ if $x \notin \mathbb{Z}\alpha$, and $R_\alpha(x_\pm) = (x+\alpha)_\pm$ otherwise. One can show that R_α is minimal subshift. From unique ergodicity of irrational rotations we deduce unique ergodicity of R_α. Thus we can consider a Hilbert space $L^2(X_\alpha, \mu)$ with unique R_α-invariant Borel probability measure on X_α. This defines a unitary operator $U_T : L^2(X, \mu_\alpha) \to L^2(X, \mu_\alpha)$ by $U_\alpha(f) = f \circ R_\alpha^{-1}$. Comparing spectra of these unitary operators we deduce that for all irrational α, α' with $\alpha \ne \alpha'$ the subshifts $R_\alpha, R_{\alpha'}$ are not flip conjugate.

The proof of amenability of topological full groups of Cantor minimal systems will be postponed to the later sections. In fact, we will give two different proofs of this result: one using embedding of the topological full group into the group of integers, and another by realizing it as Vershik transformations of a Bratteli diagram.

1. The topological full group of Cantor minimal systems. Definition and basic facts

We begin with basic definitions. The Cantor space is denoted by $\mathbf{C}$, it is characterized up to a homeomorphism as a compact, metrizable, perfect and totally disconnected topological space. The group of all homeomorphisms of the Cantor space is denoted by $Homeo(\mathbf{C})$. A *Cantor dynamical system* $(T, \mathbf{C})$ is the Cantor space together with its homeomorphism $T \in Homeo(\mathbf{C})$.

Let A be a finite set called the alphabet. A basic example of Cantor space is the set $A^{\mathbb{Z}}$ of all sequences in A indexed by integers, and equipped with the product topology. A sequence $\{\alpha_i\}$ converges to α in this space if and only if for all n there exists i_0 such that for all $i \geq i_0$, we have that α_i coincides with α on the interval $[-n, n]$.

The basic example of a Cantor dynamical system is *the shift* on $A^{\mathbb{Z}}$, i.e., the map $s : A^{\mathbb{Z}} \to A^{\mathbb{Z}}$ is defined by

$$s(x)(i) = x(i - 1)$$

for all $x \in A^{\mathbb{Z}}$.

The system $(T, \mathbf{C})$ is *minimal* if there is no non-trivial closed T-invariant subset in $\mathbf{C}$. Equivalently, the closure of the T-orbit of any point p in $\mathbf{C}$ coincides with $\mathbf{C}$:

$$\overline{\{T^i p : i \in \mathbb{Z}\}} = \mathbf{C}$$

One of the basic examples of a Cantor minimal system is *the odometer*, defined by the map $\sigma : \{0, 1\}^{\mathbb{N}} \to \{0, 1\}^{\mathbb{N}}$:

$$\sigma(x)(i) = \begin{cases} 0, & \text{if } i < n, \\ 1, & \text{if } i = n, \\ x(i), & \text{if } i > n \end{cases}$$

where $x \in \{0, 1\}^{\mathbb{N}} \backslash \{\overline{1}\}$, $\overline{1}$ is constant one sequence, and n is the smallest integer such that $x(n) = 0$. Define $\sigma(\overline{1}) = \overline{0}$. One can verify that the odometer is a minimal homeomorphism.

While the shift is not minimal, one can construct many Cantor subspaces of $A^{\mathbb{Z}}$ on which the action of the shift is minimal. Closed and shift-invariant subsets of $A^{\mathbb{Z}}$ are called *subshifts*.

A sequence $\alpha \in A^{\mathbb{Z}}$ is *homogeneous*, if for every finite interval $J \subset \mathbb{Z}$, there exists a constant $k(J)$, such that the restriction of α to any interval of the size $k(J)$ contains the restriction of α to J as a subsequence. In other words, for any interval J' of the size $k(J)$, there exist $t \in \mathbb{Z}$ such that $J + t \subset J'$ and $\alpha(s + t) = \alpha(s)$ for every $s \in J$.

THEOREM 4.1. *Let A be a finite set, T be the shift on $A^{\mathbb{Z}}$, $\alpha \in A^{\mathbb{Z}}$ and*

$$X = \overline{Orb_T(\alpha)}.$$

Then the system (T, X) is minimal if and only if α is homogeneous.

PROOF. Assume that the sequence $\alpha \in A^{\mathbb{Z}}$ is homogeneous. Let $\beta \in \overline{Orb_T(\alpha)}$. In order to show that X is minimal, it suffices to show that $\alpha \in \overline{Orb_T(\beta)}$. That is, that for any interval J there exists m such that $T^m \beta = \alpha$ on J.

Take any interval I of length bigger then $k(J)$. We can find s such that $\beta = T^s \alpha$ on J, thus $T^{-s} \beta = \alpha$ on $J + s$. Since the size of $I + s$ is bigger then $k(J)$, there is t such that $J + t \subset I + s$ and $T^t \alpha = \alpha$ on I, hence $\alpha = T^{-t} \alpha$ on $J + t$. Thus on the interval $J + t$ we have $T^{-s} \beta = \alpha = T^{-t} \alpha$, therefore $T^{t-s} \beta = \alpha$ on J. Since J is arbitrary, it follows that $\alpha \in \overline{Orb_T(\beta)}$ and that X is minimal.

Assume now that (T, X) is a minimal system. To reach a contradiction assume that α is not homogeneous. Then there exists an interval J such that for any n there is an interval I_n of size bigger then n with the property that the restriction of α to I_n does not contain the restriction of α to J. Choose a subsequence n_k such that the length of I_{n_k} is an increasing sequence. Choose m_k such that $I_{n_k} - m_k$ is a nested sequence of intervals whose union is $\mathbb{Z}$. Consider the sequence $T^{m_k} \alpha$, and find a subsequence that converges, say to β (this is possible since X is compact).

It is clear that β does not contain the restriction of α to J. Thus $\alpha \notin \overline{Orb_T(\beta)}$, which gives a contradiction. $\qquad\qquad\qquad\qquad\qquad\qquad\qquad\qquad\qquad\qquad\qquad$ $\square$

The topological full group. The central object of this chapter is the topological full group of a Cantor minimal system.

The topological full group of $(T, \mathbf{C})$, denoted by $[[T]]$, is the group of all $\phi \in Homeo(\mathbf{C})$ for which there exists a continuous function $n : \mathbf{C} \to \mathbb{Z}$ such that

$$\phi(x) = T^{n(x)}x \text{ for all } x \in \mathbf{C}.$$

Since $\mathbf{C}$ is compact, the function $n(\cdot)$ takes only finitely many values. Moreover, for every value k, the set $n^{-1}(k)$ is clopen. Thus, there exists a finite partition of $\mathbf{C}$ into clopen subsets such that $n(\cdot)$ is constant on each piece of the partition.

Kakutani-Rokhlin partitions. Let T be a minimal homeomorphism of the Cantor space $\mathbf{C}$, we can associate a partition of $\mathbf{C}$ as follows.

Let D be a non-empty clopen subset of $\mathbf{C}$. It is easy to check that for every point $p \in \mathbf{C}$ the minimality of T implies that the forward orbit $\{T^k p : k \in \mathbb{N}\}$ is dense in $\mathbf{C}$. Define the first return function $t_D : D \to \mathbb{N}$:

$$t_D(x) = \min(n \in \mathbb{N} : T^n(x) \in D).$$

Since $t_D^{-1}[0, n]$ is clopen as a finite union of clopen sets, it follows that t_D is continuous. Thus we can find natural numbers N, k_1, ..., k_N and a partition

$$D = D_1 \sqcup D_2 \sqcup \ldots \sqcup D_N$$

into clopen subsets, such that t_D restricted to D_i is equal to k_i for all $1 \le i \le N$.

This gives a decomposition of $\mathbf{C}$, called *a Kakutani-Rokhlin partition*:

$$\mathbf{C} = (D_1 \sqcup T(D_1) \sqcup \ldots \sqcup T^{k_1-1}(D_1)) \sqcup$$
$$\sqcup (D_2 \sqcup T(D_2) \sqcup \ldots \sqcup T^{k_2-1}(D_2)) \sqcup \ldots$$
$$\ldots \sqcup (D_N \sqcup T(D_N) \sqcup \ldots \sqcup T^{k_N-1}(D_N))$$

The family of decompositions $D_i \sqcup T(D_i) \sqcup \ldots \sqcup T^{k_i}(D_i)$ is called *a tower* over D_i. The base of the tower is defined to be D_i and the top of the tower is $T^{k_i}(D_i)$.

Refining of the Kakutani-Rokhlin partitions. Let $\mathcal{P}$ be a finite clopen partition of $\mathbf{C}$ and let

$$\mathbf{C} = (D_1 \sqcup T(D_1) \sqcup \ldots \sqcup T^{k_1-1}(D_1)) \sqcup$$
$$\sqcup (D_2 \sqcup T(D_2) \sqcup \ldots \sqcup T^{k_2-1}(D_2)) \sqcup \ldots$$
$$\ldots \sqcup (D_N \sqcup T(D_N) \sqcup \ldots \sqcup T^{k_N-1}(D_N))$$

be the Kakutani-Rokhlin partition over a clopen set D in $\mathbf{C}$. There exists a refinement of the partition of $D_i = \bigsqcup_{j=1}^{j_i} D_{i,j}$ such that the partition

$$(D_{1,1} \sqcup T(D_{1,1}) \sqcup .. \sqcup T^{k_1-1}(D_{1,1})) \sqcup .. \sqcup (D_{1,j_1} \sqcup T(D_{1,j_1}) \sqcup .. \sqcup T^{k_1-1}(D_{1,j_1})) \sqcup \ldots$$
$$\sqcup (D_{N,1} \sqcup T(D_{N,1}) \sqcup .. \sqcup T^{k_N-1}(D_{N,1})) \sqcup \ldots$$
$$\sqcup (D_{N,j_N} \sqcup T(D_{N,j_N}) \sqcup .. \sqcup T^{k_N-1}(D_{N,j_N}))$$

of $\mathbf{C}$ is a refinement of $\mathcal{P}$. Indeed, this can be obtained as follows. Assume there exists a clopen set $A \in \mathcal{P}$ such that $A \cap T^i(D_j) \ne \emptyset$ and $A \Delta T^i(D_j) \ne \emptyset$ for some i, j. Then we refine the partition $\mathcal{P}$ by the sets $T^s(T^{-i}(A) \cap D_j)$, $0 \le s \le k_j$. Since $\mathcal{P}$ is finite this operation is exhaustive.

2. Basic facts on dynamics on the Cantor space

We collect basic facts and definitions on dynamics on the Cantor space and several lemmas on minimal homeomorphisms to which we will refer several times in later sections.

The *support* of a homeomorphism T of the Cantor space $\mathbf{C}$ is defined by

$$supp(T) = \overline{\{x \in \mathbf{C} : T(x) \neq x\}}.$$

Generally, the support of a homeomorphism does not need to be open. However, for any minimal homeomorphism T, the support of each element of the topological full group $[[T]]$ is a clopen set. This follows immediately from the definition of $[[T]]$.

A homomorphism $T \in Homeo(\mathbf{C})$ is called *periodic*, if every orbit of T is finite, and *aperiodic* if every orbit is infinite. It has *period n* if every orbit has exactly n elements.

LEMMA 4.2. Let $T \in Homeo(\mathbf{C})$ be a periodic homeomorphism of period n. Then there exists a clopen set $A \subset \mathbf{C}$ such that

$$\mathbf{C} = \bigsqcup_{i=0}^{n-1} T^i(A).$$

PROOF. For any $x \in \mathbf{C}$ let $U_x \subset \mathbf{C}$ be a clopen neighborhood such that $T^i(U_x) \cap U_x = \emptyset$ for all $1 \leq i \leq n$, where n is the period of T. Since $\mathbf{C}$ is compact there are $x_1, \ldots, x_k$ such that $\mathbf{C} = \bigcup_{1 \leq i \leq k} U_{x_i}$. Let $A_1 = U_{x_1}$ and

$$A_{j+1} = A_j \bigcup \left(U_{x_{j+1}} \backslash \bigcup_{i=1}^{n-1} T^i(A_j) \right).$$

It is trivial to check that the statement holds for $A := A_n$. $\qquad\square$

LEMMA 4.3. Let $T \in Homeo(\mathbf{C})$ be a minimal homeomorphism. Then for any $g \in [[T]]$ and $n \in \mathbb{N}$ the set

$$\mathcal{O}_n = \{x \in \mathbf{C} : |Orb_g(x)| = n\}$$

is clopen.

PROOF. Let $\mathbf{C} = \bigcup_{i \in I} A_i$ be a finite clopen partition of $\mathbf{C}$ such that the restriction of g to each piece of the partition coincides with some power of T.

Denote by $\{B_j\}_{j \in J}$ the refinement of $\{A_i\}_{i \in I}$ and the sets $\{T^{-k}(A_i)_{i \in I}\}$, $1 \leq k \leq n$. Thus

$$g|_{B_j} = T^{m_j}|_{B_j},$$

for some $\{m_j\}_{j \in J}$.

Let $x \in \mathcal{O}_n$, we will show that there is a neighborhood of x inside $\mathcal{O}_n$. Let $j_0, \ldots, j_n$ be such that $T^k x \in B_{j_k}$ for all $0 \leq k \leq n$. Then we have $g^n(x) = x$ for all $x \in \mathcal{O}_n$ and therefore

$$T^s x = x, \text{ where } s = \sum_{0 \leq k \leq n} m_{j_k}.$$

But this can happen only if $s = 0$, hence $B_{j_0} \subseteq \mathcal{O}_n$. This implies that $\mathcal{O}_n$ is open.

Moreover, we have the decomposition

$$\mathcal{O}_n = \{x \in \mathbf{C} : g^n(x) = x\} \backslash \bigcup_{m < n} \{x \in \mathbf{C} : g^m(x) = x\},$$

which implies that $\mathcal{O}_n$ is closed. $\qquad\square$

Invariant Borel measures on the Cantor set. The set of Borel measures on a compact space X is separable, compact in the weak*-topology coming from the dual of the space $C(X)$ of all continuous functions on X. Let T be a homeomorphism of X, denote by $\mathcal{M}(T)$ the space of all T-invariant Borel probability measures on X. The classical Krylov-Bogolyubov theorem, [25] states that $\mathcal{M}(T)$ is non-empty. For example, for a given $x \in X$ it contains a cluster point μ of the following sequence

$$\mu_n = \frac{1}{n} \sum_{i=1}^{n} T^i \circ \delta_x,$$

where δ_y is a Dirac measure concentrated on $y \in X$. To verify that μ is T-invariant, let $f \in C(X)$, then

$$\int f d\mu_n = \frac{1}{n} \sum_{i=1}^{n} f(T^i(x))$$

and

$$\int f d(T \circ \mu_n) = \frac{1}{n} \sum_{i=1}^{n} f(T^{i+1}(x)).$$

Then

$$\left| \int f d\mu_n - \int f d(T \circ \mu_n) \right| \leq 2/n \|f\|,$$

which implies the claim.

The following lemma will be useful in the process of constructing new elements in the topological full group.

LEMMA 4.4. *Let $A \subset \mathbf{C}$ be a clopen set and $T \in Homeo(\mathbf{C})$ be a minimal homeomorphism. Then for every $\varepsilon > 0$ there exists a partition of A into clopen sets*

$$A = \bigsqcup_{i \in I} A_i$$

such that for every $\mu \in \mathcal{M}(T)$ and $i \in I$ we have $\mu(A_i) < \varepsilon$.

PROOF. It is sufficient to show the statement for $A = \mathbf{C}$. Let $\varepsilon = 1/n$ and choose a clopen set $D \subset \mathbf{C}$ such that the sets $T^k(D)$, $1 \leq k \leq n$, are pairwise disjoint. Since μ is T-invariant, we have $\mu(D) \leq 1/n$. Now the Kakutani-Rokhlin partition of $\mathbf{C}$ over D satisfies the statement. □

3. Simplicity of the commutator subgroup

The commutator subgroup of a group Γ is a group generated by all elements of the form $[g, h] = ghg^{-1}h^{-1}$ and denoted by Γ'. In this section we will show simplicity of $[[T]]'$ for a Cantor minimal system $(T, \mathbf{C})$. This is a result of Matui, [106]. We will follow a simplified proof of Bezuglyi and Medynets, [21].

We start with the following theorem of Glasner and Wiess, [62], which will be crucial in the proof.

THEOREM 4.5 (Glasner-Weiss). *Let T be a minimal homeomorphism of a Cantor set $\mathbf{C}$ and let $A, B \subseteq \mathbf{C}$ be clopen subsets such that for every $\mu \in \mathcal{M}(T)$, we have $\mu(B) < \mu(A)$. Then there exists $g \in [[T]]$ with $g(B) \subset A$ and $g^2 = id$.*

PROOF. Let $f = \chi_A - \chi_B$, then f is continuous and by the assumptions $\int f d\mu > 0$ for all $\mu \in \mathcal{M}(T)$. There exist a constant $c > 0$ such that

$$\inf(\int f d\mu : \mu \in \mathcal{M}(T)) > c.$$

Indeed, assume that this is not the case and the infimum reaches 0 on some sequence of measures in $\mathcal{M}(T)$. If μ is a cluster point of this sequence in the weak*-topology, we obtain $\mu(A) = \mu(B)$, which is a contradiction.

Let us show now that there exists n_0, such that for all $x \in \mathbf{C}$ and all $n \geq n_0$ we have

$$(4) \qquad \frac{1}{n} \sum_{i=0}^{n-1} f(T^i x) > c.$$

To reach a contradiction assume that there exists an increasing sequence $\{n_k\}$ of natural numbers and a sequence of points $\{x_k\}$ for which

$$-1 \leq \frac{1}{n_k} \sum_{i=0}^{n_k-1} f(T^i x_k) \leq c.$$

As in the proof of the Krylov-Bogoliubov theorem, [**25**], we set

$$\mu_k = \frac{1}{n_k} \sum_{i=0}^{n_k-1} T^i \circ \delta_{x_k}.$$

Let μ be a cluster point of μ_k in the weak*-topology. Then μ is in $\mathcal{M}(T)$, on the other hand we have

$$\int f d\mu \leq c,$$

which is a contradiction.

Let n_0 be such that (4) holds for all $n \geq n_0$ and all $x \in \mathbf{C}$. Choose $D \subset \mathbf{C}$ be such that $T^i(D) \cap D = \emptyset$ for all $i \leq n_0$. This implies that the hight of each tower over D is greater then n_0. Let $D_1, \ldots, D_N$ be a refinement of a Kakutani-Rokhlin partition of D:

$$\mathbf{C} = (D_1 \sqcup T(D_1) \sqcup \ldots \sqcup T^{k_1}(D_1)) \sqcup$$
$$\sqcup (D_2 \sqcup T(D_2) \sqcup \ldots \sqcup T^{k_2}(D_2)) \sqcup$$
$$\ldots \sqcup (D_N \sqcup T(D_N) \sqcup \ldots \sqcup T^{k_N}(D_N)),$$

with the property that each piece of the partition is contained in one of the sets $A \backslash B, B \backslash A, A \cap B$ or $(A \cup B)^c$. By assumption, $k_i \geq n_0$ for all $1 \leq i \leq N$. Now taking any x in D, the inequality (4) implies that for a fixed j the number of components $T^i(D_j)$, $1 \leq i \leq k_j$ that belong to A is greater then the number of components that belongs to B. We will define g as a mapping between the pieces of the partition. Define g on D_j as a symmetry that maps $T^i(D_j)$ that belong to B onto a component that belong to A by applying a power of T. Since a Kakutani-Rokhlin partition is clopen, we can define g as a trivial map on the rest of the sets. Obviously, g is in $[[T]]$ and $g^2 = id$. $\qquad \square$

Below we give a sequence of lemmas due to Bezuglyi and Medynets, from which we deduce the main result of this section: the simplicity of the topological full group of a Cantor minimal system.

LEMMA 4.6. Let T be a minimal homeomorphism of the Cantor set. For any $g \in [[T]]$ and $\delta > 0$ there exists a decomposition $g = g_1 g_2 \ldots g_n$ such that $\mu(\mathrm{supp}(g_i)) \leq \delta$ for all $\mu \in \mathcal{M}(T)$.

PROOF. Assume firstly that $g \in [[T]]$ is periodic (as element of the group). Since $g \in [[T]]$ then by Lemma 4.2 and Lemma 4.3 we can find clopen sets A_k, $k \in I$, such that $g|_{A_k}$ has order k and

$$\mathbf{C} = \bigsqcup_{k \in I} \bigsqcup_{i=0}^{k-1} g^i(A_k).$$

By Lemma 4.4 we can partite A_k into clopen sets

$$A_k = \bigsqcup_{j=1}^{n_k} B_j^{(k)}$$

such that $\mu(B_j^{(k)}) < \delta/k$ for all $B_j^{(k)}$ and $\mu \in \mathcal{M}(T)$.
Now set

$$C_{k,j} = \bigsqcup_{i=0}^{k-1} g^i(B_j^{(k)}).$$

Define $g_{k,j}$ to be g on $C_{k,j}$ and the identity on its complement. Since all the sets are clopen, $g_{k,j}$ is continuous and $g_{k,j}$ belongs to $[[T]]$. Obviously, $g = \prod_{k,j} g_{k,j}$ and $\mu(supp(g_{k,j})) < \delta$.

Assume now that g is non-periodic. Let $k \in \mathbb{N}$ be such that $1/k < \delta$ and define

$$\mathcal{O}_{\geq k} = \{x \in \mathbf{C} : Orb_g(x) \text{ has at least } k \text{ elements}\}.$$

By Lemma 4.4 we have that the complement of $\mathcal{O}_{\geq k}$ is clopen and thus $\mathcal{O}_{\geq k}$ is clopen. Therefore, for any $x \in \mathcal{O}_{\geq k}$ there exists a clopen neighborhood U_x such that $g^i(U_x) \cap U_x = \emptyset$ for all $1 \leq i < k$. By compactness there are $x_1, \ldots, x_n \in \mathcal{O}_{\geq k}$ such that $\mathcal{O}_{\geq k} = \bigcup_{1 \leq i \leq n} U_{x_i}$. Define $B_1 = U_{x_1}$ and

$$B_{i+1} = B_i \bigsqcup \left(U_{x_{i+1}} \setminus \bigcup_{l=-k+1}^{k+1} g^l(B_i) \right).$$

Then $B = B_n$ meets every orbit of g in $\mathcal{O}_{\geq k}$. Moreover, $g^i(B) \cap B = \emptyset$ for all $1 \leq i < k$, which implies $\mu(B) \leq 1/k < \delta$ for all $\mu \in \mathcal{M}(T)$. Since the transformation T is minimal we have that the function

$$F : x \mapsto \min\{l \geq 1 : g^l(x) \in B\}$$

is continuous. Define

$$g_B(x) = \begin{cases} g^k(x), & \text{if } x \in B \text{ and } k = F(x), \\ x, & x \notin B. \end{cases}$$

It is easy to see that $g_B \in [[T]]$, $\mu(supp(g_B)) < \delta$ and $g_B^{-1} \circ g$ is periodic. Thus the statement of the lemma follows from the previous case. $\qquad \square$

LEMMA 4.7. Let $T \in Homeo(\mathbf{C})$ be a minimal homeomorphism. Then for any $f \in [[T]]'$ and $\delta > 0$ there exists $g_1, \ldots, g_n, h_1, \ldots, h_n \in [[T]]$ such that f is in the normal subgroup of $[[T]]$ generated by $[g_i, h_j]$, $1 \leq 1i, j \leq n$ and $\mu(supp(g_i) \cup supp(h_i)) < \delta$.

PROOF. Let $f = [g, h]$ for some $g, h \in [[T]]$. By Lemma 4.6 we can find $g_1, \ldots, g_n$ and $h_1, \ldots, h_n$ in $[[T]]$ such that $g = g_1 \ldots g_n$, $h = h_1 \ldots h_n$ with $\mu(supp(g_i)) < \delta/2$ and $\mu(supp(h_i)) < \delta/2$ for all $\mu \in \mathcal{M}(T)$. Since f is in the group generated by $[g_i, h_j]$, $1 \leq i, j \leq n$, we obtain the statement. $\square$

The following is a generalization of Glasner-Weiss to the commutator subgroup.

LEMMA 4.8. Let $T \in Homeo(\mathbf{C})$ be a minimal homeomorphism. If A and B are clopen subsets of $\mathbf{C}$ such that $3\mu(B) < \mu(A)$ for all $\mu \in \mathcal{M}(T)$, then there exists $f \in [[T]]'$ such that $f(B) \subset A$.

PROOF. By replacing A by $A \backslash B$ we have $2\mu(B) < \mu(A)$ for all $\mu \in \mathcal{M}(T)$ and $A \cap B = \emptyset$. Now by Theorem 4.5 we can find a symmetry $g \in [[T]]$ such that $g(B) \subset A$. Then

$$\mu(g(B)) = \mu(B) < \mu(A) - \mu(B) = \mu(A \backslash g(B)).$$

Thus, again by Theorem 4.5, we can find a symmetry $h \in [[T]]$ such that $h(g(B)) \subset A \backslash g(B)$. It is easy to check, using the properties of g and h, that $g = (hg)h^{-1}(hg)^{-1}$; we obtain $hg = [h, hg]$ and $hg(B) \subseteq A$, which implies the statement. $\square$

THEOREM 4.9. Let T be a minimal homeomorphism and let Γ be either $[[T]]$ or $[[T]]'$. Then for every normal subgroup H of Γ, we have $\Gamma' \leq H$.

PROOF. We will show that for all elements g, h in Γ their commutator $[g, h]$ is in H. Let $f \in H$. Let E be a clopen non-empty set such that $f(E) \cap E = \emptyset$. By compactness of $\mathcal{M}(T)$ we have

$$3\delta = \inf(\mu(E) : \mu \in \mathcal{M}(T)) > 0.$$

By Lemma 4.6 and Lemma 4.7, we can find $g_i, h_j \in \Gamma$ such that $g = g_1 \ldots g_n$ and $h = h_1 \ldots h_n$ and

$$\mu(supp(g_i)) < \delta/2, \quad \mu(supp(h_i)) < \delta/2$$

for all $\mu \in \mathcal{M}(T)$. We claim that for all g and h in Γ with $\mu(supp(g) \cup supp(h)) < \delta$ we have $[g, h] \in H$. Since the commutator $[g_1 \ldots g_n, h_1 \ldots h_n]$ belongs to the normal subgroup generated by $[g_i, h_j]$, the claim implies the statement.

To prove the claim put $F = supp(g) \cup supp(h)$, then $3\mu(F) < \mu(E)$. Thus we can apply Lemma 4.8 to find an element α in $[[T]]'$ such that $\alpha(F) \subseteq E$. Since H is normal, we have

$$q = \alpha^{-1} f \alpha \in H.$$

Thus

$$\overline{h} = [h, q] = (h\alpha^{-1}f\alpha h^{-1})\alpha^{-1}f^{-1}\alpha$$

and $[g, \overline{h}]$ are in H.

Since $q(F) \cap F = \emptyset$, the elements g^{-1} and $qh^{-1}q^{-1}$ commute. Hence, we have

$$[g, \overline{h}] = g(hqh^{-1}q^{-1})g^{-1}(qhq^{-1}h^{-1}) = [g, h] \in H,$$

which proves the claim. $\square$

COROLLARY 4.10 (Matui, '06). Let $T \in Homeo(\mathbf{C})$ be minimal, then $[[T]]'$ is simple.

PROOF. Since $[[T]]''$ is a normal subgroup of $[[T]]$, we can apply the theorem to obtain that $[[T]]' \leq [[T]]''$. Thus, $[[T]]'' = [[T]]'$. Let now H be a normal subgroup of $[[T]]'$. Then $[[T]]'' \leq H$, therefore $[[T]]' = H$. $\square$

4. Finite generation of the commutator subgroup of a minimal subshift

The aim of this section is to prove that every commutator subgroup of a Cantor minimal subshift is finitely generated, Theorem 4.13. This result is due to Hiroki Matui, [**106**]. Through this section we assume that T is a minimal homeomorphism of the Cantor set.

Let U be a clopen set in $\mathbf{C}$, such that U, $T(U)$ and $T^{-1}(U)$ are pairwise disjoint. Define

$$f_U(x) = \begin{cases} T(x), & x \in T^{-1}(U) \cup U \\ T^{-2}(x), & x \in T(U) \\ x, & \text{otherwise.} \end{cases}$$

Obviously, f_U is a homeomorphism of $\mathbf{C}$ and $f_U \in [[T]]$. Moreover, we claim that f_U is in the commutator subgroup $[[T]]'$. To verify the claim, define a symmetry in $[[T]]$:

$$g(x) = \begin{cases} T(x), & x \in T^{-1}(U) \\ T^{-1}(x), & x \in U. \end{cases}$$

One verifies that $f_U = [g, f_U]$ by identifying f_U with the cycle (123) and g with the cycle (12).

Consider the following set of elements of $[[T]]'$

$$\mathcal{U} = \{f_U : U \text{ is clopen set and } U, T(U), T^{-1}(U) \text{ are pairwise disjoint}\}.$$

LEMMA 4.11. *The commutator subgroup of the topological full group $[[T]]'$ is generated by $\mathcal{U}$.*

PROOF. Let H be the subgroup of $[[T]]$ generated by $\mathcal{U}$. We start by showing that if $g \in [[T]]$ and $g^3 = e$, then g is in H. It is straightforward, that H is normal. Therefore by of simplicity of $[[T]]'$ conclude that $H = [[T]]'$.

By Lemma 4.2 and Lemma 4.3 we can find a clopen set A such that A, $g(A)$ and $g^2(A)$ are pairwise disjoint and $supp(g) = A \sqcup g(A) \sqcup g^2(A)$. Let now B_i be a clopen partition of $\mathbf{C}$ such that the restriction of g to each B_i coincides with a certain power of T. Consider the following partitions of A:

$$\mathcal{P}_0 = \{B_i \cap A\}_{1 \leq i \leq n},$$
$$\mathcal{P}_1 = g^{-1}\{B_i \cap g(A)\}_{1 \leq i \leq n},$$
$$\mathcal{P}_2 = g^{-2}\{B_i \cap g^2(A)\}_{1 \leq i \leq n}.$$

Denote the common refinement of $\mathcal{P}_0$, $\mathcal{P}_1$ and $\mathcal{P}_2$ by $\{A_j\}_{1 \leq j \leq m}$. It has the property that for every $1 \leq j \leq m$ there are integers k_j, l_j such that

$$g|_{A_j} = T^{k_j}|_{A_j}, \quad g|_{g(A_j)} = T^{l_j}|_{g(A_j)}, \quad g|_{g^2(A_j)} = T^{-k_j - l_j}|_{g^2(A_j)}.$$

Now we can decompose $g = g_1 \dots g_m$ as a product of commuting elements of $[[T]]$ defined by the restriction of g to $A_j \cup g(A_j) \cup g^2(A_j)$. This implies that it is sufficient to consider the case when g is in $[[T]]$ of the order 3 and there exists a clopen set $A \subset \mathbf{C}$ such that there are k and l with

$$g|_A = T^k|_A, \quad g|_{g(A)} = T^l|_{g(A)}, \quad g|_{g^2(A)} = T^{-k-l}|_{g^2(A)}.$$

Since for any $x \in A$ there exists a clopen neighborhood $U_x \subseteq A$ such that $\{T^i(U_x)\}_{1 \leq i \leq k+l}$ are pairwise disjoint and A is compact, we can select a finite family U_x that covers A. Let $C_1, \ldots, C_n$ be the partition of A generated by this finite family. Let $g = g_1 \ldots g_n$ be the decomposition of g into a product of commuting elements of $[[T]]$ defined by taking g_i to be the restriction of g to $C_i \cup g(C_i) \cup g^2(C_i)$.

This reduces the argument to the case when $g \in [[T]]$ has the following property: $g^3 = id$ and there exists a clopen set $A \subset \mathbf{C}$ such that there are k and l with

$$g|_A = T^k|_A, \quad g|_{g(A)} = T^l|_{g(A)}, \quad g|_{g^2(A)} = T^{-k-l}|_{g^2(A)},$$

and $T^i(A) \cap T^j(A) = \emptyset$ for all $1 \leq i, j \leq k + l$. This element can be considered as a cycle $(k\ l\ k+l)$ of the permutation group S_{k+l+1} and each cycle $(i-1\ i\ i+1)$ is given by $f_{T^i(A)}$. Moreover, g is in the alternating group A_{k+l+1}, which contains all 3-cycles. Thus g is a product of elements of $\mathcal{U}$, which finishes the lemma. $\qquad\square$

Note that the proof of lemma shows slightly more. Namely, for every prime number p, any element of order p in $[[T]]$ belongs to the commutator subgroup.

LEMMA 4.12. Let U and V be clopen subsets of $\mathbf{C}$, then the following holds

(i) If $T^2(V)$, $T(V)$, V, $T^{-1}(V)$, $T^{-2}(V)$ are pairwise disjoint and $U \subseteq V$, then for $\tau_U = f_{T^{-1}(U)} f_{T(U)}$ we have

$$\tau_V f_U \tau_V^{-1} = f_{T(U)},$$
$$\tau_V^{-1} f_U \tau_V = f_{T^{-1}(U)}.$$

(ii) If V, U, $T^{-1}(U)$, $T(U) \cup T^{-1}(V)$, $T(V)$ are pairwise disjoint then

$$[f_V, f_U^{-1}] = f_{T(U) \cap T^{-1}(V)}.$$

PROOF. The proof of the lemma boils down to the identification of the elements involved in the statement with permutations.

(i). The support of $\tau_{V \setminus U}$ is disjoint from the supports of the other homeomorphism, thus

$$\tau_V f_U \tau_V^{-1} = \tau_U f_U \tau_U^{-1} = f_{T(U)},$$

where the last identity is the consequence of the identity in the symmetric group $(01234)(123)(04321) = (012)$.

(ii). Let $C = T(U) \cap T^{-1}(V)$. We can decompose $f_U = f_{T^{-1}(C)} f_{U \setminus T^{-1}(C)}$ and $f_V = f_{T(C)} f_{V \setminus T(C)}$. Thus

$$[f_V, f_U^{-1}] = [f_{T(C)}, f_{T^{-1}(C)}^{-1}] = f_{T(C)} f_{T^{-1}(C)}^{-1} f_{T(C)}^{-1} f_{T^{-1}(C)} = f_C,$$

where the last identity is equivalent to the identity in the permutation group:

$$(234)(021)(243)(012) = (012). \qquad\square$$

THEOREM 4.13. Let $T \in Homeo(\mathbf{C})$ be a minimal homeomorphism. The commutator subgroup $[[T]]'$ is finitely generated if and only if T is conjugate to a minimal subshift.

PROOF. Assume that $T \in Homeo(\mathbf{C})$ is a minimal subshift, i.e., T acts as a shift on the Cantor set $A^{\mathbb{Z}}$ for some finite alphabet A and there exists a closed T-invariant subset $X \subset A^{\mathbb{Z}}$ such that the action of T on X is minimal. Moreover, enlarging the alphabet and using the characterization of minimal subshifts in terms of homogeneous sequences, we can assume that $x(i) \neq x(j)$ for every $|i - j| < 5$ and $x \in X$.

For every $n, m \in \mathbb{N}$ and $a_i \in A$, $-m \leq i \leq n$, define the cylinder sets in X by

$$\langle\langle a_{-m} \ldots a_{-1} \underline{a_0} a_1 \ldots a_n \rangle\rangle = \{x \in X : x(i) = a_i, -m \leq i \leq n\},$$

here the underlining of a_0 means that a_0 is in the 0's coordinate of $\mathbb{Z}$-enumeration. Since $x(i) \neq x(j)$ for every $|i - j| < 5$ we have that for every cylinder set U the sets $T^{-2}(U), T^{-1}(U), U, T(U), T^2(U)$ are pairwise disjoint. Let H be the subgroup of $[[T]]'$ generated by the finite set of cylinders:

$$\{f_U : U = \langle\langle a\underline{b}c \rangle\rangle, a, b, c \in A\}.$$

We will show that $H = [[T]]'$. By Lemma 4.11 it is sufficient to show that for every cylinder set $U \in X$, we have $f_U \in H$.

Since

$$f_{T(\langle\langle \underline{a} \rangle\rangle)} = \prod_{b \in A} f_{\langle\langle \underline{a}b \rangle\rangle}, \quad f_{T^{-1}(\langle\langle \underline{a} \rangle\rangle)} = \prod_{b \in A} f_{\langle\langle \underline{b}a \rangle\rangle},$$

we immediately have that $f_{T(\langle\langle \underline{a} \rangle\rangle)}, f_{T^{-1}(\langle\langle \underline{a} \rangle\rangle)}$, and therefore $\tau_{\langle\langle \underline{a} \rangle\rangle}$ are in H. Applying Lemma 4.12 to the sets

$$U = \langle\langle a_{-m} \ldots a_{-1} \underline{a} a_1 \ldots a_n \rangle\rangle \subseteq \langle\langle \underline{a_0} \rangle\rangle = V$$

we obtain:

$$\tau_{\langle\langle \underline{a_0} \rangle\rangle} f_U \tau_{\langle\langle \underline{a_0} \rangle\rangle}^{-1} = f_{T(U)}, \quad \tau_{\langle\langle \underline{a_0} \rangle\rangle}^{-1} f_U \tau_{\langle\langle \underline{a_0} \rangle\rangle} = f_{T^{-1}(U)}.$$

Thus, it suffice to show that f_U can be generated by $U = \langle\langle a_{-m} \ldots a_{-1} \underline{a_0} a_1 \rangle\rangle$. The later follows by induction applying Lemma 4.12 (ii) to sets $U = \langle\langle a_{-m} \ldots a_{-1} \underline{a_0} a_1 \rangle\rangle$ and $V = \langle\langle a_1 \underline{a_2} \rangle\rangle$.

To prove the converse, assume that $T \in Homeo(\mathbf{C})$ is minimal and $[[T]]'$ is finitely generated. Let $g_1, \ldots, g_n$ be a generating set of $[[T]]'$ and $n_i : \mathbf{C} \to \mathbb{Z}$ be continuous maps that satisfy:

$$g_i(x) = T^{n_i(x)}x, \quad x \in \mathbf{C}.$$

Let $\mathcal{P} = \{\mathcal{P}_1, \ldots, \mathcal{P}_n\}$ be the common refinement of the partition $\{n_i^{-1}(k)\}_{k \in \mathbb{Z}}$. We will consider $\mathcal{P}$ as a finite alphabet together with shift map $s : \mathcal{P}^{\mathbb{Z}} \to \mathcal{P}^{\mathbb{Z}}$. Define a continuous map $S : \mathbf{C} \to \mathcal{P}^{\mathbb{Z}}$ by the property that $S(x)(k) = \mathcal{P}_s$, if $T^k(x) \in \mathcal{P}_s$. It is easy to verify that S is a factor map. Define a homeomorphism $f_i \in Homeo(\mathbf{C})$ by $f_i(z) = s^k(z)$ when $z(0) \subseteq n_i^{-1}(k)$. It is easy to see that $f_i \in [[s]]$ and $Sg_i = f_iS$.

Let us show that S is injective. Suppose $x, y \in \mathbf{C}$ are distinct and $S(x) = S(y)$. Let $g \in [[T]]'$ such that $g(x) \neq x$ and $g(y) = y$. By assumptions $[[T]]'$ is finitely generated, thus we can write g as a word $w(g_1, \ldots, g_n)$ in the generators $g_1, \ldots, g_n$.

$$\begin{aligned}
Sg(x) &= Sw(g_1, \ldots, g_n)(x) \\
&= w(f_1, \ldots, f_n)S(x) \\
&= w(f_1, \ldots, f_n)S(y) \\
&= Sw(g_1, \ldots, g_n)(y) \\
&= Sg(y) = S(x).
\end{aligned}$$

Hence, for some k we have $s^k S(x) = S(T^k(x)) = S(x)$, which contradicts the minimality of s and thus of T. $\qquad \square$

5. Spatial isomorphism of topological full groups

The aim of this section is to establish the following remarkable result of Giordano, Putnam and Skau, [**61**]. The part which concerns with commutator subgroups is due to Bezugliy and Medynets, [**21**].

THEOREM 4.14. Let T_1 and T_2 be two minimal homeomorphisms of the Cantor space $\mathbf{C}$, and let $\Gamma^{(i)}$ be either the topological full group $[[T_i]]$ or its commutator subgroup $[[T_i]]'$. If $\alpha : \Gamma^{(1)} \to \Gamma^{(2)}$ is an isomorphism, then it is necessarily spatial: there is a homeomorphism $\Lambda \in Homeo(\mathbf{C})$ such that

$$\alpha(g) = \Lambda g \Lambda^{-1}, \text{ for all } g \in \Gamma^{(1)}.$$

The proof will be divided into several lemmas. In this section, we assume that T is a minimal homeomorphism of the Cantor space $\mathbf{C}$, and Γ is either $[[T]]$ or $[[T]]'$.

LEMMA 4.15. For every non-empty clopen set $A \subseteq \mathbf{C}$, $x \in A$ and $k \in \mathbb{N}$, there is $h \in [[T]]'$ of period k such that $supp(h) \subset A$ and $x \in supp(h)$.

PROOF. Fix $k \in \mathbb{N}$, and let $A(n)$ be an alternating group which contains an element of order k.

By minimality of T there are $0 = k_0 < k_1 < \ldots < k_{n-1}$, such that $T^{k_i}(x) \in A$ for every $0 \leq i \leq n-1$. Let U be a sufficiently small neighborhood of x such that

$$T^{k_i}(U) \cap T^{k_j}(U) = \emptyset, \text{ for } i \neq j.$$

Now we have n pairwise disjoint sets $T^{k_i}(U)$ which are obtained one from another by applying a power of T. Thus for every permutation σ in $S(n)$ we can construct an element h_σ in $[[T]]$, which maps $T^{k_i}(U)$ to $T^{k_{\sigma(i)}}(U)$. This implies that all elements h_σ of $[[T]]$ that correspond to $\sigma \in A(n)$ belong to $[[T]]'$. Therefore we have statement of the lemma. $\square$

For a clopen set $A \subset \mathbf{C}$ we define a subgroup of Γ:

$$\Gamma_A = \{g \in \Gamma : supp(g) \subseteq A\}.$$

Let F be a subset of Γ, define *the centralizer* of F in Γ by

$$C_\Gamma(F) = \{g \in \Gamma : gh = hg \text{ for all } h \in F\}.$$

Clearly, $F \subseteq C_\Gamma(C_\Gamma(F))$ and $C_\Gamma(F_1 \cup F_2) = C_\Gamma(F_1) \cap C_\Gamma(F_2)$ for all subsets F_1 and F_2 of Γ.

LEMMA 4.16. Let $A_1, \ldots, A_n$ be clopen subsets of $\mathbf{C}$, then the following holds:

(i) If $\Gamma_{A_1} = \Gamma_{A_2}$, then $A_1 = A_2$;

(ii) The centralizer of $\Gamma_{A_1} \cup \ldots \cup \Gamma_{A_n}$ in Γ is equal to $\Gamma_{\bigcap_i A_i^c}$;

(iii) $\Gamma_{A_1} \cap \Gamma_{A_2} = \Gamma_{A_1 \cap A_2}$.

PROOF.   (i) Assume $A_1 \backslash A_2 = \emptyset$. By Lemma 4.15, we can find an involution $g \in [[T]]'$ such that $supp(g) \subseteq A_1 \backslash A_2$. Thus, $g \in \Gamma_{A_1} \backslash \Gamma_{A_2}$, which is a contradiction.

(ii) Suppose $g \in C_\Gamma(\Gamma_{A_1} \cup \ldots \cup \Gamma_{A_n})$. To reach a contradiction assume $g \notin \Gamma_{\bigcap_i A_i^c}$, i.e., there are $i \leq n$ and $B \subseteq A_i$ such that $g(B) \cap B \neq \emptyset$. We can find $h \in \Gamma_{A_i}$ such that $supp(h) \subseteq B$ and $C \subseteq B$ is such that $h(C) \cap C = \emptyset$. Hence,

$$gh(C) \neq hg(C) = g(C),$$

this implies $g \notin C_\Gamma(\Gamma_{A_i})$, which is a contradiction. The backwards inclusion is obvious.

(iii) This is immediate from the definitions.   □

Let $\pi \in \Gamma$ be an involution, then its support is a clopen set and we can define the following sets:

$$C_\pi = \{g \in \Gamma : g\pi = \pi g\};$$
$$U_\pi = \{g \in C_\pi : g^2 = e, g(hgh^{-1}) = (hgh^{-1})g \text{ for all } h \in C_\pi\};$$
$$V_\pi = \{g \in \Gamma : gh = hg \text{ for all } h \in U_\pi\};$$
$$S_\pi = \{g^2 : g \in V_\pi\};$$
$$W_\pi = \{g \in \Gamma : gh = hg \text{ for all } h \in S_\pi\}.$$

The following lemma is due to Bezuglyi and Medynets, [21].

LEMMA 4.17. Let Γ be either the topological full group $[[T]]$ or its commutator subgroup $[[T]]'$. The subsets C_π, U_π, V_π, S_π and W_π of Γ have the following properties:

(i) $g(supp(\pi)) = supp(\pi)$ for every $g \in C_\pi$;
(ii) $supp(g) \subset supp(\pi)$ for every $g \in U_\pi$;
(iii) If A is a π-invariant clopen set, then $\pi|_A \in U_\pi$;
(iv) $V_\pi \subset C_\pi$;
(v) If $g \in V_\pi$, then $g(B) \subset B \cup \pi(B)$ for all $B \subset supp(\pi)$;
(vi) If $g \in V_\pi$, then $g^2(B) = B$ for every clopen set $B \subseteq supp(\pi)$;
(vii) If $g \in S_\pi$, then $supp(g) \subseteq supp(\pi)^c$;
(viii) For any clopen set $C \subseteq supp(\pi)^c$, there is an involution $g \in S_\pi$ supported on C;
(ix) $W_\pi = \Gamma_{supp(\pi)}$.

PROOF.   (i) It is easy to check that $supp(g\pi g^{-1}) = g(supp(\pi))$. Since $g\pi g^{-1} = \pi$ we get $g(supp(\pi)) \subseteq supp(\pi)$. Since π is an involution we get $g(supp(\pi)) = supp(\pi)$ for every $g \in C_\pi$.

(ii) To reach a contradiction suppose there ia a clopen set $A \subseteq supp(\pi)^c$ such that $g(A) \cap A = \emptyset$. By Lemma 4.15, we can find $h \in \Gamma$ with support in A and such that for some $V \subset A$ we have $h^i(V) \cap V = \emptyset$, for $i = 1, 2$. In this case $h \in C_\pi$. On the other hand

$$g(hgh^{-1})(V) = g^2 h^{-1}(V) = h^{-1}(V),$$
$$(hgh^{-1})g(V) = hg^2(V) = h(V).$$

Since $h^{-1}(V) \neq h(V)$, we get $g \notin U_\pi$. Hence, $supp(g) \subset supp(\pi)$ for every $g \in U_\pi$;

(iii) Let A be a π-invariant clopen set. Obviously, $\pi|_A$ commutes with π, thus $\pi|_A$ is in C_π. Fix $h \in C_\pi$, if $x \in A \cap h(A)$ then

$$\pi|_A(h\pi|_A h^{-1})(x) = ((h\pi|_A h^{-1}))\pi|_A(x) = x,$$

and in case $x \in A \cup h(A^c)$ we have

$$\pi|_A(h\pi|_A h^{-1})(x) = ((h\pi|_A h^{-1}))\pi|_A(x) = \pi(x),$$

Thus, $\pi|_A \in U_\pi$

(iv) The inclusion $V_\pi \subset C_\pi$ is straightforward from the fact $\pi \in U_\pi$.

(v) Let $g \in V_\pi$. To reach a contradiction suppose there is a clopen set B such that $g(B) \not\subseteq B \cup \pi(B)$. Set $B' = B \cup \pi(B)$ and $C = g(B')\backslash B'$. Then $\pi(B') = B'$ and $C \neq \emptyset$. By ((iv)) we have $\pi g(B') = g\pi_{B'} = g(B')$ and therefore

$$\pi(C) = \pi(g(B')\backslash B') = \pi g(B')\backslash \pi(B') = g(B')\backslash B' = C.$$

Now by ((i)) and ((iv)) we have $g(supp(\pi)) = supp(\pi)$. Since $B \subset supp(\pi)$, this implies $B' \subseteq supp(\pi)$. Therefore we can decompose $C = C_1 \cup C_2$ such that $\pi(C_1) = C_2$. By construction, $g(C) \cap C = \emptyset$. By ((iii)) we obtain $\pi|_C \in U_\pi$ and

$$\pi|_C g(C_1) = g(C_1) \neq g(C_2) = g\pi|_C(C_1).$$

Hence, $g \notin V_\pi$, therefore $g(B) \subset B \cup \pi(B)$ for all $B \subset supp(\pi)$;

(vi) Let $g \in V_\pi$, to reach a contradiction assume that there is $B \subset supp(\pi)$ such that $g^2(B) \neq B$. Taking a smaller subset of B and again denoting it by B we can assume

$$g(B) \cap B = g^2(B) \cap B = \emptyset.$$

By ((v)), we have $g(B) \subseteq B \cup \pi(B)$ and

$$g^2(B) \subseteq g(B) \cup g\pi(B) = g(B) \cup \pi g(B).$$

Since $g(B) \cap B = \emptyset$, we conclude $g(B) \subseteq \pi(B)$ and $g^2(B) \subseteq \pi g(B) \subseteq \pi^2(B) = B$.

(vii) Follows immediately from ((vi)).

(viii) Let $C \subseteq supp(\pi)^c$ be a clopen set. By Lemma 4.15, there is a periodic homeomorphism of order 4 with support in C. By ((ii)), $g \in V_\pi$, therefore $g^2 \in S_\pi$.

(ix) It follows from ((vii)) that $\Gamma_{supp(\pi)} \subset W_\pi$. If $g \in W_\pi$ and for some $B \subset supp(\pi)^c$ we have $g(B) \cap B = \emptyset$, then by ((viii)) there is an involution $h \in S_\pi$ supported on B. Let C be such that $h(C) \cap C = \emptyset$. Then $hg(C) = g(C) \neq gh(C)$, which implies $gh \neq hg$, contradicting the choice of g. Hence, $W_\pi = \Gamma_{supp(\pi)}$. $\square$

As a direct consequence of Lemma 4.17 ((ix)) and Lemma 4.16 we have the following lemma.

LEMMA 4.18. Let $\pi_1, \ldots, \pi_n, \rho_1, \ldots, \rho_n \in \Gamma$ be involutions. Then

$$\bigcup_i supp(\pi_i) = \bigcup_i supp(\rho_i)$$

if and only if

$$C_\Gamma(W_{\pi_1} \cup \ldots \cup W_{\pi_n}) = C_\Gamma(W_{\rho_1} \cup \ldots \cup W_{\rho_n})$$

We quote here without a proof the following classical theorem of Stone.

THEOREM 4.19 (Stone). Homeomorphisms of the Cantor space $\mathbf{C}$ are in one-to-one correspondence with the automorphisms of the Boolean algebra $\mathcal{B}$ of clopen sets of $\mathbf{C}$. In other words, for every automorphism α of $\mathcal{B}$ there exists a unique $\hat{\alpha} \in Homeo(\mathbf{C})$ such that $\alpha(A) = \hat{\alpha}(A)$ for every clopen set A.

PROOF OF THE GIORDANO-PUTNAM-SKAU (THEOREM 4.14). By   Stone's theorem it is sufficient to define Λ on clopen sets of $\mathbf{C}$. By Lemma 4.15 for any clopen $A \subseteq \mathbf{C}$ there is a finite family of involutions $\pi_1, \ldots, \pi_n$ in $\Gamma^{(1)}$ such that

$$\bigcup_i supp(\pi_i) = A^c.$$

By Lemma 4.16 and Lemma 4.17 ((ix)) we have

$$C_{\Gamma^{(2)}}(W_{\alpha(\pi_1)} \cup \ldots \cup W_{\alpha(\pi_n)}) = C_{\Gamma^{(2)}}(\Gamma^{(2)}{}_{supp(\alpha(\pi_1))} \cup \ldots \cup \Gamma^{(2)}{}_{supp(\alpha(\pi_n))})$$
$$= C_{\Gamma^{(2)}}(\Gamma^{(2)}{}_{supp(\alpha(\pi_1))^c \cap \ldots \cap supp(\alpha(\pi_n))^c})$$
$$= C_{\Gamma^{(2)}}(\Gamma^{(2)}{}_{\Lambda(A)}),$$

where $\Lambda(A) = supp(\alpha(\pi_1))^c \cap \ldots \cap supp(\alpha(\pi_n))^c$. By Lemma 4.18, Λ is a well defined map.

We claim that Λ is an automorphism of the Boolean algebra of clopen subsets of $\mathbf{C}$. We will prove this claim in several steps below.

We start by showing that $\Lambda(A_1 \cap A_2) = \Lambda(A_1) \cap \Lambda(A_2)$ for every clopen A_1 and A_2 in $\mathbf{C}$. If $\pi_1, \ldots, \pi_n \in \Gamma^{(1)}$ and $\rho_1, \ldots, \rho_m \in \Gamma^{(1)}$ are involutions such that

$$A_1^c = \bigcup_i supp(\pi_i) \quad \text{and} \quad A_2^c = \bigcup_i supp(\rho_i),$$

then

$$(A_1 \cap A_2)^c = \bigcup_i supp(\pi_i) \cup \bigcup_i supp(\rho_i),$$

therefore

$$\Gamma^{(2)}{}_{\Lambda(A_1 \cap A_2)} = C_{\Gamma^{(2)}}(W_{\alpha(\pi_1)} \cup \ldots \cup W_{\alpha(\pi_n)} \cup W_{\alpha(\rho_1)} \cup \ldots \cup W_{\alpha(\rho_m)})$$
$$= C_{\Gamma^{(2)}}(W_{\alpha(\pi_1)} \cup \ldots \cup W_{\alpha(\pi_n)}) \cap C_{\Gamma^{(2)}}(W_{\alpha(\rho_1)} \cup \ldots \cup W_{\alpha(\rho_m)})$$
$$= \Gamma^{(2)}{}_{\Lambda(A_1)} \cap \Gamma^{(2)}{}_{\Lambda(A_2)} = \Gamma^{(2)}{}_{\Lambda(A_1) \cap \Lambda(A_2)}.$$

It follows $\Lambda(A_1 \cap A_2) = \Lambda(A_1) \cap \Lambda(A_2)$.

Let us show now that $\Lambda(A^c) = \Lambda(A)^c$ for every clopen A in $\mathbf{C}$. Let $\pi_1, \ldots, \pi_n \in \Gamma^{(1)}$ and $\rho_1, \ldots, \rho_m \in \Gamma^{(1)}$ be involutions such that

$$A^c = \bigcup_i supp(\pi_i) \quad \text{and} \quad A = \bigcup_i supp(\rho_i).$$

Since $C_{\Gamma^{(1)}}(\Gamma^{(1)}{}_A) = \Gamma^{(1)}{}_{A^c}$ we obtain

$$C_{\Gamma^{(1)}}(C_{\Gamma^{(1)}}(W_{\pi_1} \cup \ldots \cup W_{\pi_n})) = C_{\Gamma^{(1)}}(W_{\rho_1} \cup \ldots \cup W_{\rho_m})$$

and

$$C_{\Gamma^{(2)}}(C_{\Gamma^{(2)}}(W_{\alpha(\pi_1)} \cup \ldots \cup W_{\alpha(\pi_n)})) = C_{\Gamma^{(2)}}(W_{\alpha(\rho_1)} \cup \ldots \cup W_{\alpha(\rho_m)})$$

which implies

$$\Gamma^{(2)}{}_{\Lambda(A)} = C_{\Gamma^{(2)}}(W_{\alpha(\rho_1)} \cup \ldots \cup W_{\alpha(\rho_m)})$$
$$= C_{\Gamma^{(2)}}(C_{\Gamma^{(2)}}(W_{\alpha(\pi_1)} \cup \ldots \cup W_{\alpha(\pi_n)}))$$
$$= C_{\Gamma^{(2)}}(\Gamma^{(2)}{}_{\Lambda(A)}) = \Gamma^{(2)}{}_{\Lambda(A)}.$$

Hence, $\Lambda(A^c) = \Lambda(A)^c$ for every clopen A in $\mathbf{C}$.

Since $\emptyset = supp(e)$, we have $\Lambda(\mathbf{C}) = \mathbf{C}$ and $\Lambda(\emptyset) = \emptyset$. Thus, Λ is an endomorphism of $\mathcal{B}$.

It is easy to see that Λ is also bijective. Indeed, its inverse is defined as follows. If B is a clopen set and $\pi_1, \ldots, \pi_n \in \Gamma^{(2)}$ are such that

$$B^c = \bigcup_i supp(\pi_i),$$

then $\Lambda^{-1}(B)$ is defined to be

$$\Gamma^{(1)}{}_{\Lambda^{-1}(B)} = C_{\Gamma^{(1)}}(W_{\alpha^{-1}(\pi_1)} \cup \ldots \cup W_{\alpha^{-1}(\pi_n)})$$

Thus Λ is an automorphism of the Boolean algebra and by Stone's theorem it defines a homeomorphism of the Cantor space, which we denote again by Λ.

If $\pi \in \Gamma^{(1)}$ is an involution, then $\Lambda(supp(\pi)) = supp(\alpha(\pi))$. Indeed,

$$\Lambda(supp(\pi))^c = \Lambda(supp(\pi)^c) = supp(\alpha(\pi))^c.$$

Hence, $\Lambda(supp(\pi)) = supp(\alpha(\pi))$.

We claim that for any clopen set B and $g \in \Gamma^{(1)}$ we have

$$\alpha(g)(B) = \Lambda g \Lambda^{-1}(B).$$

To reach a contradiction assume that this is not the case. Let a clopen set B and $g \in \Gamma^{(1)}$ satisfy

$$B \cap \alpha(g^{-1})\Lambda g \Lambda^{-1}(B) = \emptyset.$$

Let $\pi \in \Gamma^{(2)}$ be an involution such that $supp(\pi) \subseteq B$. Then by the previous paragraph, $\alpha^{-1}(\pi)$ is supported on $\Lambda^{-1}(B)$, thus, $g\alpha^{-1}(\pi)g^{-1}$ is supported on $g\Lambda^{-1}(\pi)$. This implies that $\alpha(g\alpha^{-1}(\pi)g) = \alpha(g)\pi\alpha(g^{-1})$ is supported on $\Lambda g \Lambda^{-1}(B)$. On the other hand $\alpha(g)\pi\alpha(g^{-1})$ is supported on $\alpha(g)(B)$, which implies that $\alpha(g)(B) \cap \Lambda g \Lambda^{-1}(B) \neq \emptyset$, contadicting the choice of B. $\qquad\square$

6. Boyle's flip conjugacy theorem

Two homeomorphisms ϕ and ψ of the Cantor space $\mathbf{C}$ are *flip conjugate*, if there is $\alpha \in Homeo(\mathbf{C})$ such that either $\phi = \alpha\psi\alpha^{-1}$ or $\phi = \alpha\psi^{-1}\alpha^{-1}$.

THEOREM 4.20 (Boyle-Tomiyama, [30]). *Let ϕ and ψ be minimal homeomorphisms of the Cantor space $\mathbf{C}$. If $\alpha \in Homeo(\mathbf{C})$ is such that the map*

$$g \mapsto \alpha g \alpha^{-1} \in [[\psi]], g \in [[\phi]],$$

is an isomorphism, then ϕ and ψ are conjugate.

PROOF. Replacing ϕ by $\alpha\phi\alpha^{-1}$ we can assume that α is identity and $[[\phi]] = [[\psi]]$. Let $n : X \to \mathbb{Z}$ be the cocycle that defines ψ in $[[\phi]]$, i.e.,

$$\psi(x) = \phi^{n(x)}(x), \text{ for every } x \in \mathbf{C}.$$

Define

$$f(k, x) = \begin{cases} -n(\psi^{-1}(x)) - \ldots - n(\psi^k(x)), & \text{if } k < 0 \\ 0, & \text{if } k = 0 \\ n(x) + \ldots + n(\psi^{k-1}(x)), & \text{if } k > 0 \end{cases}$$

Is satisfies $\psi^k(x) = \phi^{f(k,x)}$ for all $k \in \mathbb{Z}$ and the cocycle identity:

$$f(k_l, x) = f(k, \psi^l(x)) + f(l, x).$$

Fix N such that $n(x) \leq N$ for all $x \in X$. The cocycle identity implies

$$|f(k \pm 1, x) - f(k, x)| \leq N$$

and

$$|f(k, \psi(x)) - f(k, x)| \leq |f(k+1, x) - f(k, x)| + |f(-1, \psi(x))| \leq 2N.$$

Since $\psi^k(x) = \phi^{f(k,x)}(x)$ we have that the map $k \mapsto f(k, p)$ is bijective for any fixed $p \in \mathbf{C}$. Therefore for any $p \in \mathbf{C}$ there is K such that

$$[-N, N] \subseteq \{f(k, p) : k \in [-K, K]\}.$$

By continuity of n, for a fixed k we have that $f(k, \cdot)$ is continuous, thus for any $p \in \mathbf{C}$ there exists a neighborhood U_p of p such that

$$[-N, N] \subseteq \{f(k, y) : k \in [-K, K]\}$$

for all $y \in U_p$. By compactness we can take K to be large enough so that this holds for all $x \in \mathbf{C}$.

Note that $f(K, x) \neq 0$ for all $x \in X$. Moreover $f(K, x) > 0$ if and only if $f(k, x) > 0$ and $f(-k, x) < 0$ for all $n \geq K$. Similarly, $f(K, x) < 0$ if and only if $f(k, x) < 0$ and $f(-k, x) > 0$ for all $n \geq K$. Define the sets:

$$A = \{x \in \mathbf{C} : f(k, x) > 0\} \text{ and } B = \{x \in \mathbf{C} : f(k, x) < 0\}.$$

It is easy to check that these sets are clopen, ϕ-invariant and $\mathbf{C} = A \sqcup B$. Thus, either $A = \emptyset$ or $B = \emptyset$. By replacing ψ by ψ^{-1} we can assume that $A = \mathbf{C}$. Define a function $c : \mathbf{C} \to \mathbb{N}$ as follows

$$
\begin{aligned}
c(x) &= |[-KN, \infty]) \cap \{f(i, x) : i \leq 0\}| \\
&= |[-KN, \infty]) \cap \{f(i-1, \psi(x)) + n(x) : i \leq 0\}| \\
&= |[-KN, \infty]) \cap \{f(i, \psi(x)) + n(x) : i \leq 0\}| - 1 \\
&= |[-KN - n(x), \infty]) \cap \{f(i, \psi(x)) : i \leq 0\}| - 1 \\
&= |[-KN, \infty]) \cap \{f(i, \psi(x)) : i \leq 0\}| + n(x) - 1 \\
&= c(\psi(x)) + n(x) - 1.
\end{aligned}
$$

Thus, $1 + c(x) = c(\psi(x)) + n(x)$. Consider $g(x) = \phi^{c(x)}x$. Note that

$$\phi g(x) = \phi^{1+c(x)} = \phi^{n(x)+c(\psi(x))}(x) = \phi^{c(\psi(x))}\psi(x) = g\psi(x).$$

This implies that $\phi^k g = g\psi^k$ and hence g is surjective. If $g(x) = g\psi^k(x)$ for some k, then $\phi^k g(x) = g(x)$, which is impossible. Thus, g is bijective. Since c is continuous, g is a homeomorphism, hence, we have the statement of the theorem. $\square$

Theorem 4.20 together with Theorem 4.14 implies the following classical theorem.

COROLLARY 4.21 (Giordano, Putnam and Skau, [**61**]). Two minimal homeomorphism of the Cantor space have isomorphic full groups if and only if they are flip conjugated.

7. Examples of non-isomorphic topological full groups

An explicit example of a minimal subshift ϕ can be obtained as follows. Consider an irrational number α and the rotation $r_\alpha : z \mapsto z + \alpha$ on the circle $\mathbb{R}/\mathbb{Z}$. Now define a set X_α by replacing each $x \in \mathbb{Z}\alpha \subset \mathbb{R}/\mathbb{Z}$ with the pair $\{x_-, x_+\}$. Let $\pi : X_\alpha \to \mathbb{R}/\mathbb{Z}$ be the projection (that maps x_- and x_+ to x). Let $R_\alpha : X_\alpha \to X_\alpha$ be defined by $R_\alpha(x) = x + \alpha$ if $x \notin \mathbb{Z}\alpha$, and $R_\alpha(x_\pm) = (x + \alpha)_\pm$ otherwise. We have that $\pi R_\alpha = r_\alpha \pi$.

Take any $x, y \in \mathbb{R}/\mathbb{Z}$ and denote by $(x, y)_c \subset \mathbb{R}/\mathbb{Z}$ the open interval which is obtained by going counterclockwise from x to y. We introduce a topology on X_α by stating that for each $x, y \in \mathbb{Z}\alpha$ the set $\pi^{-1}(x, y)_c \cup \{x_-, y_+\}$ is open.

LEMMA 4.22. X_α is a Cantor space and R_α is a homeomorphism.

PROOF. Denote by $[x, y]_\alpha = \pi^{-1}(x, y)_c \cup \{x_-, y_+\}$. Then X_α is the disjoint union of $[x, y]_\alpha$ and $[y, x]_\alpha$. Since every $[x, y]_\alpha$ is open, it follows that it is also closed. Since the set $\alpha\mathbb{Z}$ is dense in $\mathbb{R}/\mathbb{Z}$, it follows that each point in X_α is an intersection of such clopen subsets, and thus X_α is totally discontinuous. It is clear that no point is isolated, and that X_α is second countable, and so it is a Cantor set.

Finally, since $R_\alpha^{-1}[x, y]_\alpha = [x - \alpha, y - \alpha]_\alpha$, it follows that R_α is continuous. Clearly, so is R_α^{-1}. $\square$

We also have the following

LEMMA 4.23. R_α is a subshift.

PROOF. Let $x \in \alpha\mathbb{Z} - \{0\}$. Denote by $Y_1 = [0, x]_\alpha \subset X_\alpha$, and let Y_0 be the complement of Y_1. Both Y_0 and Y_1 are clopen sets, and therefore the characteristic function $\chi = \chi_{Y_1} : X_\alpha \to \{0, 1\}$ is continuous. Define $\phi : X_\alpha \to \{0, 1\}^{\mathbb{Z}}$ by the rule $\phi(x)(n) = \chi(R_\alpha^{-n}x)$. It is easy to check that ϕ conjugates R_α to the shift on $\{0, 1\}^{\mathbb{Z}}$. It is left to show that ϕ is injective. Take different $y, y' \in X_\alpha$. Since $\alpha\mathbb{Z}$ is dense, there is n such that $R_\alpha^n y \in Y_0$ and $R_\alpha^n y' \in Y_1$. Thus $\phi(y) \neq \phi(y')$. $\square$

Unique ergodicity

We are going to show that the groups $[[R_\alpha]]$ are nonisomorphic for different α. It follows from the Giordano-Putnam-Skau result that it suffices to show that R_α are not flip-conjugate for different α. Precisely, for $\alpha \neq \alpha'$ there is no homeomorphism $\phi : X_\alpha \to X_{\alpha'}$ such that $\phi R_\alpha = R_{\alpha'}\phi$ or $\phi R_\alpha = R_{\alpha'}^{-1}\phi$. This provides uncountably pairwise non-isomorphic topological full groups.

In order to proceed, we need to introduce several definitions.

DEFINITION 4.24. A homeomorphism $T : X \to X$ is called uniquely ergodic if there is a unique Borel probability measure μ_T which is T-invariant.

Note that if $T : X \to X$ and $S : Y \to Y$ are both uniquely ergodic, and if a continuous map $f : X \to Y$ intertwines T and S, it follows that $f_*\mu_T = \mu_S$, since $f_*\mu_T$ is obviously S-invariant.

If T is uniquely ergodic, we can talk about the Hilbert space $L^2(X)$, implying that the measure on X is μ_T. Define by $U_T : L^2(X) \to L^2(X)$ the unitary operator $U_T(\phi) = \phi \circ T^{-1}$.

LEMMA 4.25. Suppose that $T : X \to X$ and $S : Y \to Y$ are both uniquely ergodic, and let $f : X \to Y$ be a homeomorphism which intertwines T and S. Then U_T and U_S are conjugate, in particular they have the same spectra.

PROOF. By above, for a continuous map $f : X \to Y$ that intertwines T and S, the map $U_f : L^2(Y) \to L^2(X)$ is norm-preserving, and $U_S U_f = U_f U_T$. If f is a homeomorphism, then U_f is an isometry, and so $U_T = U_f{}^* U_S U_f$. The equality of spectra follows. $\square$

PROPOSITION 4.26. *The homeomorphism R_α is uniquely ergodic for any irrational α.*

PROOF. Suppose X is compact and $T : X \to X$ is a continuous map. For a continuous map $f : X \to \mathbb{R}$ and $n \geq 1$ set

$$A_n(f)(x) = \frac{1}{n} \sum_{j=1}^{n} f(T^j x)$$

Suppose that for any continuous f, $A_n(f)$ converges uniformly to some constant (depending on f but independent of x). Then T is uniquely ergodic. Indeed, define $\mu(f) = \lim_n A_n(f)(x)$. It is easy to see that the map $f \mapsto \mu(f)$ is linear and $f \geq 0$ implies $\mu(f) \geq 0$. By Riesz representation theorem, this defines a Borel measure on X. Since $\mu(f) = \mu(f \circ T)$, the measure μ is T-invariant.

Suppose that ν is another Borel probability measure on X which is T-invariant. Since $A_n(f)(x) \to \mu(f)$ uniformly in x, we can integrate both sides with respect to ν. By T-invariance of ν

$$\int A_n(f) \, d\nu = \frac{1}{n} \sum_j \int f(T^j x) \, d\nu(x) = \int f \, d\nu = \nu(f)$$

And so $\nu(f) = \mu(f)$. Thus $\nu = \mu$ and so μ is the unique T-invariant measure on X.

Let us now show that for all $x \in \mathbb{R}/\mathbb{Z}$

$$A_n(f)(x) = \frac{1}{n} \sum_{j=1}^{n} f(R_\alpha^j x)$$

converges to a constant. First note, that any continuous function can be uniformly approximated by trigonometric polynomials $\sum_n c_n e^{2i\pi nx}$, the the Stone-Weierstrass theorem. So it suffices to show the convergences for such polynomials. Also, $A_n(f)$ is linear in f, and thus it suffices to show the convergence for functions $e^{2i\pi mx}$. We have in case $m \neq 0$,

$$A_n(e^{2i\pi mx}) = \frac{1}{n} \sum_{j=1}^{n} e^{2i\pi m(x+j\alpha)} = e^{2i\pi mx} \frac{1}{n} \sum_{j=1}^{n} e^{2i\pi mj\alpha} =$$

$$e^{2i\pi mx} \frac{1 - e^{2i\pi mn\alpha}}{n(1 - e^{2i\pi m\alpha})}$$

which clearly goes to 0 as $m \to \infty$. □

LEMMA 4.27. *The homeomorphism $R_\alpha : X_\alpha \to X_\alpha$ are uniquely ergodic, and the spectrum of U_{R_α} is $\{e^{2i\pi n\alpha} \mid n \in \mathbb{Z}\}$.*

PROOF. Let ν be an R_α-invariant measure on X_α. Then $\pi_* \nu$ is an r_α-invariant measure on $\mathbb{R}/\mathbb{Z}$, and so by uniqueness $\pi_* \nu$ is the Lebesgue measure. The subset $\{x_\pm \mid x \in \alpha\mathbb{Z}\}$ must have measure ν zero, since it is countable and R_α-invariant. Note that on the complement of this set, $\pi : X_\alpha \to \mathbb{R}/\mathbb{Z}$ is injective. It follows that π is a Borel isomorphism modulo sets of measure zero. Thus ν is unique. It also follows that $U_\pi : L^2(\mathbb{R}/\mathbb{Z}) \to L^2(X_\alpha)$ is an isometry. It follows that the spectrum of U_{R_α} is equal to the spectrum of U_{r_α}. Note now that $U_{r_\alpha}(e^{2i\pi nx}) = e^{-2i\pi n\alpha} e^{2i\pi nx}$, and that the functions $e^{2i\pi nx}$ form an orthogonal basis of $L^2(\mathbb{R}/\mathbb{Z})$. The matrix of U_{r_α} in this basis is diagonal with $\{e^{2i\pi n\alpha} \mid n \in \mathbb{Z}\}$ on the diagonal. □

COROLLARY 4.28. If $\alpha, \alpha' \in (0, 1/2)$ are irrational and different, then R_α and $R_{\alpha'}$ are not flip conjugate. This implies that $[[R_\alpha]]$ and $[[R_{\alpha'}]]$ are not isomorphic. Moreover, they have non-isomorphic commutator subgroups.

CHAPTER 5

Lamplighter actions and extensive amenability

In this chapter we discuss another analytic property of actions called called *extensively amenable actions*. Recall, that the action of a group G on a set X is amenable if there exists a G-invariant finitely additive probability measure on X. Acting on X the group G also acts on subsets of X pointwise.

DEFINITION 5.1. An action of a group G on a set X is extensively amenable if there exists a G-invariant finitely additive probability measure on finite subsets of X giving the full weight to the collection of all subsets that contain any given finite subset of X.

Extensive amenability will be a crucial tool for proving amenability in our future examples. We have proved in Theorem 2.21, that if G acts amenably on X and stabilizers of all points are amenable, then G is amenable. Thus, for a given group defined by an action on some space it is reasonable to reconstruct this space in a way that Theorem 2.21 is can be verified. In several reconstructions, extensively amenable actions guarantee that the action on the new space is amenable.

One of the reconstructions of the space is to consider *the lamplighter group*, $\mathbb{Z}/2\mathbb{Z} \wr_X G = \bigoplus_X \mathbb{Z}/2\mathbb{Z} \rtimes G$, and its action on the set $\bigoplus_X \mathbb{Z}/2\mathbb{Z}$. It was introduced in [86] in order to prove amenability of the topological full group. The idea of [86] is to embed the group G into the lamplighter group in a way that it is possible to verify amenability of the stabilizers of its action on $\bigoplus_X \mathbb{Z}/2\mathbb{Z}$. Under this notation, the action of G on X is extensively amenable if the action of its lamplighter group is amenable. All extensively amenable actions are amenable. Many groups that are defined as groups of certain transformations of spaces admit extensively amenable actions. In fact, all known non-elementary amenable groups admit such actions. In the later chapters we will introduce more technical reconstructions of the space, however extensive amenability will be useful there as well.

In the first sections we will give basic definitions of extensive amenability. The equivalence of these definitions was mostly proved in the papers [86] and [90], in several cases we omit original proofs and present some shortcuts. The crucial property is that recurrent actions imply extensive amenability, which was proved in [88]. We present three different proves of this fact. The first one uses capacity of electrical networks, the second is a more direct proof due to Narutaka Ozawa, and the last one is a relation with inverted orbits of random walks proved in [90].

In order to prove amenability of certain subgroups of the interval exchange transformation group, [90], the space was reconstructed in the following way. Instead of $\bigoplus_X \mathbb{Z}/2\mathbb{Z}$ we consider $Sym(X)$ the group all finitely supported permutations of X on which the group G acts by conjugation. Then we can form the semidirect product $Sym(X) \rtimes G$, which acts on $Sym(X)$ as on a coset space.

1. Extensive amenability: basic definition and properties

Assume that a discrete group G is acting on a set X. Consider the direct sum $\bigoplus_X \mathbb{Z}/2\mathbb{Z}$, i.e., the group of all finitely supported sequences with values in $\{0,1\}$ with addition mod 2. Another interpretation of $\bigoplus_X \mathbb{Z}/2\mathbb{Z}$ is as the set of all finite subsets of X, denoted by $\mathcal{P}_f(X)$, with multiplication given by the symmetric difference. We will use these interpretations of $\bigoplus_X \mathbb{Z}/2\mathbb{Z}$ depending on which is more appropriate to the given context.

The action of an element $g \in G$ on X induces an automorphism of $\bigoplus_X \mathbb{Z}/2\mathbb{Z}$ given by the action on the indexes of a sequence $(w_x)_{x \in X} \in \bigoplus_X \mathbb{Z}/2\mathbb{Z}$ by

$$g(w_x)_{x \in X} = (w_{g^{-1}x})_{x \in X}.$$

Thus we can form a semidirect product $\bigoplus_X \mathbb{Z}/2\mathbb{Z} \rtimes G$, which is also called *the permutational wreath product*, or *lamplighter group* of $\mathbb{Z}/2\mathbb{Z}$ and G, denoted by $\mathbb{Z}/2\mathbb{Z} \wr_X G$. The multiplication is given as follows:

$$(E,g) \cdot (F,h) = (E \Delta g(F), gh) \text{ for } g, h \in G \text{ and } E, F \in \mathcal{P}_f(X).$$

The lamplighter $\bigoplus_X \mathbb{Z}/2\mathbb{Z} \rtimes G$ acts on the cosets $\bigoplus_X (\mathbb{Z}/2\mathbb{Z} \rtimes G)/G$ by multiplication on the left, which can be viewed as an action on $\bigoplus_X \mathbb{Z}/2\mathbb{Z}$ by the following rule:

$$(E,g)(F) = g(F) \Delta E \text{ for } g \in G \text{ and } E \in \mathcal{P}_f(X).$$

One of the central ideas for applications of definitions of extensive amenability is the following. We show in Theorem 5.4 that it is equivalent to Definition 5.1.

DEFINITION 5.2. An action of G on X is **extensively amenable** if the affine action of the semidirect product $\bigoplus_X \mathbb{Z}/2\mathbb{Z} \rtimes G$ on $\bigoplus_X \mathbb{Z}/2\mathbb{Z}$ is amenable.

In fact, as we will see in Theorem 5.4, $\mathbb{Z}/2\mathbb{Z}$ can be replaced by any amenable group in the definition above.

Note that if the group G is amenable then so is $\bigoplus_X \mathbb{Z}/2\mathbb{Z} \rtimes G$, thus any action of G is extensively amenable. However, as we will see later, the action of the wobbling group $W(\mathbb{Z})$ on $\mathbb{Z}$ is extensively amenable. Nevertheless $W(\mathbb{Z})$ contains the free non-abelian group on two generators, and therefore it is non-amenable.

Consider the map $\phi : \mathcal{P}_f(X) \backslash \emptyset \to Prob(X)$, which sends a finite subset to the uniform measure on it. It is a G-map. Then extensive amenability of the action of G implies, in particular, that there exists a G-invariant mean μ on $\mathcal{P}_f(X)$. The barycenter of the push-forward of μ along ϕ is a G-invariant mean on X. Thus we have just showed the following.

LEMMA 5.3. If the action of G on X is extensively amenable, then it is amenable.

Note that the converse is not true, as we show in the later sections of this chapter. In the case of non-amenable groups it is always a difficult question to decide whether a particular amenable action is extensively amenable. A good example of this difficulty will be illustrated on the wobbling groups.

Let us first describe some preliminary notation. Consider the measure space $(\{0,1\}^X, \mu)$, where the set of all sequences in $\{0,1\}^X$ is equipped with the measure μ which is equal to the product measure of the uniform measures on $\{0,1\}$. This defines the Hilbert space $L^2(\{0,1\}^X, \mu)$ of all complex-valued square integrable functions on $\{0,1\}^X$ with respect to the measure μ and the inner product

$$\langle f, g \rangle = \int_{\{0,1\}^X} f\overline{g} \ d\mu$$

Denote by χ_A the characteristic function of a set $A \subset \{0,1\}^X$.

THEOREM 5.4. Let G act transitively on X and fix a point p in X. The following are equivalent:

  (i) The action of G on X is extensively amenable;
 (ii) There exists a sequence of unit vectors $f_n \in L^2(\{0,1\}^X, \mu)$ such that for every $g \in G$

$$\|gf_n - f_n\|_2 \to 0 \text{ and } \|f_n \cdot \chi_{\{(w_x) \in \{0,1\}^X : w_p = 0\}}\|_2 \to 1;$$

 (iii) There exists a constant $C > 0$ such that the action of G on $\mathcal{P}_f(X)$ admits a G-invariant mean giving the weight C to the collection of sets containing p;
 (iv) The action of G on $\mathcal{P}_f(X)$ admits a G-invariant mean giving the full weight to the collection of sets containing p;
  (v) The action of G on $\mathcal{P}_f(X)$ admits an G-invariant mean such that for all $E \in \mathcal{P}_f(X)$ it gives the full weight to the collection of sets containing E;

PROOF. ((ii)) $\implies$ ((i)). Let $f_n \in L^2(\{0,1\}^X, \mu)$ be a sequence of functions which satisfy ((ii)). Note that, replacing f_n with $f_n \cdot \chi_{\{w_p = 0\}}$ and normalizing we obtain a sequence of unit vectors in $L^2(\{0,1\}^X, \mu)$ such that $f_n \cdot \chi_{\{w_p = 0\}} = f_n$ and

$$\|gf_n - f_n\|_2 \to 0 \text{ for all } g \in G.$$

The group $\{0,1\}^X$ is the Pontriagin dual of $\mathcal{P}_f(X)$, with the pairing function $\{0,1\}^X \times \mathcal{P}_f(X)$ given by

$$\langle w, E \rangle = exp(i\pi \sum_{x \in E} w_x)$$

Thus we can define the Fourier transform $\hat{f} \in l^2(\mathcal{P}_f(X))$ of $f \in L^2(\{0,1\}^X, \mu)$ by

$$\hat{f}(E) = \int_{\{0,1\}^X} f(w)\langle w, E \rangle d\mu(w).$$

We will show that the sequence $\hat{f}_n$ is approximately invariant under the action of $\bigoplus_X \mathbb{Z}/2\mathbb{Z} \rtimes G$.

From the properties of the Fourier transform and the easy fact that it is G-equivariant, we have

$$\|g\hat{f}_n - \hat{f}_n\|_2 = \|(gf_n - f_n)\hat{\ }\|_2 = \|gf_n - f_n\|_2 \to 0.$$

Thus $\hat{f}_n$ remains G-invariant.

Since the action of G on X is transitive it is sufficient to show that $\hat{f}_n$ is invariant under the action of $\{p\}$:

$$\{p\}\hat{f}_n(E) = \hat{f}_n(E \Delta \{p\})$$

$$= \int_{\{0,1\}^X} f_n\langle w, E\Delta\{p\}\rangle d\mu(w)$$

$$= \int_{\{0,1\}^X} f_n \chi_{\{w_p=0\}}(w)\langle w, E\Delta\{p\}\rangle d\mu(w)$$

$$= \int_{\{0,1\}^X} f_n \chi_{\{w_p=0\}}(w) exp(i\pi \sum_{x\in E\Delta\{p\}} w(x)) d\mu(w)$$

$$= \int_{\{0,1\}^X} f_n \chi_{\{w_p=0\}}(w) exp(i\pi \sum_{x\in E} w(x)) d\mu(w)$$

$$= \hat{f}_n(E)$$

Thus $\hat{f}_n$ is $\{p\}$-invariant. Since $\hat{f}_n \in l^2(\mathcal{P}_f(X))$ are almost invariant, we have that $\hat{f}_n^2 \in l^1(\mathcal{P}_f(X))$ are also almost invariant. Indeed, this follows from Cauch-Schwarz inequality:

$$\|gf^2 - f^2\|_1 = \|(gf - f)(gf + f)\|_1$$
$$\leq \|(gf - f)\|_2 \|(gf + f)\|_2$$
$$\leq 2\|(gf - f)\|_2,$$

for every unit vector $f \in l^2(\mathcal{P}_f(X))$ and $g \in G$.

Taking a cluster point of the sequence $\hat{f}_n^2$ in weak*-topology we obtain an $\bigoplus_X \mathbb{Z}/2\mathbb{Z} \rtimes G$-invariant mean on $\mathcal{P}_f(X)$, thus the action is extensively amenable.

To show that ((i)) implies ((iii)), assume that m is a $\mathcal{P}_f(X) \rtimes G$-invariant mean on $\mathcal{P}_f(X)$. Let $\mathcal{F}_p$ be the set of all finite subsets of X containing p. Then $\{p\}.\mathcal{F}_p = \mathcal{F}_p^c$, therefore we have $m(\mathcal{F}_p) = m(\{p\}.\mathcal{F}_p) = m(\mathcal{F}_p^c) = 1/2$.

((iii)) $\implies$ ((iv)). Let now m be a G-invariant mean on $\mathcal{P}_f(X)$ with $m(\mathcal{F}_p) = C$ for some $C > 0$.

Fix $k \in \mathbb{N}$ and define G-equivariant map

$$U_k : \mathcal{P}_f(X)^k \to \mathcal{P}_f(X)$$

by

$$U_k(F_1, \ldots, F_k) = F_1 \cup \ldots \cup F_k$$

Let $m^{\times k}$ be a product measure on $\mathcal{P}_f(X)^k$, i.e., for all $F_1, \ldots, F_k \in \mathcal{P}_f(X)$ we have

$$m^{\times k}(F_1, \ldots, F_k) = m(F_1) \cdot \ldots \cdot m(F_k).$$

Note that $m^{\times k}$ is invariant under the diagonal action of G.

Define m_k to be the push-forward of $m^{\times k}$ with respect to U_k. Since U_k and $m^{\times k}$ are G-invariant, m_k is also G-invariant. Moreover, for all $E \in \mathcal{X}$ we have

$$U_k^{-1}(\mathcal{F}_p^c) \subseteq \mathcal{F}_p^c \times \ldots \times \mathcal{F}_p^c.$$

Thus $1 - m_k(\mathcal{F}_p) \leq (1 - m(\mathcal{F}_p))^k = (1 - C)^k$. Taking a cluster point in the weak*-topology we obtain a mean that satisfies ((v)).

((v)) $\implies$ ((iv)). It is obvious.

((iv)) $\implies$ ((v)). For a finite set $E \subset X$ the set of finite subsets that contain E is $\bigcap_{x \in E} \mathcal{F}_x$. Since the action of G on X is transitive we have $\mu(\mathcal{F}_x) = 1$ for every $x \in X$, thus $\mu(E) = 1$ and ((v)) follows.

((iv)) $\implies$ ((ii)). Let m be G-invariant mean giving a full weight to $\mathcal{F}_p$. Then there exists a sequence $m_n \in l^1(\mathcal{P}_f(X))$ such that $\|g.m_n - m_n\|_1 \to 0$ for all $g \in G$ and $m_n(\mathcal{F}_p) = 1$. For a sequence $w \in \{0, 1\}^X$, define

$$f_n(w) = \sum_{F \in \mathcal{P}_f(X)} m_n(F) 2^{|F|} \chi_F(w),$$

where $\chi_F(w)$ is 1 if $F \cap w \neq \emptyset$ and 0 otherwise. Since m_n is supported on $\mathcal{F}_p$ we have $f_n \cdot \chi_{\{(w_x) \in \{0,1\}^X : w_p = 0\}} = f_n$. Since $\|\chi_F\|_1 = 2^{-|F|}$ we have that $\|f_n\| = 1$.

Moreover f_n is G-invariant. Indeed,

$$\|g.f_n - f_n\| \leq \sum_{E \in \mathcal{P}_f(X)} \|m_n(E) 2^{|F|} g.\chi_F - m_n(E) 2^{|F|} \chi_F\|_1$$

$$= \sum_{E \in \mathcal{P}_f(X)} \|m_n(gE) 2^{|F|} \chi_F - m_n(E) 2^{|F|} \chi_F\|_1$$

$$= \sum_{E \in \mathcal{P}_f(X)} \|m_n(gE) - m_n(E)\|_1$$

$$= \|g.m_n - m_n\|.$$

Since $\|g.f_n^{1/2} - f_n^{1/2}\|_2^2 \leq \|g.f_n - f_n\|_1$, the implication follows. $\qquad \square$

The following lemma is an interesting observation: the group $\mathbb{Z}/2\mathbb{Z}$ is not essential for extensively amenable actions and can be replaced by any other amenable group. It was obtained in collaboration with N. Monod, another proof will appear later in the chapter, where we will discuss functorial properties of extensive amenability.

LEMMA 5.5. Assume that the action of G on X is transitive and extensively amenable. Then for any amenable group H the action of $\bigoplus_X H \rtimes G$ on $\bigoplus_X H$ is amenable.

PROOF. Fix a point p in X. We may assume that G is generated by a finite set S. Let A be a finite subset of H. For every $\varepsilon > 0$ we need to find a finite set E in $\bigoplus_X H$ such that it is ε-invariant for both S and $\{(e, h\delta_p) : h \in A\}$.

Fix $\varepsilon > 0$. By assumption, we can find a finite set $F \subset \mathcal{P}_f(X)$, which is (S, ε)-invariant and such that all elements of F contain the point p. Without loss of generality we may assume that all elements of F are of the same size, say k. Indeed, since the action of G preserves cardinality, we can decompose F as a disjoint union $F = F_1 \cup \ldots \cup F_n$ where all elements of F_i have the same cardinality. Assume that none of these components is $(S, |S| \cdot \varepsilon)$-invariant, i.e., for every F_i there exists $s \in S$ such that

$$|sF_i \backslash F_i| > \varepsilon \cdot |S| \cdot |F_i|.$$

Note that $|sF \backslash F| = \sum_{i=1}^n |sF_i \backslash F_i|$. Summing up the last equation over S we obtain:

$$\sum_{s \in S} |sF \backslash F| = \sum_{s \in S} \sum_{i=1}^n |sF_i \backslash F_i| > \varepsilon \cdot |S| \cdot \sum_{i=1}^n |F_i| = \varepsilon \cdot |S| \cdot |F|,$$

which is impossible.

Let F_A be a (A,ε)-Følner set. Consider the set taken with multiplicities:

$$E = \{\phi \in \bigoplus_X H : \mathrm{supp}(\phi) \in F, \phi(X) \subset F_A\}.$$

Here each ϕ comes with multiplicity $\{|\{C \in F : supp(\phi) \subseteq C\}|\}$. Then $|E| = |F_A|^k \cdot |F|$ and

$$|sE \backslash E| \le \varepsilon|F_A| \cdot |F| = \varepsilon|E|.$$

Moreover, for all $h \in A$ we have

$$|(e, h\delta_p)E \backslash E| \le |hF_A \backslash F_A| \cdot |F_A|^{k-1} \cdot |F| = \varepsilon/|F_A| \cdot |E|.$$

Define a function $f : \bigoplus_X H \to \mathbb{R}_+$:

$$f(\nu) = \sum_{\phi \in E} \delta_\phi(\nu) \text{ for all } \nu \in \bigoplus_X H,$$

Here we write sum instead of χ_E in order to specify that the values of f can depend on the multiplicities that appear in the set E. It is immediate that $\|f\|_1 = |E|$ and $\|g.f - f\|_1 = |sE \Delta E|$, therefore we have the statement of the lemma. $\square$

We will use the following theorem for applications in later sections. Note that we don't assume transitivity of the action.

LEMMA 5.6. An action $G \curvearrowright X$ is extensively amenable if and only if for every finitely generated subgroup H of G and every H-orbit $Y \subset X$, the action of H on Y is extensively amenable.

PROOF. Assume that the action of G on X is extensively amenable and $H < G$ is a subgroup. Assume, in addition, that a set $Y \subset X$ is invariant under the action of H, and let us show that the action of H on Y is extensively amenable. Define a $\mathcal{P}_f(Y) \rtimes H$-equivariant map on $\mathcal{P}_f(X)$ into $\mathcal{P}_f(Y)$ by intersecting a finite subset of X with Y. The push-forward of $\bigoplus_X \mathbb{Z}/2\mathbb{Z} \rtimes G$-invariant mean on $\bigoplus_X \mathbb{Z}/2\mathbb{Z}$ along our H-map is $\bigoplus_Y \mathbb{Z}/2\mathbb{Z} \rtimes H$-invariant mean on $\bigoplus_Y \mathbb{Z}/2\mathbb{Z}$.

The converse of the lemma follows from the above theorem and the fact that the amenability of the action of $\bigoplus_X \mathbb{Z}/2\mathbb{Z} \rtimes G$ on $\bigoplus_X \mathbb{Z}/2\mathbb{Z}$ is equivalent to the existence Følner sets in $\bigoplus_X \mathbb{Z}/2\mathbb{Z}$, which approximate the action of any finite set from $\bigoplus_X \mathbb{Z}/2\mathbb{Z} \rtimes G$. However, since the action of G on X is not transitive, we can switch among the orbits of G on X by adding δ_x to the finite set we want to approximate. $\square$

2. Recurrent actions: definition and basic properties

Let G be a finitely generated group with finite symmetric generating set S.

If G acts transitively on X a **Schreier graph** $\Gamma(X, G, S)$ is the graph with the set of vertices identified with X, the set of edges is $S \times X$, where an edge (s, x) connects x to $s(x)$.

Choose a measure μ on G such that support of μ is a finite generating set of G and $\mu(g) = \mu(g^{-1})$ for all $g \in G$. Consider the Markov chain on X with transition probability from x to y equal to $p(x, y) = \sum_{g \in G, g(x)=y} \mu(g)$.

DEFINITION 5.7. The action is called **recurrent** if the probability of returning to x_0 after starting at x_0 is equal to 1 for some (hence for any) $x_0 \in X$. An action is transient if it is not recurrent.

It is well known (see [**155**, Theorems 3.1, 3.2]) that recurrence of the described Markov chain does not depend on the choice of the measure μ, if the measure is symmetric, and has finite support generating the group.

DEFINITION 5.8. An action of G on X is **recurrent** if the Markov chain that corresponds to a measure supported on a symmetric finite generating set of G is recurrent.

Note that, the action of G on itself is recurrent if and only if G is virtually $\{0\}$, $\mathbb{Z}$ or $\mathbb{Z}^2$, see Theorem 3.24 in [**155**]. Moreover, all recurrent actions are amenable.

The following theorem is part of the more general Nash-Williams criteria for recurrence. It will be very useful in the applications.

THEOREM 5.9. Let Γ be a connected graph of uniformly bounded degree with set of vertices V. Suppose that there exists an increasing sequence of finite subsets $F_n \subset V$ such that $\bigcup_{n \geq 1} F_n = V$, the subsets ∂F_n are pairwise disjoint, and

$$\sum_{n \geq 1} \frac{1}{|\partial F_n|} = \infty,$$

where ∂F_n is the set of vertices of F_n adjacent to the vertices of $V \setminus F_n$. Then the simple random walk on Γ is recurrent.

We will also use a characterization of transience of a random walk on a locally finite connected graph (V, E) in terms of electrical networks. The **capacity** of a point $x_0 \in V$ is the quantity defined by

$$cap(x_0) = \inf \left\{ \left(\sum_{(x,x') \in E} |a(x) - a(x')|^2 \right)^{1/2} \right\}$$

where the infimum is taken over all finitely supported functions $a : V \to \mathbb{C}$ with $a(x_0) = 1$. We will use the following

THEOREM 5.10 ([**155**], Theorem 2.12). The simple random walk on a locally finite connected graph (V, E) is transient if and only if $cap(x_0) > 0$ for some (and hence for all) $x_0 \in V$.

In all existent applications to amenability we will use Theorem 5.9. In its turn Theorem 5.10 will serve us as a technical link to prove amenability of certain actions of groups. In order to give a complete proof of amenability of all examples mentioned in this book we will need to show that the graph condition of Theorem 5.9 implies zero capacity of the random walk. We will omit the proofs that both conditions imply recurrency and refer the reader to the book of Woess [**155**] for details. To summarize the above, in all our applications we will use only the following theorem applied to Schreier graphs of group actions.:

THEOREM 5.11. Let Γ be a connected graph of uniformly bounded degree with set of vertices V. Suppose that there exists an increasing sequence of finite subsets $F_n \subset V$ such that $\bigcup_{n \geq 1} F_n = V$, the subsets ∂F_n are pairwise disjoint, and

$$\sum_{n \geq 1} \frac{1}{|\partial F_n|} = \infty,$$

where ∂F_n is the set of vertices of F_n adjacent to the vertices of $V \setminus F_n$. Then $cap(x_0) = 0$ for some $x_0 \in V$.

PROOF. Define

$$a_n(x) = \left(\sum_{i=1}^{n} \frac{1}{|\partial F_i|} \chi_{F_i} \right) / \left(\sum_{i=1}^{n} \frac{1}{|\partial F_i|} \right).$$

Pick a point x_0, which belongs to each set F_i. Clearly $a_n(x_0) = 1$. Moreover, we have

$$\left(\sum_{x \sim x'} |a_n(x) - a_n(x')|^2 \right)^{1/2} = \left(\sum_{i=1}^{n} \frac{1}{|\partial F_i|} \right)^{1/2} / \left(\sum_{i=1}^{n} \frac{1}{|\partial F_i|} \right),$$

which obviously converges to 0.   □

3. Recurrent actions are extensively amenable

In this section we discuss the relation between recurrent actions and extensive amenability. The connecting point is the definition of extensive amenability given in Theorem 5.4 ((ii)).

Let $\mathcal{H}_i$ be a collection of Hilbert spaces indexed by a set I. Fix a sequence of unit vectors $\xi_i \in \mathcal{H}_i$. Then the algebraic (incomplete) tensor product of the $\mathcal{H}_i$ is the set of all linear combinations of $\bigotimes_{i \in I} \phi_i$, where all but finitely many ϕ_i are equal to ξ_i. It carries an inner product, which is defined by

$$\left\langle \bigotimes_{i \in I} \phi_i, \bigotimes_{i \in I} \nu_i \right\rangle = \prod_{i \in I} \langle \phi_i, \nu_i \rangle_{\mathcal{H}_i}$$

An infinite tensor product of Hilbert spaces is the Hilbert space is defined to be the completion of the algebraic tensor product by the norm defined by the above inner product.

Consider the Hilbert space of square integrable functions $L_2(\{0,1\}^X, \mu)$ with respect to the measure μ given by the product of measure m on $\{0,1\}$, where $m(0) = m(1) = \frac{1}{2}$.

It is natural to consider the Hilbert space $L_2(\{0,1\}^X, \mu)$ as an infinite tensor power of the Hilbert space $L_2(\{0,1\}^X, m)$.

A function $f \in L_2(\{0,1\}^X, \mu)$ is called *a product of independent random variables* if there are functions $f_x : \{0,1\} \to \mathbb{C}$ such that $f(w) = \prod_{x \in X} f_x(w_x)$. Equivalently, if we consider $L_2(\{0,1\}^X, \mu)$ as the infinite tensor power, then the condition that f is a product of random independent variables means that f is an elementary tensor in $L_2(\{0,1\}^X, \mu)$.

THEOREM 5.12. Let G be a finitely generated group acting transitively on a set X and fix a point p in X. There exists a sequence of functions $\{f_n\}$ in $L_2(\{0,1\}^X, \mu)$ with $\|f_n\|_2 = 1$ given by a product of random independent variables that satisfy

   (i) $\|g f_n - f_n\|_2 \to 0$ for all $g \in G$,
   (ii) $\|f_n \cdot \chi_{\{(w_x) \in \{0,1\}^X : w_p = 0\}}\|_2 \to 1$,

if and only if the action of G on X is recurrent.

PROOF 1. Denote by (X, E) the Schreier graph of the action of G on X with respect to S. Suppose that the simple random walk on (X, E) is recurrent. By Theorem 5.10, there exists $a_n = (a_{x,n})_x$ a sequence of finitely supported functions such that $a_{p,n} = 1$ and

$$\sum_{x \sim x'} |a_{x,n} - a_{x',n}|^2 \to 0.$$

Without loss of generality we may assume that $0 \le a_{x,n} \le 1$. Indeed, we can replace all values $a_{x,n}$ that are greater than 1 by 1 and those that are smaller than 0 by 0, this would not increase the differences $|a_{x,n} - a_{x',n}|$.

For $0 \le t \le 1$ consider the unit vector $\xi_t \in L_2(\{0,1\}, m)$ defined by

$$(\xi_t(0), \xi_t(1)) = (\sqrt{2}\cos(t\pi/4), \sqrt{2}\sin(t\pi/4)).$$

Define $f_{x,n} = \xi_{1-a_{x,n}}$ and $f_n = \bigotimes_{x \in X} f_{x,n}$.

To show that $\|gf_n - f_n\|_2 \to 0$ for all $g \in G$, is the same as to show that $\langle gf_n, f_n \rangle \to 1$ for all $g \in \Gamma$. It is sufficient to show this for $g \in S$. Since $\cos(x) \ge e^{-x^2}$, whenever $|x| \le \pi/4$, we have

$$\langle gf_n, f_n \rangle = \prod_x \langle f_{x,n}, f_{gx,n} \rangle$$

$$= \prod_x \cos \frac{\pi}{4}(a_{x,n} - a_{gx,n})$$

$$\ge \prod_x \exp\left(-\frac{\pi^2}{16}(a_{x,n} - a_{gx,n})^2\right)$$

$$\ge \exp\left(-\frac{\pi^2}{16}\sum_{x \sim x'} |a_{x,n} - a_{x',n}|^2\right).$$

By the selection of the $a_{x,n}$, the last value converges to 1.

Since $f_{p,n} = \xi_0 = (1,0)$ we have

$$f_n \chi_{\{(w_x) \in \{0,1\}^X : w_p = 0\}} = f_n.$$

Let us prove the other direction of the theorem. Define the following pseudometric on the unit sphere of $L_2(\{0,1\}, m)$ by

$$d(\xi, \eta) = \inf_{w \in \mathbb{C}, |w|=1} \|w\xi - \eta\| = \sqrt{2 - 2|\langle \xi, \eta \rangle|}.$$

Assume that there is a sequence of products of random independent variables $\{f_n\}$ in $L_2(\{0,1\}^X, \mu)$ that satisfy the conditions of the theorem, i.e.,

$$f_n(w) = \prod_{x \in X} f_{n,x}(w_x).$$

We can assume that the product is finite. Replacing $f_{n,x}$ by $f_{n,x}/\|f_{n,x}\|$ we can assume that $\|f_{n,x}\|_{l_2(\{0,1\}, m)} = 1$. Define $a_{x,n} = d(f_{x,n}, 1)$. It is straightforward that $(a_{x,n})_{x \in X}$ has finite support and

$$\lim_n a_{p,n} = \sqrt{2 - \sqrt{2}} > 0.$$

Moreover for every $g \in G$

$$|\langle gf_n, f_n \rangle| = \prod_x |\langle f_{n,x}, f_{n,gx} \rangle|$$

$$= \prod_x (1 - d(f_{n,x}, f_{n,gx})^2/2)$$

$$\le \exp\left(-\sum_x d(f_{n,x}, f_{n,gx})^2/2\right).$$

Since by assumption $|\langle gf_n, f_n\rangle| \to 1$ and $\sum_x d(f_{n,x}, f_{n,gx})^2 \geq 0$ we have

$$\sum_x d(f_{n,x}, f_{n,gx})^2 \to 0.$$

By definition of the Schreier graph and by the triangle inequality for d,

$$\sum_{(x,x')\in E} |a_{x,n} - a_{x',n}|^2 = \sum_{g\in S}\sum_x |a_{x,n} - a_{gx,n}|^2$$

$$\leq \sum_{g\in S}\sum_x d(f_{n,x}, f_{n,gx})^2 \to 0.$$

This proves that $cap(p) = 0$ in (X, E), and hence by Theorem 5.10 that the simple random walk on (X, E) is recurrent. □

A more direct proof of extensive amenability from recurrence of the action is the following.

DIRECT PROOF OF RECURRENCE IMPLIES EXTENSIVE AMENABILITY. We again use the characterization of recurrence in terms of capacity, which implies that there exists a sequence of finitely supported functions $a_n : X \to \mathbb{R}_+$ such that for a fixed point $p \in X$ we have $a_n(p) = 1$ for all n and

$$\|ga_n - a_n\|_2 \to 0 \text{ for all } g \in G.$$

Moreover, we can assume $0 \leq a_n(x) \leq 1$ for all $x \in X$ and n.

Define $\xi_n : \mathcal{P}_f(X) \to \mathbb{R}_+$ by $\xi_n(\emptyset) = 1$ and

$$\xi_n(F) = \prod_{x\in F} a_n(x).$$

We claim that $\nu_n := \xi_n/\|\xi_n\|_2 \in l^2(\mathcal{P}_f(X))$ is almost invariant under the action of $\mathcal{P}_f(X) \rtimes G$. Thus taking a cluster point in the weak*-topology of $\nu_n^2 \in l_1(\mathcal{P}_f(X))$ we obtain a $\mathcal{P}_f(X) \rtimes G$-invariant mean on $\mathcal{P}_f(X)$.

To prove the claim, note that since $a_n(p) = 1$ for all n the functions ν_n are automatically invariant under the action of $\{p\} \in \mathcal{P}_f(X)$. From the transitivity of the action of G on X we have that it is sufficient to show that ν_n are almost invariant under the action of G. Since $\|g\nu_n - \nu_n\| = 2 - 2\langle g\nu_n, \nu_n\rangle$, it is sufficient to show that $\langle g\nu_n, \nu_n\rangle \to 1$. The direct verification shows that

$$\|\xi_n\|^2 = \langle \xi_n, \xi_n\rangle$$

$$= \prod_{x\in X} \left(1 + a_n(x)^2\right)$$

$$= \prod_{x\in X} \left(1 + a_n(g^{-1}x)^2\right)$$

and

$$\langle g\xi_n, \xi_n\rangle = \prod_{x\in X} \left(1 + a_n(g^{-1}x)a_n(x)\right).$$

Thus we have

$$\left(\frac{\langle \xi_n, \xi_n\rangle}{\langle g\xi_n, \xi_n\rangle}\right)^2 = \prod_{x\in X} \frac{\left(1 + a_n(x)^2\right)\left(1 + a_n(g^{-1}x)^2\right)}{\left(1 + a_n(g^{-1}x)a_n(x)\right)^2}.$$

Since $\log(t) \leq t - 1$ for all $t > 0$ and $0 \leq a_n(x) \leq 1$ we have

$$
\begin{aligned}
0 \leq 2\log \frac{\langle \xi_n, \xi_n \rangle}{\langle g\xi_n, \xi_n \rangle} \\
= \sum_{x \in X} \log \frac{\left(1 + a_n(x)^2\right)\left(1 + a_n(g^{-1}x)^2\right)}{\left(1 + a_n(g^{-1}x)a_n(x)\right)^2} \\
\leq \sum_{x \in X} \frac{\left(a_n(x) - a_n(g^{-1}x)\right)^2}{\left(1 + a_n(g^{-1}x)a_n(x)\right)^2} \\
\leq \|ga_n - a_n\|^2 \to 0.
\end{aligned}
$$

$\square$

4. Extensions of actions

In this section we prove that extensive amenability is preserved under extensions. Denote by G_y the stabilizer of y in G. The proof the next theorem is very similar to the proof of the Theorem 2.21.

THEOREM 5.13. *Let G act on two sets X, Y and let $q: X \to Y$ be a G-map. If $G \curvearrowright Y$ is extensively amenable and if $G_y \curvearrowright q^{-1}(y)$ is extensively amenable for every $y \in Y$, then $G \curvearrowright X$ is extensively amenable. The converse holds if q is surjective.*

PROOF. Let m_1 be a mean on $\mathcal{P}_f(Y)$ as in Theorem 5.4 ((iv)). Then for all $y \in Y$ there is a mean m_y on $\mathcal{P}_f(q^{-1}(y))$ giving full weight to the subsets of $q^{-1}(y)$ that contain any given finite subset of $q^{-1}(y)$ and with the property that m_{gy} is the push-forward by g of the mean m_y for all $y \in Y$ and $g \in G$. Indeed, by the assumption that $G_y \curvearrowright q^{-1}(y)$ is extensively amenable we can take such a G_y-invariant mean m_y on $\mathcal{P}_f(q^{-1}(y))$ for each y in a fixed G-transversal of Y, and, for $y' = gy$ in the G-orbit of such y, define $m_{y'}$ as the push-forward of m_y by g. This definition does not depend on g because m_y is G_y-invariant, and this defines the requested mean on $\mathcal{P}_f(q^{-1}(y'))$.

Let now $A = \{y_1, \ldots, y_n\} \in \mathcal{P}_f(Y)$, denote by m_A the mean on $\mathcal{P}_f(X)$ defined by

$$
m_A(f)
$$
$$
= \frac{1}{n!} \sum_{\sigma:\, \{1,\ldots,n\} \to A} \int_{q^{-1}(\sigma(1))} \cdots \int_{q^{-1}(\sigma(n))} f(\cup_{i=1}^n B_i)\, dm_{\sigma(1)}(B_n) \ldots dm_{\sigma(n)}(B_1).
$$

where the average is taken over all bijections σ, which in particular implies that m_A does not depend on the chosen ordering of the elements of A. By the properties of the means m_y, we have that the push-forward of m_A by $g \in G$ is m_{gA}, and m_A gives full weight to the subsets of X that contain any given subset of $q^{-1}(A)$. These properties ensure that the mean m on $\mathcal{P}_f(X)$ defined by

$$
m: f \in \ell^\infty(\mathcal{P}_f(X)) \mapsto \int_{\mathcal{P}_f(Y)} m_A(f)\, dm_1(A),
$$

is G-invariant and gives full weight to the subsets of X that contain any given subset of X, which proves extensively amenable of the the action of G on X.

To prove the converse let m be a mean on $\mathcal{P}_f(X)$ as in Theorem 5.4. Again, by Theorem 5.4, the action of the subgroup G_y on the subset $q^{-1}(y)$ of X is extensively amenable for all $y \in Y$. Consider a map

$$q' \colon A \in \mathcal{P}_f(X) \mapsto \{q(a), a \in A\} \in \mathcal{P}_f(Y).$$

The map

$$f \in \ell^\infty(\mathcal{P}_f(Y)) \mapsto m(f \circ q')$$

is a G-invariant mean that gives full weight to the sets containing every finite subset of $q(Y)$. This proves that $G \curvearrowright q(Y)$ is extensively amenable. $\qquad\square$

Recall, that transitive actions of groups are always given by actions on the coset space by the stabilizer of a point. We have the following description of transitive actions, by applying the theorem to the quotient map and spaces $X = G/F$ and $Y = G/H$.

COROLLARY 5.14. Let $F < H < G$ be groups. Then the action of G on G/F is extensively amenable if and only if both the actions of H on H/F and G on G/H are extensively amenable.

COROLLARY 5.15. Assume that two actions $G \curvearrowright X$ and $H \curvearrowright Y$ are extensively amenable. Then

(i) The diagonal action of $G \times H$ on $X \times Y$ is extensively amenable.
(ii) Let G act trivially on Y, and let H^X act by $(h_x)_{x \in X} \cdot (x, y) = (x, h_x y)$. Then the action of $H^X \rtimes G$ on $X \times Y$ is extensively amenable.

PROOF. ((i)) follows from Theorem 5.13 applied for the actions of $G \times H$ on $X \times Y$ and X with trivial action of H on Y, and $q \colon X \times Y \to X$ the first coordinate projection. On the other hand ((ii)) is Theorem 5.13 for the actions on $H^X \rtimes G$ on $X \times Y$ and X taken with the trivial action of H^X for the same projection q. $\qquad\square$

5. Functorial properties of extensive amenability

The functorial approach to extensive amenability was introduced in [**90**], the exposition of which we will follow. In this section, we consider a functor F from the category of finite sets with morphisms given by bijections to the category of amenable groups with morphisms given by homomorphisms. Since the class of amenable groups is preserved under taking direct limits, we can extend such a functor to all sets with injective maps as morphisms by setting $F(X)$ to be the direct limit of $F(Y)$ as Y runs over the directed set $\mathcal{P}_f(X)$. We still denote the resulting functor by the same letter F.

Here we list examples of such functors.

EXAMPLE 5.16. Given an action of G on X and on $\bigoplus_X \mathbb{Z}/2\mathbb{Z}$, we define a functor as $F(X) = \bigoplus_X \mathbb{Z}/2\mathbb{Z}$.

EXAMPLE 5.17. For a set X we define a functor $F(X) = \mathrm{Sym}(X)$, the group of finitely supported permutations of a set X, on which G acts by conjugation.

EXAMPLE 5.18. Fix a finite ring R with unit. Consider the functor $F(Y)$ given by the group of invertible matrices over R indexed by a finite set Y, with the "corner" inclusions. For an infinite set X, the group $F(X)$ is a stable linear group which we denote by $GL_{(X)}(R)$ (it is the usual one when X is countable). As a variation, we can define $F(Y)$ to be the group $EL_Y(R)$ generated by elementary matrices; this yields stable elementary groups $EL_X(R)$ for arbitrary sets X.

EXAMPLE 5.19. Fix again a finite ring R. Given a finite set Y consider the (unstable) Steinberg group or degree $|Y|$ over R. Then for X general we obtain a (stable) Steinberg group which we denote by $\mathrm{St}_{(X)}(R)$. Thus we have a natural transformation given by the morphisms $\mathrm{St}_{(X)}(R) \to EL_X(R)$ (recall that these are isomorphisms if R is a finite field).

Any group action $G \curvearrowright X$ yields an action $G \curvearrowright F(X)$ by automorphisms. Thus we can consider a semi-direct product group $F(X) \rtimes G$. We can identify $F(X)$ with the coset space $(F(X) \rtimes G)/G$, and let $F(X) \rtimes G$ act on it by left multiplication.

THEOREM 5.20. Let F be a functor from the category of sets to the category of amenable groups, which maps each finite set to a finite group. If the action of a group G on X is extensively amenable, then the action of $F(X) \rtimes G$ on $F(X)$ is extensively amenable.

PROOF. Assume that the action of G on X is extensively amenable. Let m be a G-invariant mean on $\mathcal{P}_f(X)$ giving full weight to the collection of subsets that contain any given finite subset. Let F be a functor from the category of finite sets to the category of finite groups.

We first prove that the action of $F(X) \rtimes G$ on $F(X)$ is amenable. Then we will see how to adapt the proof to show that the action is extensively amenable.

For a finite set A, let m_A be the uniform probability measure on $F(A)$, which is a finite group by assumption. We denote by m_A^X the mean on $F(X)$ obtained by push-forward through $F(A) \to F(X)$; this mean is $F(A)$-invariant by construction. Observe also that we have $gm_A^X = m_{gA}^X$ for every $g \in G$.

We obtain a mean $\overline{m}$ on $F(X)$ by integrating m_A^X over m; more precisely, given $f \in \ell^\infty(F(X))$ we define

$$\overline{m}(f) = \int_{\mathcal{P}_f(X)} m_A^X(f) dm(A).$$

This mean is G-invariant by construction and we claim that it is also $F(X)$-invariant. It is enough to show that m is $F(A)$-invariant for every finite subset A of X. But this holds because m gives full weight to the set of finite subsets containing A, and since m_B^X is $F(A)$-invariant whenever B contains A. $\square$

COROLLARY 5.21. Let $G \curvearrowright X$ be an extensively amenable action and let F be a functor from the category of sets to the category of amenable groups, which maps each finite set to a finite group. A subgroup H of $F(X) \rtimes G$ is amenable as soon as the intersection $H \cap (\{1\} \times G)$ is so.

PROOF. To prove that H is amenable we find an amenable action of H with amenable stabilizers. Let e be the unit element of $F(X)$, and consider the action of H on the H-orbit of e. By Theorem 5.22 and Theorem 5.4, this action is extensively amenable and, in particular, it is amenable. Moreover the stabilizer of e is $H \cap (\{1\} \times G)$ which by assumption is amenable. So is every other stabilizer, which is a conjugate of the stabilizer of e. This implies that H is amenable. $\square$

A more general theorem has been proved in [90]. In particular, it was shown that for any functor described above, one gets an equivalent definition of extensive amenability of the action of G on X. Since we will need only Theorem 5.20 for the applications, we don't provide the proof of its stronger version.

We say that the functor F is *tight* on X if for all (equivalently, for some) $x \in X$ the morphism $F(X \setminus \{x\}) \to F(X)$ is not onto.

THEOREM 5.22. Let F be a functor from the category of finite sets to the category of amenable groups. If the action $G \curvearrowright X$ is extensively amenable, then the action $F(X) \rtimes G \curvearrowright F(X)$ is extensively amenable. Conversely, assume that the action $F(X) \rtimes G \curvearrowright F(X)$ is amenable. If the functor F is tight on X, then $G \curvearrowright X$ is extensively amenable.

In particular, amenability of the action $F(X) \rtimes G \curvearrowright F(X)$ does not depend on the choice of the functor F provided that it is tight on X. Moreover, for the actions of type $F(X) \rtimes G \curvearrowright F(X)$ we have that the notions of amenability and extensive amenability coincide.

Here are more examples that satisfy Theorem 5.22:

EXAMPLE 5.23. The constant functor $F(Y) = A$ for any given amenable group A. We also have the modified constant functor F_0 defined by $F_0(Y) = A$ for all non-empty sets Y and $F_0(\varnothing)$ being the trivial group.

EXAMPLE 5.24. More generally, fix an amenable group A. Consider the functor F which maps any finite set Y to A^Y with the obvious extension map on inclusions. Then for a general set X we have $F(X) = \bigoplus_X A$, the restricted product.

It is straightforward to verify that all examples above are tight on every set X except some degenerate cases: Example 5.23, Example 5.24 with A trivial and X nonempty, and in Examples 5.17, 5.18 and 5.19 one should exclude $|X| = 1$. Thus the converse of the Theorem 5.22 holds for these functors, which gives more characterizations of extensive amenability. The application of Theorem 5.22 to Example 5.24 provides another proof of Lemma 5.5.

6. Extensively amenable and amenable actions

In this section we will use wobbling groups to produce a group with amenable but not extensively amenable action.

For a finitely generated group Γ we denote by $W(\Gamma)$ the wobbling group with base space Γ considered with the graph distance on its Cayley graph. The following lemma is a straightforward consequence of Lemma 5.3.

LEMMA 5.25. Let Γ be a finitely generated group. If there exists a $W(\Gamma) \ltimes P_f(\Gamma)$-invariant mean on $P_f(\Gamma)$ then Γ is amenable.

We have one more relation between metric spaces and properties of groups.

LEMMA 5.26. Let X and Y be metric spaces and let $i : X \to Y$ be an injective map such that for every $R > 0$ we have

$$\sup\{d(i(x), i(x')) : d(x, x') \leq R\} < \infty.$$

If the action of $W(Y)$ on Y is extensively amenable then so is the action of $W(X)$ on X.

PROOF. The map i allows to define an embedding $W(X) \subset W(Y)$ by defining for $g \in W(X)$ its action on Y by $g \cdot i(x) = i(g \cdot x)$ and $g \cdot y = y$ if $y \notin i(X)$.

Assume that the action of $W(Y)$ on Y is extensively amenable and fix $x_0 \in X$. By Theorem 5.4 there is a mean m on $P_f(Y)$ that is $W(Y)$-invariant and that gives full weight to the collection of sets containing $i(x_0)$. Consider the map $\mathcal{P}_f(Y) \to \mathcal{P}_f(X)$ given by $A \mapsto i^{-1}(A)$. This map is $W(X)$-equivariant, so the push-forward of m by this map is $W(X)$-invariant. Also the preimage of the collection of all subsets containing x_0 contains all sets which contain $i(x_0)$. Thus by Theorem 5.4 the action of $W(X)$ on X is extensively amenable. $\qquad\square$

Lemma 5.26 and Lemma 5.3 imply that for $W(Y) \ltimes \mathcal{P}_f(Y)$ to act amenably on $\mathcal{P}_f(Y)$ it is necessary that $W(X)$ act amenably on X for all $X \subset Y$.

THEOREM 5.27. Let (X, d) be a metric space with bounded geometry, i.e. each ball in X of a prescribed size has the same (finite) maximum number of points.. Suppose we have an injective and Lipschitz map from the infinite binary tree to X. Then the action of $W(X)$ on X is not extensively amenable.

PROOF. Consider a Lipschitz injective map from the free group with two generators into the infinite binary tree and hence in X. Then the statement follows from Lemma 5.25 and Lemma 5.26. $\qquad\square$

We showed in Lemma 2.25 that for amenable graphs, in particular, for Cayley graphs of finitely generated amenable groups, the action of the wobbling group on them is amenable.

There are many examples of finitely generated amenable groups which contain the infinite binary tree in their Cayley graph. An elementary amenable group with exponential growth, by [**37**] contains a free subsemigroup. In [**71**], R. Grigorchuk disproved a conjecture of Rosenblatt proving that the lamplighter group $\mathbb{Z}/2\mathbb{Z} \wr G$ contains an infinite binary tree, here G is Grigorchuk's 2-group of intermediate growth.

We remark that non-amenable groups always contain a copy of the infinite binary tree in their Cayley graphs, [**18**, Theorem 1.5].

7. Inverted orbits of random walks

We now give a more probabilistic reformulation of extensive amenability. To simplify the statements we make the assumption that $G = \langle S \rangle$ is finitely generated and acts transitively on X. We fix a symmetric probability measure μ on G with support S and a base point $x_0 \in X$. We can consider the (left) random walk $(g_n)_{n \geq 0}$ on G defined by $g_0 = e$ and $g_n = h_n g_{n-1}$ for $n \geq 1$, where $(h_i)_{i \geq 1}$ are independent identically distributed by the law μ.

An inverted orbit is a random subset $\mathbf{O}_n$ of X defined by

$$(5) \qquad \mathbf{O}_n = \{x_0, g_1^{-1} x_0, \ldots, g_n^{-1} x_0\}.$$

If G is not abelian, the inverted orbit need not have the same distribution as the directed orbit of the random walk on X. Moreover it does not have to be connected as a subset in the Schreier graph of the action of G on X. Understanding inverted orbits is central to the study of growth and random walks on permutational wreath products, see [**4,10,11**]. It is sometimes convenient to consider the following variation of inverted orbit

$$(6) \qquad \mathbf{O}'_n = \{x_0, h_n x_0, h_n h_{n-1} x_0, \ldots, h_n \cdots h_1 x_0\}.$$

For a fixed n, $\mathbf{O}_n$ and $\mathbf{O}'_n$ have the same distribution, although the joint distributions of the processes $(\mathbf{O}_n)_n$ and $(\mathbf{O}'_n)_n$ differ. The next proposition shows that proving extensive amenability of an action $G \curvearrowright X$ boils down to estimate the asymptotic behavior of the distribution of $|\mathbf{O}_n|$.

PROPOSITION 5.28. Fix $G \curvearrowright X$, $x_0 \in X$ and μ as before. The following properties are all equivalent to extensive amenability.

(i) $\lim_{n\to\infty} -\frac{1}{n} \log \mathbb{E}(2^{-|\mathbf{O}_n|}) = 0$.
(ii) For every $\varepsilon > 0$ we have $\mathbb{P}(|\mathbf{O}_n| < \varepsilon n) > e^{-\varepsilon n}$ for infinitely many n's.
(iii) There exists a sequence of events $A_n \subset S^n$ verifying $-\frac{1}{n} \log \mu_n(A_n) \to 0$, conditioned to which $\frac{1}{n}\mathbb{E}(|\mathbf{O}_n| : A_n) \to 0$.

In particular, these conditions do not depend on μ and x_0.

In the last part we denote μ_n the probability measure on the space of n-steps trajectories S^n of the random walk. Here $\mathbb{E}(|\mathbf{O}_n| : A_n) = \mathbb{E}(|\mathbf{O}_n|1_{A_n})/\mu_n(A_n)$ denotes the expectation of $|\mathbf{O}_n|$ conditioned to the event that the trajectory up to time n belongs to A_n.

PROOF. Recall that extensively amenability of $G \curvearrowright X$ is equivalent to amenability of the action $\bigoplus_X \mathbb{Z}/2\mathbb{Z} \rtimes G \curvearrowright \bigoplus_X \mathbb{Z}/2\mathbb{Z}$. Since we assume that G is finitely generated and acts transitively on X, the wreath product $\bigoplus_X \mathbb{Z}/2\mathbb{Z} \rtimes G$ is finitely generated and acts transitively on $\bigoplus_X \mathbb{Z}/2\mathbb{Z}$. Thereby if we fix any non degenerate symmetric, finitely supported probability measure ν on $\bigoplus_X \mathbb{Z}/2\mathbb{Z} \rtimes G$ we can consider the Schreier graph Γ associated with the action $\bigoplus_X \mathbb{Z}/2\mathbb{Z} \rtimes G \curvearrowright \bigoplus_X \mathbb{Z}/2\mathbb{Z}$ with generating set $\mathrm{supp}(\mu)$ and base-point the trivial configuration $f_0 = \emptyset$. The left random walk on $\bigoplus_X \mathbb{Z}/2\mathbb{Z} \rtimes G$ with step measure ν then induces a nearest neighbour random walk (f_n) on Γ.

By Kesten's amenability criterion, see Appendix 4, amenability of the action $\bigoplus_X \mathbb{Z}/2\mathbb{Z} \rtimes G \curvearrowright \bigoplus_X \mathbb{Z}/2\mathbb{Z}$ is equivalent to

$$(7) \qquad \lim_{n\to\infty} -\frac{1}{n} \log \mathbb{P}(f_n = f_0) = 0.$$

Moreover, it is sufficient to show this for any choice of ν with the above properties. Thus, we can choose ν to be the *switch-walk-switch* measure $\widetilde{\mu}$ on $\bigoplus_X \mathbb{Z}/2\mathbb{Z} \rtimes G$ associated with the measure μ on G and to the base-point $x_0 \in X$. Recall that if λ is the uniform probability measure on $\{0_{\bigoplus_X \mathbb{Z}/2\mathbb{Z}}, \delta_{x_0}\} \subset \bigoplus_X \mathbb{Z}/2\mathbb{Z}$ then by definition $\widetilde{\mu} = \lambda * \mu * \lambda$, where λ and μ are naturally seen as probability measures on $\bigoplus_X \mathbb{Z}/2\mathbb{Z} \rtimes G$. With this choice of ν it is then easy to see that f_{n+1} is obtained from f_n through the following steps: first change the value of $f_n(x_0)$ to a uniform random value in $\mathbb{Z}/2\mathbb{Z}$ to obtain a new f_n', then translate f_n' to $f_n'' = h_{n+1} \cdot f_n'$ where $h_{n+1} \in G$ has distribution μ, finally randomize again $f_n''(x_0)$ to obtain f_{n+1}. It follows from this description that $\mathrm{supp}\, f_n \subset \mathbf{O}_n'$ for every n, where $\mathbf{O}_n'$ is as in (6). Moreover f_n lights each point in $\mathbf{O}_n'$ independently with probability $1/2$. From this we immediately get

$$\mathbb{P}(f_n = f_0) = \mathbb{E}(2^{-|\mathbf{O}_n'|}) = \mathbb{E}(2^{-|\mathbf{O}_n|}).$$

The equivalence between and ((i)) and extensive amenability follows.

If condition ((ii)) holds, then for every $\varepsilon > 0$,

$$\mathbb{E}(2^{-N_n}) \geq \mathbb{E}(2^{-N_n}1_{N_n<\varepsilon n}) \geq 2^{-\varepsilon n}\mathbb{P}[N_n < \varepsilon n],$$

which is by assumption greater that $2^{-2\varepsilon n}$ for infinitely many n's. Hence ((i)) holds.

Suppose ((ii)) does not hold. This means that there exists $\varepsilon > 0$ such that $\mathbb{P}[N_n < \varepsilon n] < 2^{-\varepsilon n}$ for all n large enough. For such n we can therefore write

$$\mathbb{E}(2^{-N_n}) = \mathbb{E}(2^{-N_n}(1_{N_n \geq \varepsilon n} + 1_{N_n < \varepsilon n}) \leq 2 \cdot 2^{-\varepsilon n},$$

which implies that $\mathbb{E}(2^{-N_n})$ decays exponentially. Thus, ((i)) and ((ii)) are equivalent.

Condition ((ii)) implies ((iii)) by a diagonal extraction argument.

To see that ((iii)) implies ((i)), observe that

$$2^{-|\mathbf{O}_n|} \geq 2^{-|\mathbf{O}_n|} 1_{A_n}$$

and, therefore, by Jensen's inequality,

$$-\frac{1}{n} \log \mathbb{E}(2^{-|\mathbf{O}_n|}) \leq -\frac{1}{n} \log \mathbb{E}(2^{-|\mathbf{O}_n|} 1_{A_n})$$

$$\leq -\frac{1}{n} \log \mu_n(A_n) - \frac{1}{n} \mathbb{E}(|\mathbf{O}_n| : A_n) \log 2 \to 0. \qquad \square$$

Proof of "recurrent implies extensive amenability" using inverted orbits

As an application of the previous section we give a probabilistic proof of the fact that recurrent actions are extensively amenable without relying on capacity of random walks. Recall, a group action $G \curvearrowright X$ is called *recurrent* if for every symmetric, finitely supported probability measure μ on G and every $x_0 \in X$, the random walk $(g_n x_0)$ on the orbit of x_0 induced by the left random walk on G is recurrent. If G is finitely generated, it is sufficient to check this for a symmetric, finitely supported probability measure with generating support. Equivalently it is sufficient to check that for every $x \in X$ and for a symmetric, finite generating set S of G the Schreier graph $\Gamma(G, x_0, S)$ is recurrent for the simple random walk.

The following lemma is used in [11], Lemma 3.1, and [4].

LEMMA 5.29. Assume that G is finitely generated and the action $G \curvearrowright X$ is transitive. Then $G \curvearrowright X$ is recurrent if and only if $\frac{1}{n} \mathbb{E}|\mathbf{O}_n| \to 0$ for some (equivalently for any) non-degenerate symmetric, finitely supported probability measure μ on G.

PROOF. Let $T = \min\{n \geq 1 : g_n x_0 = x_0\} \in \mathbb{N} \cup \{\infty\}$. We have

$$\mathbb{E}|\mathbf{O}_{n+1}| - \mathbb{E}|\mathbf{O}_n| = \mathbb{P}(g_{n+1}^{-1} x_0 \notin \mathbf{O}_n)$$

$$= \mathbb{P}(h_{n+1}^{-1} x_0 \neq x_0, \, h_n^{-1} h_{n+1}^{-1} x_0 \neq x_0, \ldots, h_1^{-1} \cdots h_{n+1}^{-1} x_0 \neq x_0)$$

$$= \mathbb{P}(T > n+1)$$

Since, by symmetry, $(h_{n+1}^{-1}, h_n^{-1} h_{n+1}^{-1}, \ldots, h_1^{-1} \cdots h_{n+1}^{-1})$ has the same law as $(g_1, \ldots g_{n+1})$. This computation shows that

$$\frac{1}{n} \mathbb{E}|\mathbf{O}_n| \to \mathbb{P}(T = \infty),$$

which vanishes if and only if $G \curvearrowright X$ in recurrent. $\qquad \square$

PROOF OF THEOREM 5.12. Without loss of generality we may assume that G is finitely generated and acts transitively on X. By convexity

$$-\frac{1}{n} \log \mathbb{E}(2^{-|\mathbf{O}_n|}) \leq \frac{1}{n} \mathbb{E}(|\mathbf{O}_n|) \log 2 \to 0,$$

where we used Lemma 5.29. Then Proposition 5.28 implies extensive amenability.

$\square$

Theorem 5.10 is a particular case of a more general criterion of recurrency, which is due to Nash-Williams [**127**], which can be also found in the book of W. Woess [**155**, Corollary 2.20]. A part of the equivalent definitions in Theorem 5.4 are in [**86**]. A relation of functors with extensive amenability is done in [**90**], exposition of which we followed. The inverted orbits approach to extensive amenability also comes from [**90**].

The second part of the proof that recurrence implies extensive amenability, which is more direct and does not use the equivalent definitions listed in Theorem 5.4 was communicated to the author by N. Ozawa.

CHAPTER 6

Amenability of topological full groups

Let G be a group generated by a finite symmetric set S. Assume that it acts on a topological space $\mathcal{X}$ by homeomorphisms. The action of G on $\mathcal{X}$ is *minimal*, if there are no closed proper G-invariant subset in $\mathcal{X}$. In other words, every orbit of G is dense in $\mathcal{X}$. We will consider only minimal actions in this chapter.

Recall, *the topological full group* of G is the group of all homeomorphisms h of $\mathcal{X}$ such that for every $x \in \mathcal{X}$ there exists a neighborhood of x such that restriction of h to that neighborhood is equal to restriction of an element of G. We denote this group by $[[G]]$. If $\mathcal{X}$ is a compact space, then for each element $g \in [[G]]$ there exists a clopen finite partition of $\mathcal{X}$ such that at each piece of this partition g acts as a certain element of G. It is natural to call such groups *piecewise G-groups*. Consider G as a metric space, with distance $d(\cdot, \cdot)$ given by the distance in the Cayley graph. Let $W(G)$ be the wobbling group defined in the Section 10, i.e., the group of bijections g of G with property

$$\sup\{d(g\gamma, \gamma) : \gamma \in G\} < \infty.$$

Assume now, that $\mathcal{X}$ is compact, and G acts minimally on $\mathcal{X}$. Then the associated topological full group $[[G]]$ is a subgroup of $W(G)$. Indeed, fix a point p in $\mathcal{X}$, then the orbit of this point $\{\gamma p : \gamma \in G\}$ is dense in $\mathcal{X}$. Therefore the following map π_p is an injective homomorphism of $[[G]]$ into $W(G)$:

$$g(\gamma p) = \pi_p(g)(\gamma)p, \text{ for all } g \in [[G]], \gamma \in G.$$

In particular, this embedding, by Theorem 2.26 we have that topological full groups of minimal $\mathbb{Z}^d$-actions do not admit property (T) subgroups. In this chapter we use this idea to study several classes of groups coming from minimal $\mathbb{Z}^d$-actions: topological full group of Cantor minimal system, interval exchange transformation groups and products of Cantor minimal systems.

We start with the result of Nicolas Monod and the author which states that the topological full group of any minimal homeomorphism T of the Cantor space is amenable. This is a classical example of a topological full group of a $\mathbb{Z}$-action. The proof we follow is not original, and is based on the recurrence of the $W(\mathbb{Z})$ action on $\mathbb{Z}$. We refer the reader to Chapter 4 for a detailed exposition of algebraic properties of this group. The proof of amenability heavily relies on the properties of subgroups of $W(\mathbb{Z})$. Namely, all minimal actions of $\mathbb{Z}$ on the Cantor space has a strong property: *ubiquitous pattern property*. This is related to homogeneous sequences defined in the Section 1.

As it is described in Chapter 5, we consider the action of the lamplighter $\bigoplus_{\mathbb{Z}} \mathbb{Z}/2\mathbb{Z} \rtimes W(\mathbb{Z})$ on the cosets $\bigoplus_{\mathbb{Z}} (\mathbb{Z}/2\mathbb{Z} \rtimes W(\mathbb{Z})) / W(\mathbb{Z})$ by multiplication on the left. The idea of the proof of amenability of $[[T]]$ is to consider the following embedding

$$[[T]] < W(\mathbb{Z}) \ni g \mapsto (g(\mathbb{N}), g) \in \bigoplus_{\mathbb{Z}} \mathbb{Z}/2\mathbb{Z} \rtimes W(\mathbb{Z}),$$

and its action on $\bigoplus_{\mathbb{Z}} \mathbb{Z}/2\mathbb{Z}$. Since the action of $W(\mathbb{Z})$ on $\mathbb{Z}$ is recurrent, by Theorem 5.12, we know that this action is extensively amenable. On the other hand, we will deduce that this action has amenable stabilizers, thus, by Theorem 2.21 we conclude that $[[T]]$ is amenable.

Unfortunately, this strategy does not work for all minimal $\mathbb{Z}^d$-actions, as it was proved in [**52**] that there are minimal $\mathbb{Z}^2$-actions with non-amenable topological full groups. One of the reasons of non-amenability for this group is that the stabilizers of the action (via its embedding into the lamplighter group) are not amenable.

One the other hand, it is possible to reduce amenability of topological full groups of several minimal $\mathbb{Z}^d$-actions to extensive amenability of $W(\mathbb{Z}^d)$ on $\mathbb{Z}^d$. Recall from the Chapter 5, that we know that such actions are amenable only for the recurrent cases, i.e., when $d = 1, 2$. An example of such minimal $\mathbb{Z}^d$-action on the Cantor space, where this reduction is possible, is an interval exchange transformation group.

An interval exchange transformation is a piece-wise linear bijection of the interval $X = [0, 1)$ which is given by an orientation and length preserving rearrangement of subintervals in some finite partition of X. The group of all interval exchange transformations is shortly denoted by IET. We will consider IET as the group of arc exchange transformation of the circle $\mathbb{R}/\mathbb{Z}$.

Interval exchange transformations have been a popular object of study in dynamical systems and ergodic theory, in particular in studying billiards. The exchange of two intervals is equivalent to a rotation of the circle. The exchanges of three or more intervals were first considered by Katok and Stepin [**95**]. The systematic study started since the paper by Keane [**96**], who introduced the terminology. For an introduction and account of the results, see the survey by Viana [**152**] or the book of Katok and Hasselblatt [**94**].

A very basic question on IET is the conjecture of Katok:

CONJECTURE 6.1. Does IET contain a non-abelian free group?

This conjecture attracted a lot of attention recently. In 2011, Dahmani-Fujiwara-Guirardel, [**43**] showed that free subgroups in IET are *rare*, that is a group generated by *a generic pair* of interval exchange transformations is not free.

Finitely generated subgroups of the interval exchange transformation group can be realized as subgroups of topological full groups of minimal $\mathbb{Z}^d$-actions on Cantor set.

1. Amenability of topological full groups of Cantor minimal system: first proof

Let T be a minimal homeomorphism of the Cantor space $\mathbf{C}$. Recall, the construction of the embedding of the topological full group $[[T]]$ into the wobbling group of integers. By minimality, the full topological group $[[T]]$ acts on any T-orbit faithfully. Identifying an orbit of T with $\mathbb{Z}$ we have that $[[T]]$ is a subgroup of $W(\mathbb{Z})$. More precisely, fix a point $p \in \mathbf{C}$ and define a homomorphism

$$\pi_p \colon [[T]] \longrightarrow W(\mathbb{Z})$$

by the formula
$$g(T^j p) = T^{\pi_p(g)(j)} p, \text{ for all } g \in [[T]], j \in \mathbb{Z}.$$
The homomorphism π_p is injective, since the orbit of p is dense.

A subgroup G of $W(\mathbb{Z})$ has the *ubiquitous pattern property* if for every finite set $F \subseteq G$ and every $n \in \mathbb{N}$ there exists a constant $k = k(n, F)$ such that for every $j \in \mathbb{Z}$ there exists $t \in \mathbb{Z}$ such that $[t - n, t + n] \subseteq [j - k, j + k]$ and for every $i \in [-n, n]$ and every $g \in F$ one has $g(i + t) = g(i) + t$.

LEMMA 6.2. *Let (T, C) be a Cantor minimal system, then $\pi_p([[T]])$ has the ubiquitous pattern property.*

PROOF. Fix a finite subset F in $[[T]]$ and let $n \in \mathbb{N}$. By definition there is a finite clopen partition $\mathcal{P}$ of $\mathbf{C}$ such that each $g \in F$ is a power of T when restricted to any element of $\mathcal{P}$. Thus there is an open neighborhood V of p such that for all $i \in [-n, n]$ the set $T^i V$ is contained in some $D \in \mathcal{P}$. We have that the set
$$\bigcup_{q \geq 1} \bigcup_{|r| \leq q} T^r V$$
is non-empty open and T-invariant. By minimality of T, this set coincides with $\mathbf{C}$. By compactness, there is $q \in \mathbb{N}$ such that
$$\mathbf{C} = \bigcup_{|r| \leq q} T^r V.$$
Set $k = k(n, F) = q + n$. For all $j \in \mathbb{Z}$
$$C = T^{-j} C = T^{-(j+q)} V \cup \ldots \cup T^{-(j-q)} V$$
Therefore there is an integer $t \in [j - q, j + q]$ such that $p \in T^{-t} V$. In particular, we have
$$[t - n, t + n] \subseteq [j - k, j + k].$$
Now $T^t p \in V$ and thus both $T^i p$ and $T^{i+t} p$ are in $T^i V$ for all i. Therefore, when $i \in [-n, n]$, every $g \in F$ acts on $T^i p$ and on $T^{i+t} p$ as the same power of T. By identification of the T-orbit of p with $\mathbb{Z}$, we have that the last property is exactly the ubiquitous pattern property of subgroups of $W(\mathbb{Z})$.   □

It is known that the stabilizer of the orbit of positive powers of T, i.e., of the set $\{T^j p : j \in \mathbb{N}\}$, in the topological full group of a minimal Cantor system is locally finite [**61**]. We give an alternative proof of this fact.

LEMMA 6.3. *The stabilizer of natural numbers, $Stab_{[[T]]}(\mathbb{N})$, under the action of $[[T]]$ on $\mathbb{Z}$ is locally finite.*

PROOF. Let F be a finite subset in $Stab_{[[T]]}(\mathbb{N})$. We will show that $\mathbb{Z}$ can be decomposed as a disjoint union of F-invariant finite intervals with uniformly bounded length. This implies that the group generated by F is finite, since it is a subgroup of a power of a finite group and therefore $Stab_{[[T]]}(\mathbb{N})$ is locally finite.

Let $c = \max(|g(j) - j| : j \in \mathbb{Z}, g \in F)$. Let $k = k(c, F)$ be the constant from the definition of the ubiquitous pattern property. Decompose $\mathbb{Z}$ as a disjoint union of consecutive intervals I_i of the length $2k + 1$ and such one of the intervals is $[-k, k]$. Let $E_0 = [0, 2N]$ and $t_0 = 0$. Then by the ubiquitous pattern property we can find $E_i \subseteq I_i$ and t_i such that $E_i = E_0 + t_i$ and $g(s) + t_i = g(s + t_i)$ for every $g \in F$ and $s \in E_0$.

Since none of the positive integers are mapped by F to negative integers and by the choice of E_n we have that the intervals $[t_i, t_{i+1}]$ are F-invariant. Moreover, the length of each $[t_i, t_{i+1}]$ is bounded by $2|I_i| = 4k + 2$. Thus the group generated by F is finite and therefore $Stab_{[[T]]}(\mathbb{N})$ is locally finite. $\square$

Now we have all the ingredients needed to prove amenability of $[[T]]$.

THEOREM 6.4. Let $(T, \mathbf{C})$ be a Cantor minimal system. Then the topological full group $[[T]]$ is amenable.

PROOF. Let G be a finitely generated subgroup of $[[T]] < W(\mathbb{Z})$. The following map $\pi : G \to \mathcal{P}_f(\mathbb{Z}) \rtimes G$ is an injective homomorphism

$$\pi(g) = (g(\mathbb{N})\Delta\mathbb{N}, g).$$

Indeed,

$$\begin{aligned}
\pi(g)\pi(h) &= (g(\mathbb{N})\Delta\mathbb{N}, g) \cdot (h(\mathbb{N})\Delta\mathbb{N}, h) \\
&= (g(\mathbb{N})\Delta\mathbb{N}\Delta gh(\mathbb{N})\Delta g(\mathbb{N}), gh) \\
&= (gh(\mathbb{N})\Delta\mathbb{N}, gh) \\
&= \pi(gh).
\end{aligned}$$

By the property of $W(\mathbb{Z})$ we can select a strictly increasing to $\mathbb{Z}$ sequence of intervals $[-n_i, n_i]$ such that the boarder of $[-n_i, n_i]$ under the generating set of G is contained in $[-n_{i+1}, n_{i+1}]$ and is of uniformly bounded size. By Theorem 5.9 we have that the action of G on $\mathbb{Z}$ is recurrent. Therefore, by Theorem 5.12, this action is extensively amenable. Thus it is left to show that the action of $\pi([[T]])$ on $\mathcal{P}_f(\mathbb{Z})$ has amenable stabilizers.

Consider firstly the stabilizer of the empty set, $Stab_{\pi(G)}(\emptyset)$. Let $g \in Stab_{\pi(G)}(\emptyset)$, then

$$(g(\mathbb{N})\Delta\mathbb{N}, g)(\emptyset) = g(\mathbb{N})\Delta\mathbb{N} = \emptyset.$$

Therefore $Stab_{\pi(G)}(\emptyset) = Stab_G(\mathbb{N})$, which is amenable by Lemma 6.3.

To show that stabilizers of all other points are amenable, note that the action of G on $\mathbb{Z}$ is amenable. This follows either from extensive amenability or more straightforward by taking $F_n = [-n, n]$ as a Følner sequence for the action of G on $\mathbb{Z}$.

To reach a contradiction assume that there exists $E = \{x_0, \dots, x_n\} \in \mathcal{P}_f(\mathbb{Z})$ such that $Stab_{\pi(G)}(E)$ is not amenable. We have that the group $Stab_{\pi(G)}(E) \cap Stab_G(x_0)$ is also not amenable. Indeed, the action of $Stab_{\pi(G)}(E)$ on the orbit of x_0 is amenable and the stabilizers of points of this action are conjugate to $Stab_{\pi(G)}(E) \cap Stab_G(x_0)$, thus, Theorem 2.21 applies. Repeating this argument we obtain that the group $Stab_{\pi(G)}(E) \cap Stab_G(x_0) \cap \dots \cap Stab_G(x_n)$ is not amenable. However, for $g \in Stab_{\pi(G)}(E) \cap Stab_G(x_0) \cap \dots \cap Stab_G(x_n)$, we have

$$(g(\mathbb{N})\Delta\mathbb{N}, g)(E) = g(E)\Delta g(\mathbb{N})\Delta\mathbb{N} = E\Delta g(\mathbb{N})\Delta\mathbb{N} = E$$

this implies $g(\mathbb{N})\Delta\mathbb{N} = \emptyset$ and therefore $Stab_{\pi(G)}(E) \cap Stab_G(x_0) \cap \dots \cap Stab_G(x_n)$ is a subgroup of the amenable group $Stab_{\pi(G)}(\emptyset)$, contradicting to our assumption. Thus, G is amenable. Since every finitely generated subgroup of $[[T]]$ is amenable, $[[T]]$ is also amenable. $\square$

2. The interval exchange transformation group

An interval exchange transformation is a right-continuous bijection of the interval $X = [0, 1) = \mathbb{R}/\mathbb{Z}$ which is given by an orientation and length preserving rearrangement of subintervals in some finite partition of X. The group of all interval exchange transformations is shortly denoted by IET. We can also think of IET as the group of arc exchange transformation of the circle $\mathbb{R}/\mathbb{Z}$.

For a given interval exchange transformation $g \in$ IET, we can associate a finite subset of $\mathbb{R}/\mathbb{Z}$, called *the set of angles:*

$$\alpha(g) = \{gx - x, x \in \mathbb{R}/\mathbb{Z}\}$$

Let $\Lambda < \mathbb{R}/\mathbb{Z}$ be a finitely generated subgroup of the circle. By finite generation, Λ is isomorphic to $\mathbb{Z}^d \oplus F$, for some finite abelian group F. The *rank* of Λ is the rank of its torsion-free part $rank(\Lambda) = d$.

We denote by IET(Λ) the group of all interval exchange transformations such that the angles of all its elements are in Λ. Note that Λ is invariant under the action of IET(Λ), and more generally every coset $x + \Lambda$ for $x \in \mathbb{R}/\mathbb{Z}$ is invariant under its action. Obviously, any finitely generated subgroup of IET is contained in IET(Λ) for some Λ.

In particular, Katok's conjecture boils down to determining whether or not IET(Λ) contains a free subgroup for some finitely generated $\Lambda < \mathbb{R}/\mathbb{Z}$.

3. Realization of finitely generated subgroups of IET as subgroups of the full topological group of $\mathbb{Z}^d$

In this section we present a realization of finitely generated subgroups of IET as subgroups of the full topological group of a Cantor minimal action of a finitely generated abelian group.

A realization of the Cantor set associated with the circle that provides continuos action of IET on it goes back to [**40**]. It is similar to the examples of topological full groups that come from a rotation of the circle discussed in the Section 7. The action of an irrational rotation on the Cantor set is minimal. Let $G <$ IET be a finitely generated subgroup generated by a finite set S of interval exchange transformations. By adding a rotation by an irrational angle, we can always assume that the action of G on $\mathbb{R}/\mathbb{Z}$ is minimal.

THEOREM 6.5. *Let G be a finitely generated infinite subgroup of IET. Then G is a subgroup of the topological full group of a minimal action of $\mathbb{Z}^d \oplus F$ on the Cantor set $\mathbf{C}$, where F is a finite Abelian group. Moreover, each copy of $\mathbb{Z}$ in the topological full group acts minimally on $\mathbf{C}$.*

PROOF. By adding an extra element to the generating set, we can assume that G contains a rotation by some irrational $\alpha \in \mathbb{R}/\mathbb{Z}$. Let $\mathcal{B}$ be the set of all points of discontinuity of all elements in G unified with the set $\alpha\mathbb{Z}$. Now define a set $\mathbf{C}$ by replacing each $x \in \mathcal{B}$ with the pair $\{x_-, x_+\}$ and keeping the rest of the points unchanged. Take any $x, y \in \mathbb{R}/\mathbb{Z}$ and denote by $(x, y)_c \subset \mathbb{R}/\mathbb{Z}$ the open interval which is obtained by going counterclockwise from x to y. We introduce a topology on X_α by declaring that for each $x, y \in \alpha\mathbb{Z}$ the set $\pi^{-1}(x, y)_c \cup \{x_-, y_+\}$ is open. By exactly the same reasoning as in Lemma 4.22, we have that $\mathbf{C}$ is the Cantor space, and G acts on it by homeomorphisms.

The density of an orbit implies that the rotation acts minimally on $\mathbf{C}$. In fact, each copy of $\mathbb{Z}$ acts minimally, since it acts as irrational rotation of the circle. Thus, G is a subgroup of $[[\mathbb{Z}^d \oplus F]]$ for some d and a finite Abelian group F, where the action of each copy of $\mathbb{Z}$ is minimal. $\square$

Let G be a finitely generated subgroup of IET. Assume that it contains all rotations that are involved in the piece-wise action of its generating set. With this assumption the set $\alpha(G)$ becomes an abelian group isomorphic to some $\mathbb{Z}^d \oplus F$ for some finite Abelian group F. Moreover, since the action of each element involves a finite number of rotations, we can conclude that G is a subgroup of the wobbling group $W(\mathbb{Z}^d \oplus F)$. Thus, by Theorem 2.26 we have the following result of Dahmani-Fujiwara-Guirardel, [**43**].

COROLLARY 6.6. IET does not contain a Kazhdan property (T) subgroups.

4. Amenability of subgroups of IET of low ranks

Recall, IET(Λ) is the subgroup of all $g \in$ IET such that the angle $gx - x$ is in Λ for every $x \in \mathbb{R}/\mathbb{Z}$. From the construction in the previous section, if $\Lambda = \mathbb{Z}$, then the group IET(Λ) is amenable, since the construction gives an embedding of IET(Λ) into the topological full group of a Cantor minimal system. In this section, we will show that if the rank of the group Λ is equal to d and the action of $W(\mathbb{Z}^d)$ on $\mathbb{Z}^d$ is extensively amenable, then IET(Λ) is amenable. Since the case $d = 1, 2$ corresponds to a recurrent action, we obtain the following theorem of [**90**].

THEOREM 6.7. Let Λ be finitely generated subgroup of $\mathbb{R}/\mathbb{Z}$. If $\mathrm{rk}(\Lambda) \leq 2$, then IET($\Lambda$) is amenable.

Our goal is to apply Corollary 5.21 to the functor given by $F(A) = \mathrm{Sym}(A)$ the symmetric group. This extends to an infinite set as $F(X) = \mathrm{Sym}_\infty(X)$, the group of permutations of X with finite support (see Example 5.17). If $G \curvearrowright X$ we recall that we have an action of G on $\mathrm{Sym}_\infty(X)$ by conjugation. For $\tau \in \mathrm{Sym}_\infty(X)$ and $g \in G$ we set ${}^g\tau = g\tau g^{-1}$.

LEMMA 6.8. If the action of the wobbling group $W(\mathbb{Z}^d)$ on $\mathbb{Z}^d$ is extensively amenable, then for every Λ with $\mathrm{rk}(\Lambda) = d$, the action of group IET(Λ) on $\mathbb{R}/\mathbb{Z}$ is extensively amenable.

PROOF. Let $\Lambda = \mathbb{Z}^d \oplus F$ for some finite group F of cardinality n. The wobbling group $W(\mathbb{Z}^d \oplus F) = W(\mathbb{Z}^d \times \{1, \ldots, n\})$ is a subgroup of the wobbling group $W(\mathbb{Z}^d)$. Indeed, we can embed the set $\mathbb{Z}^d \times \{1, \ldots, n\}$ into $\mathbb{Z}^d$ as follows. Let us express it firstly by $\mathbb{Z}^{d-1} \times \mathbb{Z} \times \{1, \ldots, n\}$, then we identify $\mathbb{Z} \times \{1, \ldots, n\}$ with a subset in $\mathbb{Z}$ by mapping $\mathbb{Z}$ into $(n + 1)\mathbb{Z}$ and (z, f) into $f + (n + 1)z$. It is easy to check that this embedding gives the embedding of the wobbling groups. This implies that if the action of $W(\mathbb{Z}^d)$ on $\mathbb{Z}^d$ is extensively amenable, then the action of $W(\mathbb{Z}^d \oplus F)$ on $\mathbb{Z}^d \oplus F$ is extensively amenable for all finite groups F.

Let now $H < $ IET(Λ) be a finitely generated subgroup, equipped with a finite symmetric generating set S. For $x \in \mathbb{R}/\mathbb{Z}$ let $\Gamma(x, H, S)$ be the orbital Schreier graph for the action of H on Hx. We have an injective map

$$\Gamma(x, H, S) \to \Lambda$$

$$y \mapsto y - x$$

where the difference is taken in $\mathbb{R}/\mathbb{Z}$. This map takes values in Λ since $y = hx$ for some $h \in H < \mathrm{IET}(\Lambda)$. It is not hard to check that this map is bi-Lipschitz embedding (for some constant depending on the generating set S of H only). By Lemma 2.27, we have that the action of H on Hx is exactly the action of a wobbling group $W(\mathbb{Z}^d \oplus E)$ for some finite set E. Since the action of $W(\mathbb{Z}^d)$ on $\mathbb{Z}^d$ is assumed to be extensively amenable, we can conclude that the action of H on Hx is also extensively amenable. Thus, but Theorem 5.4, we have that the action of H on $\mathbb{R}/\mathbb{Z}$ is extensively amenable as well. $\qquad\square$

This lemma implies implies that for $\mathrm{rk}(\Lambda) \leq 2$ the group $\mathrm{IET}(\Lambda)$ is amenable. The following lemma completes the proof of Theorem 6.7.

LEMMA 6.9. *A subgroup $G < \mathrm{IET}$ is amenable if and only if the action $G \curvearrowright \mathbb{R}/\mathbb{Z}$ is extensively amenable.*

PROOF. One implication is obvious: amenability of the group implies extensive amenability of the action.

If we replace the convention that interval exchanges are right-continuous by the condition that they are left continuous, we get a group of bijections of $\mathbb{R}/\mathbb{Z}$ that we denote by $\widetilde{\mathrm{IET}}$. The map $g \in \mathrm{IET} \mapsto \widetilde{g} \in \widetilde{\mathrm{IET}}$, where $\widetilde{g}$ is the unique left-continuous map that coincides with g except on the points of discontinuity of g, is a group isomorphism. Then

$$\tag{8} \tau_g = \widetilde{g}g^{-1}$$

is a bijection of $\mathbb{R}/\mathbb{Z}$ with finite support equal to the points of discontinuity of g^{-1}. Moreover

$$\tag{9} \tau_{gh} = \widetilde{gh}h^{-1}g^{-1} = \tau_g g \tau_h g^{-1} = \tau_g({}^g\tau_h),$$

so that the map

$$\iota \colon \mathrm{IET} \to \mathrm{Sym}_\infty(\mathbb{R}/\mathbb{Z}) \rtimes \mathrm{IET}$$
$$g \mapsto (\tau_g, g)$$

is an injective group homomorphism. Observe that $\tau_g = 1$ if and only if g is continuous, i.e. a rotation. If $G < IET$ is a subgroup, the restriction of ι to G takes values in $\mathrm{Sym}(\mathbb{R}/\mathbb{Z}) \rtimes G$. Moreover $\iota(G) \cap \{1\} \times G$ consists of rotations and thereby is amenable. The conclusion follows from Corollary 5.21. $\qquad\square$

In [86] we consider all stabilizers of the action of $\pi(G)$ on $\mathcal{P}_f(\mathbb{Z})$. The idea that it is enough to show amenability of the stabilizer of the empty set belongs to Yves de Cornulier and can be found in the report of N. Bourbaki seminar [41].

CHAPTER 7

Subgroups of topological full groups of intermediate growth

In this chapter we consider subgroups of topological full group. In [**117**], Nekrashevych gave examples of Burnside simple groups of intermediate growth. While Nekrashevych uses the terminology of groupoids in his work, we made the choice to use the language of topological full groups. The main idea of simplicity and finite generacy of these groups is already developed in the Chapter 4, where we showed the result of Matui that the commutator subgroup of the full topological group is simple and finitely generated.

Of course, it is a purely a matter of preference and some of the readers might find the language of groupoids more appealing to them.

1. Multisections

Let G be a group acting on a Cantor set X.

DEFINITION 7.1. A *multisection* M of degree n (or *n-section*) is a set of disjoint clopen subsets $U_1, \ldots, U_n$ and elements $\{g_{ij} \in G\}_{i,j=1}^n$ so that $g_{ij}(U_j) = U_i$ and $g_{ij}g_{jk} = g_{ik}$ on U_k for all $1 \leq i, j, k \leq n$.

We say that any bisection (g_{ij}, U_j) is a *part* of such a multisection, and that the multisection *extends* the bisection (g_{ij}, U_i).

If N is an m-section with $m \geq n$, given by subsets $U_1, \ldots, U_n, U_{n+1}, \ldots, U_m$ and elements $\{g_{ij} \in G\}_{i,j=1}^m$, then we say that N is an *extension* of M. If for a multisection M of degree n there is an extension N of degree $n+k$ then we call M *k-extendable*.

Note that in order to specify an n-section M it is enough to have a set U_1 and elements $g_{i1} \in G$, $2 \leq i \leq n$ such that the sets $U_1, g_{21}(U_1), \ldots, g_{n1}(U_1)$ are pairwise disjoint, since then we can define $U_i = g_{i1}(U_1)$ and $g_{ij} = g_{i1}g_{j1}^{-1}$. If $V \subset U_1$ is a clopen subset, then the sets $V, g_{21}(V), \ldots, g_{n1}(V)$ are still disjoint and thus also define an n-section. We will sometimes denote as M_V and call M restricted to V.

Note that the map $V \mapsto M_V$ is a bijection from the set of all subsets of U_1 to the set all multisections that are restrictions of M. We will transfer the usual notation for sets operations while talking about corresponding multisections. Thus $M_1 = M_2 \setminus M_3$ if $M_i = M_{V_i}$ and $V_1 = V_2 \setminus V_3$, etc. In particular we will talk about unions and disjoint unions of multisections.

DEFINITION 7.2. Let M be a multisection of degree n. For a permutation $\sigma \in S_n$ define a homeomorphism σ_M of X by the rule that for all $1 \leq i \leq n$ it equals to $g_{\sigma(i),i}$ on U_i and identity elsewhere. The image of S_n is a subgroup of $[[G]]$ denoted by $S(M)$, and the image of A_n by $Alt(M)$.

In what follows we use words like *transpositions* and *3-cycles* by which we mean the images of cycles of length 2 or 3 in $S(M)$ for some multisection M.

DEFINITION 7.3. We define the group $S(G)$ as a subgroup of $[[G]]$ generated by all transpositions and $Alt(G)$ as a subgroup of $[[G]]$ generated by all 3-cycles.

We will now prove the following proposition that treats the case when G is generated by its elements of order two. It will be needed later on. Recall that a *partition* of X is a set of subsets of X whose disjoint union is X. We say that a partition is g-invariant for $g \in G$, if each set in it is g-invariant. In that case, for any set A in the partition we can define an element $\tau_{g,A}$ of $[[G]]$ that is g on A and the identity everywhere else.

PROPOSITION 7.4. Let G be generated by a finite set S of elements of order two. Suppose H is a finitely generated subgroup of $S(G)$. Then for each $s \in S$ there is a partition $\mathcal{P}_s$ of X into clopen sets, such that $\mathcal{P}_s$ is s-invariant and the group generated by $\{\tau_{s,A} \mid s \in S, A \in \mathcal{P}_s\}$ contains H.

PROOF. It will suffice to show the following. Let $g \in G$, $s \in S$ and $x \in X$. (Recall that $s^2 = 1$.)

If the points x, sx, gsx are all distinct, then there is a clopen neighborhood $U \ni x$ such that U, sU, gsU are disjoint. Define α_g to be g on sU, g^{-1} on gsU and 1 elsewhere. Define α_{gs} similarly. Define also τ_s to be s on $U \cup sU$ and 1 elsewhere. Then it is easy to check that $\alpha_{gs} = \tau_s \alpha_g \tau_s$.

If the points x, gx, sgx are all distinct, then there is a clopen U such that U, gU, sgU are disjoint. Then $\alpha_{sg} = \tau_s \alpha_g \tau_s$.

If $sx = x$ and $gx \neq x$, then there is a clopen $U \ni x$ such that U, gU are disjoint. Moreover, by considering $U \cap sU$ we may assume that $sU = U$. Then $\alpha_{gs} = \tau_s \alpha_g \tau_s$, where τ_s is s on U and 1 elsewhere.

If $gx \neq x$ and $sgx = gx$ then there is a clopen $U \ni x$ such that U, gU are disjoint and $sgU = gU$. Then $\alpha_{sg} = \tau_s \alpha_g \tau_s$.

These four statements allow, by using induction on the length of $g \in G$, to place any transposition in $S(G)$ in a group generated by elements of the form $\tau_{s,A}$ for some clopen set A. If $H \leq S(G)$ is finitely generated, it is a subgroup of some group generated by a finite number of transpositions, and so we are done.   □

DEFINITION 7.5. For a homeomorphism f of X we denote by $\mathrm{supp}(f)$ the closure of the set of all $x \in X$ such that $f(x) \neq x$. If M is a multisection we define $\mathrm{supp}(M) = \cup_1^n U_i$.

Note that if $f \in S(M)$ then $\mathrm{supp}(f) \subset \mathrm{supp}(M)$.

Let M be a multisection of degree n, given by subsets $U_1, \ldots, U_n$ and elements $\{g_{ij} \in G\}_{i,j=1}^n$. Let $f \in [[G]]$ be such that for each $1 \leq i \leq n$ we have that $f = f_i$ on U_i for some $f_i \in G$, then the subsets $f(U_1), \ldots, f(U_n)$ and the elements $f g_{ij} f^{-1}$ define a multisection which we denote by fMf^{-1}. It follows that $Alt(fMf^{-1}) = f Alt(M) f^{-1}$.

We will often need to draw some conclusions about group $Alt(M)$ by representing M as a union of $M_1 \cup \cdots \cup M_k$ and the knowledge of the groups $Alt(M_q)$.

LEMMA 7.6. Let M be a multisection and $M = \cup_{q=1}^k M_k$. Then $Alt(M)$ is a subgroup of the group generated by all $Alt(M_q)$, $1 \leq q \leq k$ if the degree of M is at least 5 or if all M_q are disjoint.

PROOF. If the union $M = \cup_{q=1}^{k} M_k$ is disjoint then all groups $Alt(M_q)$ commute with each other and $Alt(M) \leq \prod Alt(M_q)$ by the 'diagonal' inclusion

$$\sigma_M \mapsto \prod \sigma_{M_q}$$

for $\sigma \in S_n$.

Let us suppose that the degree is at least 5. We will prove it for $k = 2$, the general case follows by induction. Let $M = M_1 \cup M_2$. Define multisections $N_1 = M_1 \setminus M_2$, $N_2 = M_1 \cap M_2$ and $N_3 = M_2 \setminus M_1$. Then M is the disjoint union of N_1, N_2, N_3. We have the diagonal inclusions $Alt(M) \leq Alt(N_1) \times Alt(N_2) \times Alt(N_3)$, $Alt(M_1) \leq Alt(N_1) \times Alt(N_2)$ and $Alt(M_2) \leq Alt(N_2) \times Alt(N_3)$. To show that $Alt(M) \leq \langle Alt(M_1), Alt(M_2) \rangle$ it suffices to show that $Alt(M) = \langle Alt(M_1), Alt(M_2) \rangle$. This is equivalent to the fact that $\{(\sigma, \sigma, 1) \mid \sigma \in A_n\}$ and $\{(1, \sigma, \sigma) \mid \sigma \in A_n\}$ generate all of A_n^3. Note that

$$[(\sigma, \sigma, 1), (1, \tau, \tau)] = (1, [\sigma, \tau], 1)$$

Moreover, if $n \geq 5$ then A_n is simple and so $[A_n, A_n] = A_n$. Thus this subgroup contains $1 \times A_n \times 1$, and therefore is equal to A_n^3. □

THEOREM 7.7. Let G be a group that acts minimally on a Cantor space X. Then $Alt(G)$ is simple.

PROOF. Let H be a nontrivial normal subgroup in $Alt(G)$. We first show that there is a clopen U such that for any 5-section M with $\text{supp}(M) \subset U$ we have $Alt(M) \leq H$.

Take $g \in H \setminus \{1\}$ and find a clopen set U such that $g(U) \cap U = \emptyset$. Let M be a 5-section supported in U, and let $h_1, h_2 \in Alt(M)$. Then $g h_1 g^{-1}$ is supported in $g(U)$, and hence $g h_1 g^{-1}$ commputes with h_1, h_2. It follows that $[[g^{-1}, h_1], h_2] = [h_1, h_2]$. Since H is normal in $Alt(G)$ we have that $[h_1, h_2] = [[g^{-1}, h_1], h_2] \in H$. It follows that $Alt(M) = [Alt(M), Alt(M)] \leq H$.

Note now that if N is a 3-section in U, then we also have $Alt(N) \leq H$. Indeed, if N can be extended to a 5-section in U then it follows from what we have already established. Note that if $x \in \text{supp}(N)$ then by minimality of the action of G there is a clopen $x \in V$ so that N_V extends to a 5-section in U. By compactness we can decompose N as a finite disjoint union $\cup N_i$ so that each N_i extends to a 5-section in U. Then $Alt(N) \leq \prod Alt(N_i) \leq Alt(G)$.

If M is a multisection on sets $V_1, \ldots, V_n$ and three out of these V_i lie in U, then $Alt(M) \leq H$. Indeed, a 3-cycle σ in $Alt(M)$ with support in U belongs to H, and since H is normal in G then also the normal closure of σ is in H. The normal closure of a 3-cycle in any alternating group A_n is the whole A_n.

Let now N be an arbitrary 3-section. We have to show that $Alt(N) \leq H$. Again by the minimality of the action of G, for any $x \in \text{supp}(N)$ there is clopen $x \in V$ so that N_V extends to a 6-section with three of its base sets in U. By above it follows that $Alt(N_V) \leq H$. By compactness we can write a disjoint union $N = \cup N_i$ with such extendable N_i. It follows that $Alt(N) \leq \prod Alt(N_i) \leq H$. □

2. Adding two multisections together

Recall that in order to define an $(n+1)$-section it is enough to have n elements $g_i \in G$, $1 \leq i \leq n$ and a clopen V so that the sets $V, g_1(V), \ldots, g_n(V)$ are disjoint. Suppose now that we have two multisections M and N given by $V, g_1, \ldots, g_n$ and

$W, h_1, \ldots, h_m$. Suppose also that $\text{supp}(N) \cap \text{supp}(M) = V \cap W$. Let $U = V \cap W$. Note that the sets $U, g_1(U), \ldots, g_n(U), h_1(U), \ldots, h_m(U)$ are disjoint, and denote the corresponding $(n+m+1)$-section by L.

LEMMA 7.8. $Alt(L) \leq \langle Alt(N), Alt(M) \rangle$.

PROOF. Let $L_1 = M_U$ and $L_2 = N_U$. Note that $Alt(L_1)$ and $Alt(L_2)$ are subgroups of $Alt(L)$. Denote also $M' = M \setminus L_1$ and $N' = N \setminus L_2$. It follows that the multisections M', N', L are disjoint and, thus, $Alt(M'), Alt(N'), Alt(L)$ pairwise commute.

We have that $Alt(M)$ is the diagonal subgroup in $Alt(M') \times Alt(L_1)$

$$Alt(M) = \{\sigma_{M'}\sigma_{L_1} : \sigma \in A_{n+1}\}$$

The same holds for $A(N)$

$$Alt(N) = \{\sigma_{N'}\sigma_{L_2} : \sigma \in A_{m+1}\}$$

It follows that $[\sigma_{M'}\sigma_{L_1}, \sigma_{M'}\sigma_{L_2}] = [\sigma_{L_1}, \sigma_{L_2}]$, thus the group $\langle Alt(N), Alt(M) \rangle$ contains the normal closure of $[Alt(L_1), Alt(L_2)]$. It will suffice to show that the normal closure of $[Alt(L_1), Alt(L_2)]$ in $Alt(L)$ is the whole group $Alt(L)$. This follows from the fact that

$$A_s = [A(\{1, \ldots, k\}), A(\{k, \ldots, s\})].$$

$\square$

3. Bisections

We call a bisection a pair (g, U) with $g \in G$ and a clopen subset U of X. The domain of (g, U) is U and its range is $g(U)$.

We define the inverse

$$(g, U)^{-1} = (g^{-1}, g(U)),$$

and the product by

$$(g, U)(f, V) = (gf, V \cap f^{-1}(U))$$

if $V \cap f^{-1}(U) \neq \emptyset$, otherwise the product is undefined.

We say that a bisection (g, V) is contained in (g, U) if $V \subset U$.

4. Finitely generated actions

DEFINITION 7.9. The action of group G on X is called expanding if $X \subset A^G$ for some finite set A.

We say that a set S of bisections *generates* the action of G on X if for any $g \in G, x \in X$ and any neighborhood U of x there is a neighborhood V of x in U so that (g, V) is a product of bisections from $S \cup S^{-1}$. Note that if S is generating, it follows that for any x there is a bisection in S whose domain contains x. It also easily follows that if we replace any bisection (g, U) in S by its 'partitioning' (g, V_1), $\ldots, (g, V_k)$, where $U = \cup_i V_i$, then the set we obtain is also generating.

LEMMA 7.10. If the action of a finitely generated group G on X is expanding then there is a finite set of bisections S that generates the action.

PROOF. Suppose G is generated by a symmetric set $g_1, \ldots, g_n$. Set $C_a^h = X \cap \{w \in A^G : w(h^{-1}) = a\}$ for $a \in A$. Consider $S = \{(g_i, C_a^e) : 1 \leq i \leq n, a \in A\}$. We first show that for any open U in X there is $V \subset U$ such that (e, V) is a product of elements of S.

We have

$$(g_{i_1}, C_{a_1}^e) \cdots (g_{i_m}, C_{a_m}^e) = (g_{i_1} \cdots g_{i_m}, C_{a_1}^{g_{i_m} \cdots g_{i_1}} \cap \cdots \cap C_{a_{m-2}}^{g_{i_m} g_{i_{m-1}}} \cap C_{a_{m-1}}^{g_{i_m}} \cap C_{a_m}^e).$$

If follows that if we choose g_{i_j} so that the path $e, g_{i_m}, g_{i_m} g_{i_{m-1}}, \cdots, g_{i_m} \cdots g_{i_1}$ passes through sufficiently many elements of G then, for appropriately chosen $a_i's$ the product above equals to (g, V) for $g = g_{i_1} \cdots g_{i_m}$ and some $V \subset U$. Now $(e, V) = (g, V)^{-1}(g, V)$.

Let now (g, U) be any bisection. We can find a product of S that equals to (g, W). By above there is $V \subset U$ such that (e, V) is also a product of elements in S. It follows that $(g, W \cap V) = (g, W)(e, V)$ is a product of elements from S and $W \cap V \subset U$. $\square$

Let P be a finite partition of X. We say that a subset of X is *subordinate* to P if it lies completely in some element of P. We will say that a bisection is *subordinate* to P if its domain and range are subordinate to different elements of P. We also say that a set S of bisections is *subordinate* to P if all its bisections are subordinate to P. Finally, a multisection M is *subordinate* to P if its base sets $U_1, \ldots, U_n$ are all subordinate to different elements of P.

We will need some additional properties of sets of bisections S.

PROPOSITION 7.11. Suppose that the action of G on X is expanding, and let P be any partition of X. Then there is a finite generating set of bisections S so that $S = S^{-1}$ and

    (a) S is subordinate to P.
    (b) For any $x \in X$ there are at least three bisections in S so that their domains contain x and they map x to three different elements of P.

PROOF. Let's start from a finite generating set of bisections T given by Lemma 7.10. Let $(g, U) \in T$. If for $x \in U$ the points $x, g(x)$ are in different elements of P, choose a clopen neighborhood V_x of x so that V_x and $g(V_x)$ completely lie in different elements of P. If $x, g(x)$ lie in the same element of P choose first $h_x \in G$ so that $x, h_x(x)$ lie in different elements of P, and then choose a clopen $V_x \ni x$ so that the pair $V_x, h_x(V_x)$ completely lie in different elements of P and the same is true about the pair $h_x(V_x), g(V_x)$. Since the set U is compact and the sets V_x form a cover of U we can choose a finite subcover $V_1, V_2, \ldots, V_k$. For each V_i either $V_i, g(V_i)$ lie in different elements of P or there is $h_i \in G$ so that this is true about pairs $V_i, h_i(V_i)$ and $h_i(V_i), g(V_i)$. Let us now remove (g, U) in T and add bisections (g, V_i) or $(h_i, V_i), (gh_i^{-1}, h_i(V_i))$. Note that in the latter case $(g, V_i) = (gh_i^{-1}, h_i(V_i))(h_i, V_i)$. Since V_i form a cover of U it easily follows that the new set of bisections is still generating. Repeating this procedure for all elements of T we get a generating set that satisfies property (a).

To obtain property (c) it will suffice to start from a set S that satisfies (a) and add some additional bisections so that (b) holds. We can do it in a similar fashion. For any $x \in X$ there is $(g_x, U_x) \in S$ with $x \in U_x$ since S is generating. Choose now $t_x, q_x \in G$ so that all three points $g_x(x), t_x(x), q_x(x)$ lie in different elements of P. Choose also clopen neighborhoods V_x, W_x so that $t_x(V_x), q_x(W_x)$ are subordinate to P. Since the diagonal in X^3 is compact, we can choose a finite subcover in $U_x \times V_x \times W_x$, so that $\{(x,x,x) \mid x \in X\} \subset \cup_i U_i \times V_i \times W_i$. It follows that for any $x \in X$ there is i so that $(g_i, U_i) \in S$, x is in all U_i, V_i, W_i and they lie in different elements of P.

This will provide a set S that satisfies both properties (a), (b). Finally, replacing it with $S \cup S^{-1}$ we obtain a symmetric generating set of bisections that satisfies all the conditions of the Proposition. $\qquad\square$

THEOREM 7.12. *Suppose that an action of G on X is minimal and expansive. Then $Alt(G)$ is finitely generated.*

PROOF. Let P be a partition of X with at least 5 elements, and let S be a finite generating set of bisections as Proposition 7.11. Let (g, U) be a bisection from $S \cup S^2 \cup S^3$ subordinate to P. For $x \in U$ find a neighborhood $V_x \subset U$ so that (g, V_x) is part of a 5-section M_x subordinate to P. More explicitly this means that M_x is given by elements h_1^x, h_2^x, h_3^x so that subsets $V_x, g(V_x), h_1^x(V_x), h_2^x(V_x), h_3^x(V_x)$ belong to different elements of P. By compactness we can find a finite number of such M_x so that corresponding sets V_x cover U. If we do it for all such bisections in $S \cup S^2 \cup S^3$ we will obtain a finite set F of 5-sections subordinate to P. We will show that the (finite) set $\cup_{M \in F} Alt(M)$ generates $Alt(G)$. For the time being denote the group generated by $\cup_{M \in F} Alt(M)$ by A_F.

We need a preliminary lemma:

LEMMA 7.13. *Let (g, U) be subordinate to P and $x \in U$. Then there is a clopen neighborhood V of x in U, so that (g, V) is a part of a 5-section L subordinate to P and such that $Alt(L) \leq A_F$.*

PROOF. Since S is generating, there is a bisection of g in S^k for some k so that its domain is a neighborhood of x in U. The proof will be by induction on k. Clearly it is true for $k = 1, 2, 3$. We now write this bisection as a product of elements in S^2 and S^{k-2}:
$$(g_1, U_1)(g_2, U_2)$$
with $g = g_1 g_2$, $(g_1, U_1) \in S^2$ and $(g_2, U_2) \in S^{k-2}$ and such that its domain $U_2 \cap g_2^{-1}(U_1)$ is a neighborhood of x in U. Denote $y = g_2(x) \in U_1$. By Proposition 7.11 (b) there is $(g', U') \in S$ so that $y \in U'$ and $x, g(x), g'(y)$ lie in 3 different parts of P. Consider the product
$$(g_1, U_1)(g', U')^{-1}(g', U')(g_2, U_2),$$
and set $(h', W') = (g_1, U_1)(g', U')^{-1}$ and $(h, W) = (g', U')(g_2, U_2)$. Note that both $(h', W') \in S^3$ and $(h, W) \in S^{k-1}$ are subordinate to P, $g = h'h$ and $x \in W \cap h^{-1}(W') \subset U$.

Since $(h, W) \in S^{k-1}$ and it is subordinate to P, we can apply the induction hypothesis. Thus there a neighborhood W_0 of x in W and a 5-section N subordinate to P so that (h, W_0) is a part of N and $Alt(N) \leq A_F$. There there are 5 base sets of N all lying in different parts of P, there is a base set of N that lies in in a part of P which is different from parts containing $x, h(x), g(x)$. Thus we can drop two base sets of N to obtain a 3-section N' which is a part of N and which contains (h, W_0) as its part. It follows that $Alt(N') \leq Alt(N) \leq A_F$. Since $(h', W') \in S^3$ there is also a neighborhood W_0' of $h(x)$ in W' and an 5-section $M \in F$ such that the bisection (h', W_0') is a part of M. It follows analogously that there is a 3-section M' which is a part of M and which contains (h', W_0') as a part, so that supp $N' \cap$ supp M' is

$h(W_0) \cap W_0'$. Since M' is a part of M we also have that $Alt(M') \leq Alt(M) \leq A_F$. By Lemma 7.8 we have a 5-section L so that $Alt(L) \leq \langle Alt(M'), Alt(N') \rangle \leq A_F$ and both $(h', h(V))$ and (h, V) are part of L, where $V = W_0 \cap h^{-1}(W_0')$. It follows that (g, V) is also a part of L. Note that since both M' and N' are subordinate to P, so is L.   □

We will now complete the proof of the theorem. Suppose M is a 3-section subordinate to P and given by $U \subset X$ and $g, h \in G$. Let $x \in U$ Then there is a neighborhood V of x in U so that $Alt(M_V) \leq A_F$. Indeed, by the Lemma 7.13 there are neighborhoods V', V'' of x and 5-sections L', L'' subordinate to P, so that (g, V') is a part of L' and (h, V'') is a part of L'', and so that $Alt(L'), Alt(L'') \leq A_F$. Then, just as in the proof of Lemma 7.13 there are 3-sections L_1', L_1'' which are parts of L', L'' and that contain (g, V'), (h, V'') respectively, and so that supp $L_1' \cap$ supp $L_1'' = V' \cap V''$. By Lemma 7.8 we have a 5-section L such that $Alt(L) \leq A_F$ and M_V is a part of L, where $V = V' \cap V''$. Hence $Alt(M_V) \leq A_F$.

Suppose now that M is a 5-section subordinate to P, and $x \in$ supp M. Again, there is a neighborhood V of x so that $Alt(M_V) \leq A_F$. Indeed, there are two 3-sections M', M'' which are parts of M so that supp $M' \cap$ supp M'' is the base set of M that contains x. By the previous paragraph there are neighborhoods V', V'' of x so that $Alt(M_{V'}'), Alt(M_{V''}'') \leq A_F$, and thus by Lemma 7.8 $Alt(M_V) \leq \langle Alt(M_{V'}), Alt(M_{V''}) \rangle \leq A_F$.

It follows now from Lemma 7.6 that if M is a 5-section subordinate to P then $Alt(M) \leq A_F$.

Suppose now that M is any 5-section, not necessarily subordinate to P, given by $U \subset X$ and $g_1, \ldots, g_4 \in G$. Let $x \in U$. Then for a sufficiently small neighborhood V of x we can find four more elements $g_5, \ldots, g_8$ so that each 5-section M_i defined by V and $g_i, g_5, \ldots, g_8$ is subordinate to P. By above it follows that $Alt(M_i) \leq A_F$. Clearly $Alt(M_V) = \langle \cup_i Alt(M_i) \rangle$, thus $Alt(M_V) \leq A_F$. Applying again Lemma 7.6 we obtain that $Alt(M) \leq A_F$. Since M is any 5-section, it follows that $A_F = Alt(G)$.   □

5. An introduction to periodicity and intermediate growth

Suppose that G acts on a compact set X. Through this section we recall basic notations and definitions that we will use later in the chapter.

Singular points. Let $x \in X$. Define G_x as the group of all $g \in G$ that fix x (the *stabilizer* of x) and $G_{(x)}$ as the group of all such $g \in G$ that fix some neighborhood of x (the neighborhood can be different for different g.) It is easy to see that $G_{(x)}$ is a normal subgroup of G_x. Note that $G_{gx} = gG_xg^{-1}$ and $G_{(gx)} = gG_{(x)}g^{-1}$.

DEFINITION 7.14. $x \in X$ is called *G-regular* if $G_x = G_{(x)}$. That is, any element that fixes x fixes also some neighborhood of x. A point which is not *G-regular* is called *G-singular*.

Note that the sets of *G-regular* and *G-singular* points are invariant under the action of G.

We will need the following lemma

LEMMA 7.15. If $x \in X$ is *G-regular* and x_i converges x then (Γ_{x_i}, x_i) converges to (Γ_x, x) as rooted graphs.

PROOF. The structure of the orbital graph Γ_x is determined by the stabilizer G_x. In particular, the structure of the ball of radius r around x in Γ_x is determined by whether or not $gG_x = hG_x$, for $g, h \in G$ of length less than r. So it suffices to show that $g \in G_x$ iff for all sufficiently large i, $g \in G_{x_i}$. If $g \in G_{x_i}$ for all $i \geq I$, then $gx = x$ by continuity. Suppose conversely, that $g \in G_x$. Since $G_x = G_{(x)}$, it follows that g fixes some neighborhood of x. Thus $g(x_i) = x_i$ for all i so that x_i is in this neighborhood. $\qquad\square$

We now define a special type of singular points (which are called purely non-Hausdorff in [**117**].)

DEFINITION 7.16. Let $x \in X$ be a G-singular point such that for any $g \in G_x$ the set of interior points of $\mathrm{Fix}(g)$ accumulates on x. Then such x is called a *purely G-singular point*.

It is easy to see that the set of purely G-singular points is also G-invariant.

Graphs of actions. In what follows we will consider rooted oriented labeled graphs (Γ, v), which means that Γ is a graph all of whose edges are oriented and labeled by elements of some labelling set, and v is a distinguished vertex called root. The distance between vertices of Γ is the length of a shortest (unoriented) path between them. For $r > 0$ the ball $B_v(r) = B_v^\Gamma(r)$ is the rooted graph with vertices of Γ that are at distance less than r from v, and induced edges and labels, and with v as the root.

We say that the distance between (Γ_1, v_1) and (Γ_2, v_2) is 2^{-r} if r is a maximal number such that the balls $B_{v_1}^{\Gamma_1}(r)$, $B_{v_2}^{\Gamma_2}(r)$ are isomorphic as rooted oriented labeled graphs.

Suppose now that G is generated by a finite set S. For $x \in X$ we define an *orbital graph of x*, Γ_x, which an oriented S-labeled graph with the set of vertices being the orbit Gx so that for any $s \in S$ and $y \in Gx$ there is an arrow from y to sy labeled by s. We usually consider Γ_x as a *rooted* graph, where the vertex x is the root. In that case we usually denote it by (Γ_x, x). It is clearly isomorphic to the Schreier graph $(G/G_x, x)$.

We will also consider the graph of germs $\Gamma_{(x)}$. Its vertices are the *germs* (g, x), with $(g, x) = (h, y)$ if $x = y$ and there is a neighborhood of x where $g = h$. For each $s \in S$ and each germ (g, x) there is an arrow labeled by s from (g, x) to (sg, x), and the germ $(1, x)$ is the root. This rooted graph is isomorphic to the Schreier graph $G/G_{(x)}$.

We will often have to consider balls in orbital graphs, in which case we will omit the graph from the notation and denote them simply by $B_x(r)$. It will be clear from the context which orbital graph we are considering. We have the following

PROPOSITION 7.17. Suppose that the action $G = \langle S \rangle$ on X is minimal, and $x \in X$ is G-regular. Then for every $r > 0$ there is $R = R(r)$ such that for any $y \in X$ there is $z \in B_y(R)$ with $B_z(r)$ isomorphic to $B_x(r)$ (as rooted oriented labeled graphs). In fact R does not depend on x.

PROOF. Note first that $B_x(r)$ is the image of $B_e(r) \subset G$ under the map $G \to \Gamma_x$ given by $g \mapsto gx$. It follows that $B_x(r)$ is determined by the list of equalities and inequalities $gx = hx$ or $gx \neq hx$ for all possible pairs $g, h \in B_e(r)$. For any g, h such that $gx \neq hx$ there is a neighborhood U of x such that $g(U) \cap h(U) = \emptyset$. If $gx = hx$ then $h^{-1}g \in G_x$ which equals $G_{(x)}$ since x is regular, and thus there is a neighborhood U of x such that $g = h$ on U. Since there is only a finite number of pairs in $B_e(r)$ it follows that there exists a sufficiently small neighborhood U such that for all $g, h \in B_e(r)$ $gx = hx$ implies $g|_U = h|_U$ and $gx \neq hx$ implies $g(U) \cap h(U) = \emptyset$.

By minimality we have that the union of $g(U)$, $g \in G$ is the whole of X. Since X is compact, it follows that there is a finite subcover: $X = g_1(U) \cup \cdots \cup g_k(U)$. Thus for any $y \in X$ there is i so that $y \in g_i(U)$, and hence $z = g_i^{-1}(y) \in U$. It follows that for all $g, h \in B_e(r)$ we have $gx = hx$ iff $gz = hz$, and thus $B_z(r)$ is isomorphic to $B_x(r)$, so we can take $R = R(r, x)$ to be the maximum of the lengths of g_i^{-1}.

It is left to note that for each r there is only a finite number of isomorphism types of graphs $B_x(r)$, since there is only a finite number of factors of $B_e(r)$. Thus we can choose $x_1, \ldots, x_m$ so that $B_{x_i}(r)$ is a list of all possible r-balls, up to isomorphism of rooted oriented labeled graphs, and let $R_i = R(r, x_i)$. Then $R = \max(R_i)$ does not depend on x. $\qquad\square$

Actions of the infinite dihedral group. Consider now the infinite dihedral group $D = \langle a, b \mid a^2 = b^2 = 1 \rangle$. It is an easy exercise to check that if $H \leq D$ then H is either trivial, the whole D, the infinite subgroup generated by ab, or it has order two. In the latter case it is conjugate to either $\langle a \rangle$ or $\langle b \rangle$. We will be interested in the corresponding Schreier graphs of D. If $H = 1$ then the Schreier graph $D/H = D$ is the Cayley graph of D which is a two-ended integer chain where each vertex is connected to the next one by a pair of edges, labeled interchangebly by a and b. The root in this this case is vertex 1.

If, on the other hand, $H = \langle a \rangle$ then the Schreier graph D/H is a one-ended chain whose starting point is the root which has a loop labeled by a attached to it. If H is just conjugate to $\langle a \rangle$ then D/H is the same graph as $D/\langle a \rangle$ but with a different root.

We will now consider how these facts relate to minimal actions of D on a compact set X Since any orbit is dense, it is infinite, and hence if $x \in X$ then D_x has to have infinite index. Thus either D_x is trivial or it is conjugate to $\langle a \rangle$ or $\langle b \rangle$. It follows that if D_x is trivial, then Γ_x is isomorphic to the Cayley graph of D, the two-sided infinite line. If D_x is conjugate to $\langle a \rangle$ then the orbit Dx contains a fixed point of a and the graph Γ_x is a one-sided line that starts from that fixed point. Note that if x is a fixed point of a or b then the graph Γ_x has a loop edge at vertex x. It follows that any D-orbit Dx contains at most one point in $\mathrm{Fix}(a) \cup \mathrm{Fix}(b)$. Namely, if $D_x = 1$ then the orbit Dx is disjoint from $\mathrm{Fix}(a) \cup \mathrm{Fix}(b)$, and if $D_x \neq 1$ then Dx intersects $\mathrm{Fix}(a) \cup \mathrm{Fix}(b)$ in one point. This in particular means that $\mathrm{Fix}(a) \cup \mathrm{Fix}(b)$ is nowhere dense.

Fragmentations of infinite dihedral group actions. Given a minimal action of D on X we will now construct a different group G and its action on X. One of the main features of this action will be that G-orbits will be the same as D-orbits, i.e. either two or one-sided chains.

DEFINITION 7.18. Let a be a homeomorphism of X of order two. A *fragmentation* of a is a finite group A of homeomorphisms of X such that for any $a' \in A$ for any $x \in X$ we have either $a'x = x$ or $a'x = ax$, and so that for any $y \in X$ there is $a'' \in A$ with $a''y = ay$. If $D = \langle a, b \rangle$ acts on X and groups A, B are fragmentations of a and b respectively, then we call the group G generated by $A \cup B$ a fragmentation of D

Using the fact that for any $y \in X$ there are $a' \in A$ and $b' \in B$ such that $a'y = ay$ and $b'y = by$, it is easy to see that for any $x \in X$ we have the equality of orbits, $Dx = Gx$.

We will need the following lemma about fragmentations

LEMMA 7.19. Let A be a fragmentation of a. If $x \notin \mathrm{Fix}(a)$ then there is a neighborhood U of x such that for each $a' \in A$ the restriction of a' to U either equals a or 1.

PROOF. If $x \notin \mathrm{Fix}(a)$ then for each $a' \in A$ there is a neighborhood V of x such that a' restricted to V is either 1 or a. Indeed, otherwise there are sequences $x_i \to x$, $y_i \to x$ such that $a'(x_i) = a(x_i)$ and $a'(y_i) = y_i$, since a' is continuous, it follows that $a'(x) = a(x) = x$.

Since A is finite, we can choose such V for each $a' \in A$ and then take their intersection to obtain U.   □

Note that any U as in the lemma defines a map $\pi = \pi_U : A \to \mathbb{Z}/\mathbb{Z}_2$, with $\pi(a') = 1$ if $a'|_U = a|_U$ and $\pi(a') = 0$ if $a'|_U = 1|_U$. Since elements of A commute with a it follows that the set aU has the same property, and $\pi_{aU} = \pi_U$. Since the set $U \cup aU$ is A-invariant, the map $\pi = \pi_{U \cup aU}$ is clearly a homomorphism $A \to \mathbb{Z}/2\mathbb{Z}$. Denote by P_π the union of all such U which correspond to homomorphisms $\pi : A \to \mathbb{Z}/2\mathbb{Z}$. It follows that $X \setminus \mathrm{Fix}(a) = \cup_\pi P_\pi$, where the union goes over all homomorphisms $\pi : A \to \mathbb{Z}/2\mathbb{Z}$

The analogous statement holds for a fragmentation B of b. If we define Q_σ to be that open sets that correspond to homomorphisms $\sigma : B \to \mathbb{Z}/2\mathbb{Z}$ and hence we can also say that $X \setminus \mathrm{Fix}(b) = \cup_\sigma Q_\sigma$.

We will now determine which points are G-regular. To do that we need the following

LEMMA 7.20. Let $G = \langle A \cup B \rangle$ be a fragmentation of $D = \langle a, b \rangle$.

  (i) if Dx is disjoint from $\mathrm{Fix}(a) \cup \mathrm{Fix}(b)$ then for any $g \in G$ there is a neighborhood U of x and $h \in D$ such that $g = h$ on U.
  (ii) If $x \in \mathrm{Fix}(a)$ then for any $g \in G$ there is a neighborhood U of x, $a' \in A$ and $h \in \{1, b, ab, bab, \dots\}$ so that $g = ha'$ on U.

A similar statement to (ii) holds for $x \in \mathrm{Fix}(b)$.

PROOF. Suppose that Dx is disjoint from $\mathrm{Fix}(a) \cup \mathrm{Fix}(b)$, and $g \in G$ is given by a word of length n over $A \cup B$. We will prove (i) by induction on n. For $n = 1$ we use Lemma 7.19. Let now $g = a'g'$ with g' given by a word of length $n - 1$. By induction there is $V \ni x$ and $h' \in D$ such that $g' = h'$ on V. Since $h'(x) \in Dx$ it is also not in $\mathrm{Fix}(a) \cup \mathrm{Fix}(b)$, and thus there is $W \ni h'(x)$ such that $a'|_W$ is either 1 or a. It follows that $g = a'g'$ equals to h' or ah' on $U = V \cap h'^{-1}(W)$. Similar reasoning holds for $g = b'g'$. This shows (i).

The statement (ii) is proved in a similar way, using Lemma 7.19 and the fact that points in Dx other then x itself do not lie in $\mathrm{Fix}(a) \cup \mathrm{Fix}(b)$, hence we can apply the first paragraph of the proof to them.   □

PROPOSITION 7.21. *If G is a fragmentation of a minimal action of D on X, then $x \in X$ is G-regular iff $Dx = Gx$ is a two-ended chain (or equivalently Gx is disjoint from $\mathrm{Fix}(a) \cup \mathrm{Fix}(b)$.) Also, if $y \in \mathrm{Fix}(a)$ then $G_y/G_{(y)} = A/A_{(y)}$.*

PROOF. Suppose that Gx is disjoint from $\mathrm{Fix}(a) \cup \mathrm{Fix}(b)$ and $g \in G_x$. By Lemma 7.20 (i) there is $h \in D$ such that $g = h$ in some neighborhood of x. Since $g(x) = h(x) = x$ we have that $h \in D_x$, which is trivial, thus $h = 1$. It follows that g is trivial in some neighborhood of x, and thus $g \in G_{(x)}$. Hence $G_x = G_{(x)}$ and so x is G-regular.

Suppose now that Dx is one-ended, and hence intersect $\mathrm{Fix}(a) \cup \mathrm{Fix}(b)$ is one point, say $y \in \mathrm{Fix}(a)$. We will show that x is G-singular. Note that G_x is conjugate to G_y and this conjugation induces an isomorphism of $G_x/G_{(x)}$ and $G_y/G_{(y)}$. Let $g \in G_y$. By Lemma 7.20 (ii) there is a neighborhood of y and where $g = ha'$ for some $h \in \{1, b, ab, bab, \dots\}$ and $a' \in A$. Since $a'(y) = y$ and $g(y) = y$ it follows that $h(y) = y$, that is $h \in D_y = \langle a \rangle$. It follows that $h = 1$. Thus $g = a'$ in some neighborhood of y. It follows that the inclusion $A \leq G_y$ induces the isomorphism $A/A_{(y)} = G_y/G_{(y)}$ since clearly $A_{(y)} = A \cap G_{(y)}$.

We now note that A_y is not equal to A. Indeed, since A is finite, $A = A_{(y)}$ implies that there is a neighborhood U of y on which all elements of A restrict to identity. By the definition of fragmentation it means that $U \subset \mathrm{Fix}(a)$. Since the action of D is minimal, $\mathrm{Fix}(a)$ is nowhere dense, a contradiction.

We therefore have that if Dx intersects $\mathrm{Fix}(a)$ in y then $G_x/G_{(x)}$ is isomorphic to $A/A_{(y)}$, which is nontrivial. Thus x is G-singular. Similarly if Dx intersects $\mathrm{Fix}(b)$ then x is G-singular.

It follows that x is G-singular if and only if $Dx = Gx$ intersects $\mathrm{Fix}(a) \cup \mathrm{Fix}(b)$. □

We will need to understand the structure of the graph of germs for G-singular points. Recall that if x is G-singular then its orbit Gx intersects $\mathrm{Fix}(a) \cup \mathrm{Fix}(b)$ in some point y, and the graph $\Gamma_{(x)}$ is just the graph $\Gamma_{(y)}$ with a different root. So it will suffice to describe the graphs $\Gamma_{(y)}$ for $y \in \mathrm{Fix}(a)$ (or $y \in \mathrm{Fix}(b)$.) We will now show that $\Gamma_{(y)}$ looks like a 'star' with $|A/A_{(y)}|$ rays, with each ray isomorphic to the one-ended chain Γ_y.

PROPOSITION 7.22. *If $y \in \mathrm{Fix}(a)$ then the vertices of $\Gamma_{(y)}$ is the set $A/A_{(y)} \times \Gamma_y$. For each $a' \in A$ the map $v \mapsto (a'A_{(y)}, v)$ gives a graph isomorphism of Γ_y into $\Gamma_{(y)}$. Also, an edge labeled a'' connects $(a'A_{(y)}, y)$ to $(a''a'A_{(y)}, y)$, for all $a', a'' \in A$.*

PROOF. Since $\Gamma_{(y)}$ is isomorphic to $G/G_{(y)}$ it will be enough to show that $G/G_{(y)}$ is as described. Note also that Γ_y is isomorphic to G/G_y and that the projection $G/G_{(y)} \to G/G_y$ makes $G/G_{(y)}$ into a normal covering of G/G_y, with the covering group $G_y/G_{(y)}$. The last group is isomorphic to $A/A_{(y)}$ by Proposition 7.21. In fact this isomorphism corresponds to the embedding of A into the fundamental group of the graph G/G_y by the rule that assigns to each $a' \in A$ the loop at y labeled by a'. Thus the covering of G/G_y with the covering group $A/A_{(y)}$ is the graph that we get by 'unwinding' these loops. □

Limits of regular orbit graphs. Recall that if $\pi : A \to \mathbb{Z}/2\mathbb{Z}$ is a homomorphism then we denote by P_π the maximal open set such that the restriction of A on it is given by π. Suppose that $x_i \in P_\pi$ are G-regular points for which x_i converge to $y \in \mathrm{Fix}(a)$.

PROPOSITION 7.23. *The graphs Γ_{x_i} converge to $\Gamma_{(y)}/\ker(\pi)$, with roots x_i converging to the image of $(1, y)$.*

Before proving it, note that A acts on $\Gamma_{(y)}$, whose set of vertices is equal to $A/A_{(y)} \times \Gamma_y$, by left multiplication on $A/A_{(y)}$. It follows that $\Gamma_{(y)}/\ker(\pi)$ has the set of vertices $A/\ker(\pi) \times \Gamma_y$. Since $A/\ker(\pi)$ has size 2, it means that $\Gamma_{(y)}/\ker(\pi)$ consists of two copies of Γ_y, the copies of y in which are connected by edges labelled by elements of $A \setminus \ker(\pi)$, while elements in $\ker(\pi)$ label the loops at both copies of y.

PROOF. We first make a simple observation that the edge structure of an orbital graph Γ_z is determined by specifying for each vertex which elements in A and B label loops at that vertex. If $z \in P_\pi \cap Q_\sigma$ then the loops at z are labeled by $a' \in \ker(\pi)$ and $b' \in \ker(\sigma)$.

Consider the first n vertices of Γ_y, starting at y. These are $d_j y$, $0 \leq j \leq n$, where $d_{2j} = (ab)^j \in D$, and $d_{2j+1} = b(ab)^j \in D$.

Since y is in $\mathrm{Fix}(a)$, it is not in $\mathrm{Fix}(b)$ while $d_j y \notin \mathrm{Fix}(a) \cup \mathrm{Fix}(b)$ for $j \geq 1$. Therefore we can choose σ_j and π_j so that $y \in Q_{\sigma_0}$, and $d_j y \in P_{\pi_j} \cap Q_{\sigma_j}$ for $j \geq 1$.

Note now that both x_i and $a x_i$ converge to y, since $y \in \mathrm{Fix}(a)$. It follows that we can choose I so that for all $i \geq I$ the points $x_i, a x_i \in Q_{\sigma_0}$ while $d_j x_i, d_j a x_i \in P_{\pi_j} \cap Q_{\sigma_j}$ for all $1 \leq j \leq n$.

Consider now the maps from $\phi, \psi : \Gamma_y \to \Gamma_{x_i}$, given by $\phi(d_j y) = d_j x_i$ and $\psi(d_j y) = d_j a x_i$. By the reasoning above these two maps preserve the labeled edges between the first n-vertices of Γ_y, except for A-labeled edges at y. Hence they induce labeled graph isomorphisms on $B_y(n)$, the ball in Γ_y with radius n centered at y, if one one disregards the A-labeled loops at y. It is left to note that since $x_i \in P_\pi$ then in the graph Γ_{x_i} the vertices x_i and $a x_i$ are connected by the edges labeled by $a' \notin \ker(\pi)$. Therefore for a sufficiently large i, a neighborhood of x_i in Γ_{x_i} is isomorphic to the two copies of $B_y(n)$ with loops at y labeled by $a' \notin \ker(\pi)$ erased and replaced by a'-labeled edges between two copies of y. $\square$

REMARK 7.24. Let us look closer at the graph $\Gamma_{(y)}/\ker(\pi)$. Since the set of vertices of graph $\Gamma_{(y)}$ is $A/A_{(y)} \times \Gamma_y$, with A acting on the first coordinate, it follows that the set of vertices of $\Gamma_{(y)}/\ker(\pi)$ is equal to $A/\ker(\pi) \times \Gamma_y$. That is, in order to construct $\Gamma_{(y)}/\ker(\pi)$ we have to take two copies of Γ_y, and replace each A-loop at y labelled by $a \notin \ker(\pi)$ with an a-labelled edge between two copies of y. We will denote such a graph as

$$\Gamma_y^- \xrightarrow{\;P_\pi\;} \Gamma_y^+.$$

REMARK 7.25. Note that for any $y \in \mathrm{Fix}(a)$ (or $\mathrm{Fix}(b)$) there is such a sequence. Indeed, the set of G-singlular points is the G-orbit of the set $\mathrm{Fix}(a) \cup \mathrm{Fix}(b)$. The latter set is nowhere dense since the action of G on X is minimal. Since G is countable, this implies that the set of G-singular points is also nowhere dense. It follows that any neighborhood of $y \in \mathrm{Fix}(a)$ contains a G-regular point, and thus there is a sequence of them converging to y. Moreover, the number of homomorphisms $\pi : A \to \langle a \rangle$ is finite, thus we can assume that this convergent sequence is contained in a single P_π.

This allows us to prove a stronger statement than Proposition 7.17. Notice first that any ball in an orbital graph Γ_z has the form of an *interval*, i.e. is a sequence of vertices with edges being either loops or connecting a vertex to the next one.

Note that the loops at the endpoints of a ball do not belong to it. Proposition 7.17 then says that there is $R(r)$ such that if Δ is an interval of length less than r in an orbital graph of a G-regular point, and $x \in X$ then there is a copy of Δ in Γ_x at a distance less then $R(r)$ from x.

Let us now introduce an orientation on an orbital graph Γ_x, by enumerating the set of its vertices $Gx = Dx$ with elements from $\mathbb{Z}$ if it's a graph of a regular point or from $\mathbb{N}$ if it is a singular point. If Δ is an interval, then it can also be given an orientation. Then an embedding of Δ into Γ_x can either preserve or revert orientations. We state that it it possible to have both.

COROLLARY 7.26. Suppose $\mathrm{Fix}(a) \cup \mathrm{Fix}(b)$ is nonempty. Then for any $r > 0$ there is $R_1(r)$ with the following property. For any $x, y \in X$ if Δ is an interval of length r in Γ_x there are two copies of Δ in Γ_y, Δ_1 and Δ_2, such that their orientations are opposite and which are both of distance at most $R_1(r)$ from y.

Note that we do not require that the point x is G-regular, as we did in Proposition 7.17. It is substantial here that we do not include in the interval the loops at its endpoints. Otherwise, the corollary will not hold, since in the graph of a G-singular point there is a vertex whose all A-edges (or B-edges) are loops, and there are no such vertices in a graph of a G-regular point.

PROOF. Let $z \in \mathrm{Fix}(a)$ and suppose Δ be an interval of length r in Γ_x. By Lemma 7.23 we may assume that x is G-regular. Then Proposition 7.17 implies that there is an interval of length $R(r)$ in Γ_z which starts with z and contains Δ. By Lemma 7.23 there is an interval of length $2R(r) + 1$ in an orbital graph of a regular point that contains copies Δ_1 and Δ_2 with opposite orientations. Again by Proposition 7.17 there is a copy of such interval in Γ_y at distance at most $R_1(r) = R(2R(r) + 1)$ from y. $\square$

Periodicity.

THEOREM 7.27. Suppose that $G = \langle A \cup B \rangle$ is a fragmentation of a minimal dihedral action of $\langle a, b \rangle$ on X, such that $\mathrm{Fix}(a) \cup \mathrm{Fix}(b) \neq \emptyset$, and there are purely singular points. Then any element in G has finite order.

Recall that a point x is purely singular if it is singular and for any $g \in G_x$ the set of interior points of $\mathrm{Fix}(g)$ accumulates on x. By Proposition 7.21 above, any singular point is in the orbit of $\mathrm{Fix}(a) \cup \mathrm{Fix}(b)$, so we may suppose that there is $x \in \mathrm{Fix}(a)$ which is purely singular. Let us figure out what does it mean.

LEMMA 7.28. $x \in \mathrm{Fix}(a)$ is purely singular iff for any $a' \in A$ there is $\pi : A \to \mathbb{Z}/2\mathbb{Z}$ such that $\pi(a') = 0$ and P_π accumulates on x.

PROOF. Note first that in order to check whether a point x is purely singular we just have to check some set of coset representatives of $G_x/G_{(x)}$. Indeed, if $g \in G_x$ and $h \in G_{(x)}$ then the sets $\mathrm{Fix}(g)$ and $\mathrm{Fix}(gh)$ coincide in some neighborhood of x. If we assume now that $x \in \mathrm{Fix}(a)$, we have by Proposition 7.21 that $G_x/G_{(x)} = A/A_{(x)}$. Therefore we have that x is purely singular iff for any $a' \in A$ the set of interior points of $\mathrm{Fix}(a')$ accumulates on x.

If $a' \in A$ then the set of interior points of $\mathrm{Fix}(a')$ is the union of all P_π such that $\pi(a') = 0$. Indeed, any P_π is open and if $\pi(a') = 0$ then $P_\pi \subset \mathrm{Fix}(a')$. Conversely, if $y \in \mathrm{Fix}(a')$ is an interior point, it follows by Lemma 7.19 that there is $\pi : A \to \mathbb{Z}/2\mathbb{Z}$ such that $y \in P_\pi \cap \mathrm{Fix}(a')$. It follows that $\pi(a') = 0$.

It is left to note that if $\cup_{\pi:\pi(a')=0} P_\pi$ accumulates on x then, since there are a finite number of such π, there is π such that $\pi(a') = 0$ and P_π accumulates on x. □

Let $g \in G$ be an element of length m over the generating set $A \cup B$. We need to show that it has finite order, in particular that the g-orbit of any point in X is finite. To do so we first prove a preliminary lemma:

LEMMA 7.29. Let Σ be a interval in an orbital graph of a G-regular point, and let $\Delta \subset \Sigma$ be a subinterval of length m so that $\Sigma \setminus \Delta$ is the union of two intervals of lengths greater than m. Take a vertex $v \in \Delta$. There is a graph embedding ϕ of Σ into an orbital graph of G-regular point, and $k \geq 1$ so that $g^k \phi(v) \in \phi(\Delta)$.

PROOF. Note first that for any $w \in \Delta$ gw is determined by the edge labels of Σ, since the length of g is m and w is at distance at least m from both endpoints of Σ. Thus for any embedding ϕ we have $g\phi(w) = \phi(gw)$. By Corollary 7.26 there is an embedding ψ of Σ into Γ_x so that both x and the image of $\psi(gv)$ lie on the same side of $\psi(\Delta)$. Identify Γ_x with the subset $\{1\} \times \Gamma_x$ of $\Gamma_{(x)} = A/A_{(x)} \times \Gamma_x$, and consider the positive g-orbit of $\psi(v)$ in $\Gamma_{(x)}$, that is the set $\{g^k \psi(v) : k \geq 1\}$. It is either finite, in which case it will return to $\psi(\Delta)$, or infinite. In the latter case it must travel to infinity, that is, leave any finite subset of vertices. Note that gw is at distance at most m from w for any vertex w. Also note that the complement of $A/A_{(x)} \times \psi(\Delta)$ in $\Gamma_{(x)}$ is the union of two sets, finite and infinite, at distance $m + 1$ from each other. The finite set contains x and $g\psi(v)$ and thus for positive g-orbit of $\psi(v)$ to travel to infinity it must intersect some $a'A_{(x)} \times \psi(\Delta)$. Consider then $\pi : A \to \mathbb{Z}/2\mathbb{Z}$ from Lemma 7.29 such that $\pi(a') = 0$ and $x \in closure(P_\pi)$. It follows that in the graph $A/\ker(\pi) \times \Gamma_x$ the positive g-orbit of $\{1\} \times \psi(v)$ intersects $\{1\} \times \psi(\Delta)$. By Proposition 7.23 there is an orbital graph of a regular point that is arbitrarily close to $A/\ker(\pi) \times \Gamma_x$, hence a sufficiently close orbital graph contains a copy of Σ with the required properties. □

By repeatedly applying this lemma, we have the following:

LEMMA 7.30. There is an interval Δ of length m in an orbital graph of a regular point such that the g-orbit of Δ is finite.

PROOF. Let Δ be any interval of length m in an orbital graph, and let $v_0, \ldots, v_m$ be its vertices. Consider a large enough interval Σ that contains Δ, so that the previous lemma applies. It follows that there is a copy of Σ in some orbital graph of a regular point so that $g^k v_0 \in \Delta$ for some $k \geq 1$. Consider a large interval Σ_1 that contains an m-neighborhood of $v_0, \ldots, g^k v_0$. It follows that for any embedding ϕ of Σ_1 we will have $\phi(g^i v_0) = g^i \phi(v_0)$, for $0 \leq i \leq k$. Hence in any copy of Σ_1 the positive g-orbit of v_0 will return to Δ. By iteration, we can then construct an interval Σ_m in some orbital graph of a regular point, so that Σ_m contains a copy of Δ and all positive orbits of $v_0, \ldots, v_m$ return to Δ in Σ_m. □

PROOF OF THEOREM 7.27. Consider a G-regular point z and its orbital graph Γ_z. Let Δ be the interval in some orbital graph as in the previous lemma and take Σ to be the interval that contains the m-neighborhood of the g-orbit of Δ. By Proposition 7.17 on both sides of z in Γ there is a copy of Σ at the distance at most $R(m)$ from z. Note that the g-orbit of both copies of Δ in Γ_z is finite, since it is determined by the edge labels of Σ. It follows that the g-orbit of z is also finite, since otherwise it must intersect one of the two copies of Δ. Moreover, its size is at most $2(R(m) + |\Sigma|)$. Thus any regular point has a g-orbit of uniformly bounded size. It follows that there is $n \geq 1$ such that g^n fixes every regular point. Since they are dense in X, $g^n = 1$. $\qquad\square$

Intermediate Growth and inverted orbits.

DEFINITION 7.31. Let $G = \langle S \rangle$ act on a set X, and let $w = g_1 \cdots g_n$ be a word over S. We define the *inverted orbit* of $x \in X$ under w as
$$O_x(w) = \{g_1(x), g_1 g_2(x), \ldots, g_1 \ldots g_n(x)\}.$$

Let $w = g_1 \cdots g_n$ be a word over S. Set $h_t = g_1 \cdots g_t \in G$. A pair (i, j) with $i < j$ is a *first return* of x in w if $h_j x = h_i x$ but $h_j x \neq h_k x$ for $i < k < j$. The number $j - i$ is the *length* of the first return (i, j).

LEMMA 7.32. The number of first returns of x in $g_1 \cdots g_n$ is $n - |O_x(g_1 \cdots g_n)|$.

PROOF. Denote $h_t = g_1 \cdots g_t \in G$. Let $y \in O_x$, and suppose that $i_1 < i_2 < \cdots < i_k$ are the list of all indices such that $y = h_{i_1} x = \cdots = h_{i_k} x$. It follows that (i_{j-1}, i_j) is a first return of x and there are $k - 1$ of them for y. Thus the number of first returns associated to y plus one is k. Summing over all $y \in O_x$ we obtain that the number of first returns plus $|O_x|$ is n. $\qquad\square$

We define $\nu_x(n)$ as $\sup_{w:|w|=n} |O_x(w)|$. The function ν_x is clearly a nondecreasing function. Note also that since $O_x(wv) = O_x(w) \cup wO_x(v)$ we have that $|O_x(wv)| \leq |O_x(w)| + |O_x(v)|$ and thus $\nu_x(n + m) \leq \nu_x(n) + \nu_x(m)$.

We will use the following property of such functions:

LEMMA 7.33. Let $f : \mathbb{N} \to (0, \infty)$ be a nondecreasing subadditive ($f(n+m) \leq f(n) + f(m)$ for all $n, m \geq 1$) function. Then $s < l$ implies that $f(l)/l \leq 2f(s)/s$.

PROOF. Define $f(0) = 0$. Then let $l = rs + q$ for $0 \leq q < s$. We have $f(q) \leq f(s)$ and so
$$f(l) \leq rf(s) + f(q) \leq (r + 1)f(s),$$
thus
$$\frac{f(l)}{l} \leq \frac{(r+1)s}{l} \frac{f(s)}{s} \leq 2\frac{f(s)}{s}.$$
$\qquad\square$

LEMMA 7.34. Let $\delta : \mathbb{N} \to (0, \infty)$ be such that $s < l$ implies $\delta(l) \leq 2\delta(s)$, and for any $n, m \geq 1$
$$\delta(mn) \leq \rho\delta(n) + \frac{C}{m}$$
for some constants $0 < \rho < 1$ and C. Then $\delta(n) \leq C'e^{-C''\sqrt{\ln n}}$ for some constants $C', C'' > 0$ and for all $n \geq 1$.

PROOF. Let $k = \lfloor \sqrt{\ln n} \rfloor$ be the largest integer smaller than or equal to $\sqrt{\ln n}$, and let $m = \lfloor e^{\sqrt{\ln n}} \rfloor$. We have that
$$\delta(m^k) \leq \rho\delta(m^{k-1}) + \frac{C}{m} \leq \rho^2\delta(m^{k-2}) + (1+\rho)\frac{C}{m} \leq \cdots \leq$$
$$\leq \rho^k\delta(1) + (1 + \rho + \cdots + \rho^{k-1})\frac{C}{m} \leq \frac{\delta(1)}{\rho}e^{-\ln\rho^{-1}\sqrt{\ln n}} + \frac{2C}{1-\rho}e^{-\sqrt{\ln n}} \leq$$
$$C'e^{-C''\sqrt{\ln n}},$$

where $C'' = \min\left(1, \ln \rho^{-1}\right)$ and $C' = \delta(1)/\rho + 2C/(1 - \rho)$. Since $m^k \leq n$, we then obtain

$$\delta(n) \leq 2\delta(m^k) \leq 2C'e^{-C''\sqrt{\ln n}}.$$

$\square$

Linearly repetitive actions. An action of the group $G = \langle S \rangle$ is *linearly repetitive* if the function $R(r)$ from Proposition 7.17 is linear (this also implies that the function $R_1(r) = R(2R(r) + 1)$ from Corollary 7.26 is linear). Denote by L the constant such that for any $z \in X$ the ball af radius Ln in Γ_z contains all a copy of an interval I of an orbital graph, whenever $|I| \leq 2n + 1$.

Let now $G = \langle S \rangle$, $S = A \cup B$, be a fragmentation of an action of D_∞ on X.

PROPOSITION 7.35. *If the action of G on X is linearly repetitive and there is a purely G-singular point, then there are $C', C'' > 0$ such that for any $y \in X$ we have $\nu_y(n) \leq C'e^{-C''\sqrt{\ln n}}$.*

PROOF. Let x be a purely singular point. Without loss of generality, we may suppose that $x \in \mathrm{Fix}(a)$. Let $P_0, \ldots, P_{d-1}$ be the pieces of A that accumulate on x. We will also use the notation that $P_k := P_{k \bmod d}$ for any k.

We think of the graph Γ_x as a horizontal ray with the left endpoint being x. In this way, any subinterval of Γ_x has a defined orientation, so we can unambiguously talk about it's left and right ends. We construct a sequence Z_k of intervals of orbital graphs as follows. Each Z_k will be a left subinterval of Γ_x (Recall that we do not include the loops at endpoints when we consider subintervals of orbital graphs). Take Z_0 to be any such subinterval. If Z_k is constructed, consider the subinterval $Z_k^- \xrightarrow{P_k} Z_k$ of $\Gamma_x^- \xrightarrow{P_k} \Gamma_x$, which is a sequence of regular orbital graphs by the Proposition 7.23. Thus there is a copy of $Z_k^- \xrightarrow{P_k} Z_k$ in the $L|Z_k|$ neighborhood of x in Γ_x (Note that we don't have to worry about the orientation of that copy, since $Z_k^- \xrightarrow{P_k} Z_k$ is symmetric). We then take Z_{k+1} to be the left subinterval of Γ_x that starts with x and ends with this copy. Note that Z_k is both a left and right subinterval of Z_{k+1}.

We need the following lemma

LEMMA 7.36. *Suppose a word $w = g_1 \cdots g_s$ labels a path γ in $Z_k^- \xrightarrow{P_k} Z_k$, that starts at one end of it and ends at the other end. Then there is a $k - d \leq k' < k$ and a subword w' of w such that one of the two options hold:*

(a) *The path in $Z_{k'}^- \xrightarrow{P_{k'}} Z_{k'}$ that starts at an endpoint and is labelled by w' is a closed path that passes through all vertices of $Z_{k'}$. The subpath of the initial path γ, which corresponds to w', then ends at the right end of $Z_{k'}$ (considered as the left subinterval of the second Z_k in $Z_k^- \xrightarrow{P_k} Z_k$).*

(b) *The path in Z_k that starts at x and is labelled by w' is a closed path that passes through all vertices of $Z_{k'}$ (the left subinterval of Z_k.) In this case the subpath of the initial path γ, which corresponds to w', ends at one of the two vertices of the edge P_k in $Z_k^- \xrightarrow{P_k} Z_k$.*

PROOF. Let $\pi_k : A \to \mathbb{Z}/2\mathbb{Z}$ be such that $P_k = P_{\pi_k}$. Consider the covering map

$$\phi_k : \Gamma_{(x)} \to \Gamma_{(x)}/\ker \pi_k = \Gamma_x^- \xrightarrow{P_k} \Gamma_x.$$

Recall that the set of vertices of $\Gamma_{(x)}$ is $A/A_{(x)} \times \Gamma_x$. We will denote by $\tilde{Z}_k$ the induced subgraph of $\Gamma_{(x)}$ with the set of vertices $A/A_{(x)} \times Z_k$. Then we have the covering map (which we denote by ϕ_k again)

$$\phi_k : \tilde{Z}_k \to Z_k^- \xrightarrow{P_k} Z_k.$$

Denote by γ the path in $Z_k^- \xrightarrow{P_k} Z_k$ that starts at the endpoint and is labelled by $w = g_1 \cdots g_s$. Let $\tilde{\gamma}$ be the covering of γ that starts at the endpoint of $\{1\} \times Z_k$. Since γ ends at the other end of $Z_k^- \xrightarrow{P_k} Z_k$, it follows that $\tilde{\gamma}$ end at some $\{h\} \times Z_k$ with $h \notin \ker \pi_k$. Since x is a purely singular point, by the Lemma 7.28 there is $k' \in [k - d, k)$ such that $\pi_{k'}(h) = 0$. Note that $Z_{k'}$ is the left subinterval of Z_k. Consider the subgraph $A/A_{(x)} \times Z_{k'}$ of $A/A_{(x)} \times Z_k$. We clearly have two possibilities for the path $\tilde{\gamma}$. Either there is $h'' \in A$ such that some subpath of $\tilde{\gamma}$ enters the branch $\{h''\} \times Z_k$, travels farther then the right end of $\{h''\} \times Z_{k'}$, and then goes back to the beginning of $\{h''\} \times Z_k$, or there is no such h''. In the former case, part (b) of the statement of the Lemma holds. Suppose then that there is no such h''. It follows that the path $\tilde{\gamma}$ never leaves $A/A_{(x)} \times Z_{k'}$, except in the branches $\{1\} \times Z_k$ and $\{h'\} \times Z_k$. Consider now the covering map

$$\phi_{k'} : \tilde{Z}_k \to Z_k^- \xrightarrow{P_{k'}} Z_k.$$

Let γ' be the subpath of $\tilde{\gamma}$ that starts when $\tilde{\gamma}$ enters the branch $\{1\} \times Z_{k'}$ for the last time, and ends when it first leaves the branch $\{h'\} \times Z_k$. Then $\phi_{k'}(\gamma')$ satisfies part (a) of the statement of the Lemma. $\qquad\square$

Note that x is the left endpoint of all intervals Z_k, $k \geq 0$. Since the intervals Z_k are subintervals of orbital graphs of G, we can find G-regular points $z_k \in X$ such that (a copy of) Z_k is a subinterval in Γ_{z_k} with z_k as it's right endpoint. Since X is compact, we can assume that z_k converge to $z \in X$. Then either z is regular, in which case Γ_{z_k} converge to Γ_z by Lemma 7.15, or z is singular. In the latter case z is in the orbit of $\mathrm{Fix}(a) \cup \mathrm{Fix}(b)$, so assume $gz = w$ for $w \in \mathrm{Fix}(a)$ (the case $w \in \mathrm{Fix}(b)$ is similar). We can pass to a subsequence such that $g(z_k)$ belong to the same piece P of fragmentation A. Lemma 7.23 then implies that graphs Γ_{z_k} converge to $\Gamma_w/\ker \pi_P$.

In both cases Γ_{z_k} converge to a $A \cup B$-labelled bi-infinite graph that contains copies of Z_k with the same vertex as their right ends. We denote this vertex by y and the graph by Γ_y. Since Γ_y is a limit of Shreier graphs of G, it is itself a Shreier graph of G. Thus we can and will talk about action of G on (the set of vertices of) Γ_y, and the corresponding paths, inverted orbits and first returns of y.

The previous lemma then allows us to connect the inverted orbit of an arbitrary point $z \in X$ with the inverted orbits of x (our purely singular element of $\mathrm{Fix}(a)$) and y as follows.

LEMMA 7.37. For $z \in X$ and u and a word u over S, there are at least

$$\frac{1}{2d}\left(|O_z(u)| - 2L|Z_k|\right)$$

first returns of x and y in u of length bigger than $|Z_{k'}|$, for some k' so that $k - d \leq k' < k$.

PROOF. Suppose $u = g_1 \cdots g_N$. Let I_z be the interval in Γ_z of radius $L|Z_k|$, centered at z. Since the action is linearly repetitive, it follows that I_z contains a copy of $Z_k^- \xrightarrow{P_k} Z_k$. Moreover, if $\Gamma_z \setminus I_z$ has two connected components, then there are two such copies on both sides of z. Take now an element $g_1 \cdots g_l z \in O_z(u) \setminus I_z$. It follows that the path

$$z, \; g_l z, \; g_{l-1} g_l z, \; \ldots, \; g_1 \cdots g_l z$$

starts at z and ends at a point outside I_z, and hence it crosses one of the two copies of $Z_k^- \xrightarrow{P_k} Z_k$. Therefore there is a subpath γ (and a subword w of $g_1 \cdots g_l$ that labels γ) that goes from one end of $Z_k^- \xrightarrow{P_k} Z_k$ to the other end, staying inside the interval. Let now $k' \geq k - d$ and a subword w' of u be as in Lemma 7.36.

We now consider two possibilities. If the part (b) of that lemma holds, it means that w' labels at path in Γ_x that starts and ends at x and goes farther then the left subinterval $Z_{k'}$ of Γ_x. Note that by going to a subpath again, we can assume that this path is at x only at the beginning and end. That is, $w' = g_i \cdots g_j$ gives a first return (i, j) of x in u, of length bigger than $|Z_{k'}|$. In addition we must have that the part of the initial path in Γ_z, that is labelled by $g_l \ldots, g_i$, must end in one of the two vertices of P_k in one of the two copies of $Z_k^- \xrightarrow{P_k} Z_k$ in I_z. To summarize, each such element $g_1 \cdots g_l z \in O_z(u) \setminus I_z$ produces a first return of x of length bigger than $|Z_{k'}|$, and there are at most four such elements.

Suppose now that part (a) of Lemma 7.36 holds. The graph Γ_y contains a copy of Z_k with y as it's right endpoint. Since $k > k'$, $Z_{k'}^- \xrightarrow{P_{k'}} Z_{k'}$ is a right subinterval of Z_k. It follows that there is a copy of $Z_{k'}^- \xrightarrow{P_{k'}} Z_{k'}$ in Γ_y, with y as it's right endpoint. Hence the subword w' labels a closed path in Γ_y that starts and ends at y, and goes farther then $Z_{k'}$. It follows as in part (b) that there is a subword $g_i \cdots g_j$ of u that gives a first return (i, j) of y in u, of length bigger than $|Z_{k'}|$. In addition we have that the the part of the initial path in Γ_z that is labeled by $g_l, \ldots, g_i$ must end in the right end of Z_k, where Z_k is the right one in a copy of $Z_k^- \xrightarrow{P_k} Z_k$ in Γ_z. Since $k - d \leq k' < k$, and we consider two copies of $Z_k^- \xrightarrow{P_k} Z_k$ in I_z, it follows that each such element $g_1 \cdots g_l z \in O_z(u) \setminus I_z$ produces a first return of y of length bigger than $|Z_{k'}|$, and there are at most $2d$ such elements.

To summarize, each element in $O_z(u) \setminus I_z$ produces a first return of x or y of length at least $|Z_{k'}|$, and each such first return is produced by at most $2d$ elements. It is left to note that $|O_z(u) \setminus I_z| \geq |O_z(u)| - 2L|Z_k|$. $\qquad \square$

Let now $u = g_1 \cdots g_{mn}$ be a word over S of length mn, and suppose $z \in X$, or $z = y$. We have that $nm - |O_z(u)|$ is equal to the number of first returns of z in u. Let r_z be the number of such returns of length less than or equal to n, and let R_z be the number of such returns of length greater than n. Thus we have $|O_z(u)| = nm - r_z - R_z$. We can now write $u = u_1 \ldots u_m$, where each word u_i has length n. Then we also have $|O_z(u_i)| = n - r_i$, with r_i the number of first returns of z in u_i. Since any such first return is also a first return in u of length less than or equal to n, we have that $r_1 + \cdots + r_m \leq r_z$. It follows that

$$|O_z(u)| = nm - r_z - R_z \leq \sum_{i=1}^m |O_z(u_i)| - R_z \leq m\nu_z(n) - R_z.$$

Add together these inequalities for x and y:

$$(10) \qquad |O_x(u)| + |O_y(u)| \leq m(\nu_x(n) + \nu_y(n)) - (R_x + R_y),$$

where $R_x + R_y$ is the number of first returns of x and y longer than n. We can estimate it using Lemma 7.37 is we choose k appropriately. Note that by construction of Z_{k+1}, since it is the smallest left subinterval of Γ_x that contains $Z_k^- \xrightarrow{P_k} Z_k$, we have that $|Z_{k+1}| \le L|Z_k|$ by linear repetitiveness. Choose the smallest k so that $|Z_{k-d}| > n$. It follows that $|Z_{k-d}| \le Ln$. We then have for any $k - d \le k' < k$ that $|Z_{k'}| > n$ and $|Z_k| \le L_1 n$, for $L_1 = L^d$. Lemma 7.37 now implies that

$$(11) \qquad R_x + R_y \ge \frac{1}{2d}\left(|O_z(u)| - L_1 n\right)$$

Adding these inequalities for $z = x, y$ we get

$$R_x + R_y \ge \frac{1}{4d}\left(|O_x(u)| + |O_y(u)| - 2L_1 n\right)$$

Thus inequality (10) gives

$$|O_x(u)| + |O_y(u)| \le \frac{4d}{4d+1} m(\nu_x(n) + \nu_y(u)) + L_2 n$$

Taking the supremum over all words u of length nm, and setting $\nu = \nu_x + \nu_y$, we obtain

$$\nu(nm) \le \rho m \nu(n) + L_3 n$$

with $\rho = 4d/(4d+1) < 1$ and $L_3 = 4dL_2/(4d+1)$. Finally, divining by nm and denoting $\delta(n) = \nu(n)/n$,

$$\delta(nm) \le \rho \delta(n) + \frac{C}{m}$$

for $n, m \ge 1$ and $C = L_3$. Lemma 7.34 now implies that

$$\nu(n) \le C' n e^{-C'' \sqrt{\ln n}}$$

for some $C', C'' > 0$.

Take now any $z \in X$. Inequalities (10) and (11) together imply that

$$\frac{1}{2d}\left(|O_z(u)| - L_1 n\right) \le R_x + R_y \le m\nu(n)$$

Therefore we have

$$\nu_z(nm) \le 2dm\,\nu(n) + Cn$$

and so

$$\delta_z(nm) \le 2d\,\delta(n) + \frac{C}{m}$$

for $\delta_z(n) = \nu_z(n)/n$, $n, m \ge 1$ and $C = L_1$.

For any integer $k \ge 1$ take the largest integer n so that $n^2 \le k < (n+1)^2$. It follows that, by Lemma 7.33

$$\delta_z(k) \le 2\delta_z(n^2) \le 2dC' e^{-C'' \sqrt{\ln n}} + \frac{C}{n} \le C_1' e^{-C'' \sqrt{\ln n}} \le C_1' e^{-C_1'' \sqrt{\ln k}}$$

for some constants $C_1', C_1'' > 0$. $\qquad \square$

We will now again use linear repetitiveness to show that the growth of G is slower than exponential. Note that any g is determined by its action on X, that is, by the $|g|$-neighborhood of z in the orbital graph Γ_z, for all $z \in X$. By linear repetitiveness, a copy of any such orbit sits in the $L|g|$-neighborhood of a fixed point $x \in X$, and we just have to count the number of such possibilities. This is the idea of the proof of the following.

THEOREM 7.38. Let $G = \langle A \cup B \rangle$ be a fragmentation of an action of D_∞ on X. Suppose the action of G on X is linear repetitive and has a purely singular point. Then G has subexponential growth.

PROOF. Take $x \in \mathrm{Fix}(a)$ to be the purely singular point (We could have used any fixed point of X instead, but it is more convenient to use a point whose orbital graph is the half-line). Let $L > 0$ be such that the ball of radius Ln in Γ_x, centered at x contain a copy of any orbital interval of length less than n. We will need the following lemma

LEMMA 7.39. There is a constant C (that depends on L) and a subset $T \subset \mathbb{N}$ such that for each $n \geq 2$ we have $|T \cap [1, Ln]| \leq C \ln n$. If I is any subinterval of $\mathbb{N} \cap [1, Lk)$, with $|I| = k$, for some $k \leq n$, then T has nonempty intersection with the set of interior points of I.

PROOF. Let $\alpha = 1 + 1/2L$, and $T = \{\lfloor \alpha^k \rfloor \mid k \geq 0\}$. Note that if $\alpha^k < Ln$ then

$$\alpha^{k+1} - \alpha^k < Ln(\alpha - 1) = n/2 < n - 1 \text{ for } n \geq 2.$$

Therefore the distance between two consecutive points in $T \cap [1, Ln)$ is less than or equal to $n - 1$. Thus if $|I| = n$ and $I \subset \mathbb{N} \cap [1, Ln)$, then $T \cap I$ is not empty. The number of elements in T_n is no more than

$$\frac{\ln(Ln)}{\ln(\alpha)} \leq C \ln(n), \text{ for } n \geq 2$$

for some C that depends on L.   □

For a G-regular point $z \in X$ and $g = g_1 \cdots g_n \in S^n$ consider the path

$$z, g_n z, \ldots, g_1 \cdots g_n z$$

in Γ_z. Take the smallest subinterval I in Γ_z that contains all of these points as interior points. We have that $|I| = k \leq n + 2$. It follows that there is a copy I' of I in the graph Γ_x at distance at most Lk from x. If z' and w' are the corresponding copies of z and $g(z)$, it follows that $g(z') = w'$. Thus the triple I', z', w' encodes the action of g on z. Thus the list of all such triples will encode the action of g on X. Let us first figure out how many triples like that there are for a fixed word $g = g_1 \cdots g_n$. Note that z' determined the triple if $g = g_1 \cdots g_n$ is known, since then $w' = g(z')$ and I' is the smallest subinterval that contains inside the path from z' to w' labelled by g. Now, Γ_x as a metric space is isomorphic to $\mathbb{N}$. Consider the image of the set T from the above lemma. We will call it T again for simplicity. It follows from the lemma that that there is an element $t \in T$ which is an interior point of I'. It follows that $t = g_i \cdots g_n z'$, thus $z' = g_n \cdots g_i t$ and so $z' \in O_t(g_n \cdots g_1)$. Since I' is at distance at most $n + 2$ from x, it follows that $t \in T \cap [1, L(n + 2))$. Lemma 7.39 and Proposition 7.35 now imply that there are at most $Cn \ln(n) e^{-C'\sqrt{\ln(n)}}$ possibilities for z', for some constants C, C'. Therefore, for each fixed $g = g_1 \cdots g_n$ there are at most $Cn \ln(n) e^{-C'\sqrt{\ln(n)}}$ triples I', z', w' that define g.

Let us now estimate the number of such lists. Since each such list determines an element $g \in G$ of length n over S, this will also provide an estimate on the number of such elements of G.

Each such list consists of at most $Cn \ln(n) e^{-C'\sqrt{\ln(n)}}$ triples I', z', w', where $z', w' \in I'$, and I' is a subinterval of Γ_x of length at most $n + 2$ and at distance at most $L(n + 2)$ from x. There are at most $L(n + 2)^2$ such subintervals I', and there are $(n+2)^2$ choices for $z', w' \in I'$. Thus the number of possible triples is less than $L(n+2)^4 \leq C_1 n^4$, for some constant C_1. The number of such lists is then no more than

$$a_n = (C_1 n^4)^{Cn \ln(n) e^{-C'\sqrt{\ln(n)}}}$$

It suffices to check that $\ln(a_n)/n$ tends to 0. Indeed,

$$\frac{\ln(a_n)}{n} = \frac{4C(\ln(n))^2}{e^{C'\sqrt{\ln n}}} + \frac{4C \ln(n) \ln C_1}{e^{C'\sqrt{\ln n}}}$$

and $(\ln n)^2 / e^{C'\sqrt{\ln n}}$ tends to 0.

This shows that G has a growth slower than exponential. On the other hand G is infinite finitely generated and periodic by Theorem 7.27, and so cannot have polynomial growth be the theorem of Gromov. Indeed, otherwise it would be a finitely generated virtually nilpotent group which is periodic, but all such groups are finite. □

6. Examples

In this section we construct an example of a simple finitely generated group of intermediate growth. We start with the following

Examples of infinite torsion groups. Let K be an alphabet, and consider $K^{\mathbb{Z}}$. Define the homeomorphisms a, b of $K^{\mathbb{Z}}$ by the rule $a(w)(n) = w(1-n)$ and $b(w)(n) = w(-n)$ for all $n \in \mathbb{Z}$. Note that $a^2 = b^2 = 1$ is a trivial map. We also have that $ba = \sigma$ is the shift $\sigma(w)(n) = w(n+1)$. It follows that $\langle a, b \rangle = D$. The action of D on $K^{\mathbb{Z}}$ is not minimal, so we can consider some minimal D-invariant subset $X \subset K^{\mathbb{Z}}$.

PROPOSITION 7.40. Let (D, X) be a minimal action on a Cantor set X, and $x \in \text{Fix}(a)$. Then there is a fragmentation A of a such that x is a purely singular point for the group $G = \langle A \cup \{b\} \rangle$.

PROOF. Let U_n be a decreasing sequence of clopen neighborhoods of x, such that $\cap U_n = \{x\}$. Then $V_n = U_n \cap a U_n$ is a decreasing sequence of clopen a-invariant subsets with $\cap V_n = \{x\}$. By discarding some elements we can assume that each V_{n+1} is a proper subset of V_n. Let $W_n = V_n \setminus V_{n+1}$. Suppose $I_1, \ldots, I_k$ is a partition of $\mathbb{N}$ into k infinite sets. Define for each $1 \leq j \leq k$ sets $P_j = \cup_{n \in I_j} W_n$. Note that P_j's are disjoint a-invariant and open, and the closure of each P_j is $P_j \cup \{x\}$. Let also P_0 be the complement of $\cup_{1 \leq j \leq k} P_j$. Clearly P_0 is clopen and a-invariant. For $0 \leq i \leq k$ define a_i to be a on P_i and 1 on the complement. Let A_0 be the group generated by all a_i. We have that A_0 is a fragmentation of a and that it is isomorphic to $(\mathbb{Z}/2\mathbb{Z})^{k+1}$, so we can identify both groups. Let also $\pi_i, 0 \leq i \leq k$ be the coordinate projections of A_0. Consider now a subgroup A of $(\mathbb{Z}/2\mathbb{Z})^{k+1}$ such that for any i there is $a' \in A$ with $\pi_i(a') = 0$, and so that for any $a' \in A$ there is $1 \leq j \leq k$ with $\pi_j(a') = 0$. Then x is a purely G-singular point for $G = \langle A \cap \{b\} \rangle$ by Lemma 7.28. □

Note that there are plenty of such subgroups of $(\mathbb{Z}/2\mathbb{Z})^{k+1}$. Indeed, if $k = 3$, then we can take a subgroup of $(\mathbb{Z}/2\mathbb{Z})^4$ generated by $(1,1,1,0)$, $(1,1,0,1)$ and $(1,0,1,1)$. Thus if we start with a minimal $D = \langle a, b \rangle$-invariant closed subset of $K^{\mathbb{Z}}$ that contains a fixed point of a or b, then there are lots of fragmentations of D that are infinite torsion groups.

Intermediate growth group.

Linearly repetitive subshifts. Let K be a finite set. A subset $X \subset K^{\mathbb{Z}}$ which is closed and shift invariant is called a *subshift*. We call X *linearly repetitive* if there is a number L such that the following holds. For any $u, w \in X$ and finite subwords $u_1 \leq u$ and $w_1 \leq w$, then w_1 contains a copy of u_1 as long as $|w_1| \geq L|u_1|$.

THEOREM 7.41. *Suppose X is a linearly repetitive subshift which is $\langle a, b \rangle$-invariant. Let $G = \langle A \cup B \rangle$ be a fragmentation which has purely singular points and with linearly repetitive orbital graphs. Then $Alt(G)$ is a finitely generated simple periodic group of intermediate growth.*

PROOF. The group $Alt(G)$ is simple by Theorem 7.7 and finitely generated by Theorem 7.12. Since $Alt(G)$ is a finitely generated subgroup of $S(G)$, and G is generated by set $A \cup B$ whose elements have order two, we can apply Proposition 7.4. That is, for each $a' \in A$ there is an a'-invariant clopen partition $\mathcal{P}_{a'}$ and for each $b' \in B$ a b'-invariant clopen partition $\mathcal{P}_{b'}$ as in Proposition 7.4. Recall that if $Q \in \mathcal{P}_{a'}$ then $\tau_{a',Q}$ is the homeomorphism that is a' on Q and 1 on Q^c. Define A_1 to be the set of all such $\tau a', Q$. Note that A_1 is also a fragmentation of a. Similarly define B_1 to be a fragmentation of b. Proposition 7.4 then implies that the group $G_1 = \langle A_1 \cup B_1 \rangle$ contains $Alt(G)$. Thus it suffices to show that G_1 has intermediate growth.

Since G_1 is a fragmentation of $\langle a, b \rangle$ we can use Theorem 7.38. It is easy to check, using the fact that all $Q \in \mathcal{P}_{a'}$ are clopen, that a purely singular point of G will be also purely singular for G_1. Thus it is left to show that the orbital graphs of $G_1 = \langle A_1 \cup B_1 \rangle$ are linearly repetitive.

Note that we can construct an orbital graph G_1 from G orbital graph as follows. If an edge from x is labelled by $a' \in A$ in G orbital graph, and $x \in Q \in \mathcal{P}_{a'}$ then we replace this label by $\tau_{a',Q}$ and we replace similarly b-labels. The obtained graph of an orbital graph of G_1. Note now that since partitions $\mathcal{P}_{a'}$ consist of clopen sets, then there is $m \in \mathbb{N}$ such that the finite subword $x_{[-m,m]}$ of $x \in X \subset K^{\mathbb{Z}}$ determined in which element Q of a partition x lies. Since X is a linearly repetitive subshift, it follows that the obtained G_1 orbital graph is also linearly repetitive. Thus G_1 and hence $Alt(G)$ has growth less than exponential. Since $Alt(G)$ is simple, it cannot have polynomial growth by Gromov theorem, and thus it has intermediate growth. Since $Alt(G) \leq G_1$ which is periodic, $Alt(G)$ is also periodic. $\qquad\square$

6.0.1. *Substitution dynamical systems.* Let us introduce several other notions. A special way to generate a subshift is as follows. Let K^* be the set of all nonempty words over the alphabet K. Consider a map $S : K \to K^*$. We can extend it to a map $S : K^* \to K^*$ by the rule

$$S(k_1 \ldots k_m) = S(k_1) \ldots S(k_m).$$

Fix a letter $e \in K$. Define $X = X_S \subset K^{\mathbb{Z}}$ as the set of all such w that any finite subword of w appears in some $S^n(e)$. Then X is clearly a subshift. The following theorem is a partial case of a theorem in [**50**]

THEOREM 7.42. *Suppose there is L such that for any n and any subword $u \leq S^n(e)$ with $|u| \geq L$ we have that u contain letter e. Then the dynamical system (X_S, σ) is minimal and linearly repetitive.*

We will also extend S to a continuous map $K^{\mathbb{Z}} \to K^{\mathbb{Z}}$ by the rule

$$S(\ldots k_{-1} k_0 k_1 \ldots) = \ldots S(k_{-1}) S(k_0) S(k_1) \ldots$$

where the first letter of $S(k_1)$ is on the first position. We will need the following:

LEMMA 7.43. *Let $Y \subset K^{\mathbb{Z}}$ be a subshift such that $S(Y) \subset Y$. Suppose also that Y contains a sequence with letter e in it. Then $X_S \subset Y$.*

PROOF. We have that there is $w \in Y$ that contain letter e. It follows that $S^m(w) \in S^m(Y) \subset Y$ contains a subword $S^m(e)$, for any m. Consider any element $w' \in X_S$. Let u_n be the subword of w' on the positions from $-n$ to n. There is m such that $u_n \leq S^m(e)$. Find $w_n \in Y$ that contains $S^m(e)$ and therefore contains u_n. By shifting it we may assume that we have found $w_n \in Y$ with a subword u_n on the positions from $-n$ to n. It follows that $w_n \to w'$ and hence $w' \in Y$. $\square$

An example. We first construct a specific action of D. If u and w are words, then $u \leq w$ means that u is a subword of w.

Consider the map $S : \{0,1\} \to \{0,1\}^*$ defined by $S(0) = 01$, $S(1) = 10$. It follows that S and the letter 0 satisfies the condition in the previous section, hence the Theorem 7.42 implies that the corresponding subshift $X \subset \{0,1\}^{\mathbb{Z}}$ is minimal.

We will first show that X is in fact invariant with respect to the action of $D = \langle a, b \rangle$. Note the following properties for any $v \in \{0,1\}^*$

$$\overline{S(v)} = S(\overline{v}), \quad S(v)^t = S(\overline{v}^t)$$

where $(v_1 \cdots v_m)^t = v_m \cdots v_1$ and $\overline{v}$ is obtained from v by flipping 0 and 1.

LEMMA 7.44. *X is invariant with respect to the action of $D = \langle a, b \rangle$ on $\{0,1\}^{\mathbb{Z}}$.*

PROOF. Since aw or bw are just the sequence w which is flipped and possibly shifted, it suffices to show that if $u \leq S^n(0)$, then $u^t \leq S^m(0)$ for some m. Note now that $S^{2n}(0)^t = S^{2n}(0)$ and $S^{2n+1}(0)^t = S^{2n+1}(1) \leq S^{2n+2}(0)$. $\square$

We will show that X is a disjoint union of $S(X)$ and $\sigma S(X)$. We need the following technical lemma:

LEMMA 7.45. *Let $u \leq S^n(0)$. Then there is a unique way to write $u = \varepsilon u' \eta$ with ε, η either from $\{0,1\}$ or empty, and $u' = S(v')$ for some $v' \leq S^{n-1}(0)$.*

PROOF. That such a way exists is obvious. Suppose it is not unique. This means that there is a subword $u'' \leq u$ such that 2-block of u'' do not coincide with the 2-blocks of u'. That means that there is a subword 01 or 10 in u', which is not the S-image of any letter of v'. Since the letters of v' are also mapped to 01 and 10 by S, it follows that $u' = 0101 \ldots 0101$ or $1010 \ldots 1010$. On the other hand since $u \leq S^n(0)$ it follows that $n \geq 2$ and then $S^n(0)$ must consist of 4-blocks $1001 = S^2(1)$ and $0110 = S^2(0)$. Neither $0101 \ldots 0101$ nor $1010 \ldots 1010$ contain such blocks, and so u cannot be a subword of any $S^n(0)$. $\square$

We will now show that

LEMMA 7.46. *$X = S(X) \coprod \sigma S(X)$. Hence $S(X)$ is a clopen set.*

PROOF. It will follow from the fact that any $w \in X$ can be written in a unique way as a sequence of 2-blocks u_j, with $u_j \in \{01, 10\}$, so that if $u_j = S(\varepsilon_j)$ then the sequence $\ldots \varepsilon_{-1} \varepsilon_0 \varepsilon_1 \ldots$ is also in X.

Uniqueness is proved as in Lemma 7.45. That is, if there are two ways to write w as a sequence of 2-blocks, then $w = \cdots 01010101 \cdots$, but it does not contain a subword 0110 or 1001, and so w cannot be in X.

To show existence, let $u \leq w$ be any finite subword. We have $u \leq S^n(0)$ for some n. By Lemma 7.45 $u = \varepsilon u'\eta$. with $u' = S(v')$. Take $u'' \leq w$ such that $u \leq u''$ and $u'' = u_1 u' u_2$ for some two blocks u_1, u_2. Since also $u'' \leq S^m(0)$ for some m, it follows that by uniqueness in Lemma 7.45 that $u'' = S(v'')$, and $v' \leq v''$. In this way, adding blocks on both sides of u, we can construct a suquence of words $u^{(n)}$ and $v^{(n)}$ such that $u^{(n)} = S(v^n)$ and $u^{(n)}$ increases to w.   □

We have the following easily checked properties for $w \in \{0,1\}^{\mathbb{Z}}$

$$S(\sigma w) = \sigma^2 S(w), \quad aS(w) = S(a\overline{w}).$$

Note that 00 is the middle of $S^2(00) = 01100110$. It follows that $S^{2n}(00)$ is in the middle of $S^{2n+2}(00)$. If we position $S^{2n+2}(00)$ at places from $-4^{n+1} + 1$ to 4^{n+1}, then the middle part $S^{2n}(00)$ will be positioned from $-4^n + 1$ to 4^n. It follows that there is a well defined limit $\lim_n S^{2n}(00)$ in X. There is similarly defined $\lim_n S^{2n}(11)$.

LEMMA 7.47. $\mathrm{Fix}(a) = \{\lim_n S^{2n}(00), \lim_n S^{2n}(11)\}$ and $\mathrm{Fix}(b) = \emptyset$.

PROOF. Supppose $w \in \mathrm{Fix}(b)$. That means that there is a finite word $u \leq w$ of odd length such that $u^t = u$. By Lemma 7.45 we have that u can be written uniquely as $u = u'\varepsilon$ or $u = \varepsilon u'$, with $\varepsilon \in \{0,1\}$ and $u' = S(v')$, with $v' \leq S^{n-1}(0)$. Suppose $u = u'\varepsilon$. We then have $u'\varepsilon = u = u^t = \varepsilon u'^t$, and $u'^t = S(v')^t = S(\overline{v'}^t)$. This is contradiction to the uniqueness in Lemma 7.45.

Suppose now $w = aw$. We have that X is the disjoint union of $S(X)$ and $\sigma S(X)$. We have that $w \in S(X)$. Indeed, otherwise $w = \sigma S(u)$. If $u_0 = 0$ it means that $w_0 w_1 = 01$, which contradicts $aw = w$, and the same for $u_0 = 1$.

Thus $w = S(u)$. Note that $w = aw = aS(u) = S(a\overline{u})$ thus by injectivity of S we have $u = a\overline{u}$. We now have that also $u \in S(X)$. Indeed, otherwise $u = \sigma S(v)$ and then (recall that $\sigma = ba$)

$$u = a\overline{u} = a\sigma S(\overline{v}) = \sigma^{-1} aS(\overline{v}) = \sigma^{-1} S(av) = \sigma S(\sigma^{-1} av).$$

Thus $v = \sigma^{-1} av$ and so $v = bv$, thus v is in $\mathrm{Fix}(b)$ which is impossible.

We have established that $w = S^2(u)$ for some $u \in X$. Note now that $w = aw = aS^2(u) = S^2(au)$, and so $au = u$, hence $u \in \mathrm{Fix}(b)$. It follows that for any n there is $u_n \in X$ with $w = S^{2n}(u_n)$. Since $aw = w$ the pair on positions $0, 1$ of w is either 00 or 11. If it is 00, then it is 00 for all u_n. Hence w coincides with $S^{2n}(00)$ on the positions from -4^n to 4^n and so $w = \lim_n S^{2n}(00)$. The other possibility is that $w = \lim_n S^{2n}(11)$.   □

We now construct a fragmentation of a. Let $T = S^2$, and note that $aT = Ta$. Denote by $X_{\varepsilon\eta}$ the subset of X with ε at the 0th position and η at the 1st position.

LEMMA 7.48. The set $X_{00} \cup X_{11} \setminus \mathrm{Fix}(a)$ can be decomposed as a disjoint union $\coprod_{i=0}^2 P_i$ with the sets P_i open and a-invariant. Additionally, $T(P_i) \subset P_{i+1}$ (addition mod three), $T(P) \subset P$, $\sigma T(X) \cup \sigma^3 T(X) \subset P$ and $\sigma^2 T(X) \subset P_0$. The closure of each P_i is $P_i \cup \mathrm{Fix}(a)$.

PROOF. Let u and w be the two fixed points of a, so that $u \in X_{00}$ and $w \in X_{11}$. It is easy to check that $T(X_{00}) \subset X_{00}$, thus the sequence $T^n(X_{00})$ is decreasing sequence. Clearly $\cap_n T^n(X_{00}) = \{\lim_n S^{2n}(00)\}$. Similarly, $\cap_n T^n(X_{11}) = \{\lim_n S^{2n}(11)\}$. As in Proposition 7.40 let $V_n = T^n(X_{00} \cup X_{11})$ and $W_n = V_n \setminus V_{n+1}$.

Then $T(W_n) = W_{n+1}$. Denote by $P_i = \cup_{k \geq 0} W_{3k+i}$, for $i = 0, 1, 2$. We then have that $T(P_i) \subset P_{i+1}$.

It is easy to check that $T(P) = P$ and $\sigma T(X) \cup \sigma^3 T(X) \subset P$. Since $\sigma^2 T(X)$ is disjoint from $T(X)$ and hence from P, it follows that $\sigma^2 T(X)$ is in $V_0 = X_{00} \cup X_{11}$. However $V_1 \subset T(X)$ and so in fact $\sigma^2 T(X) \subset W_0 \subset P_0$. □

We have that sets P, P_0, P_1, P_2 are all a-invariant and partition $X \setminus \mathrm{Fix}(a)$. Let a' be a on P and 1 outside it. Let also a_i be a on $P_{i+1} \cup P_{i+2}$ and 1 outside it, for $i = 0, 1, 2$ (addition mod three). The group A is generated by a', a_0, a_1, a_2. It follows just as in Proposition 7.40 that both points in $\mathrm{Fix}(a)$ are purely singular for $G = \langle A \cup \{b\} \rangle = \langle a', a_0, a_1, a_2, b \rangle$.

PROPOSITION 7.49. *If $G = \langle a', a_0, a_1, a_2, b \rangle$ then the action of G on X is linearly repetitive with a purely singular point.*

PROOF. Recall that the action of G is linearly repetitive if there is a constant L such that if I is a subinterval of an orbital graph then for any $x \in X$ the $L|I|$ neighborhood of x in Γ_x contains a copy of I. Using Proposition 7.23 we can assume both that I is a subinterval of a regular orbital graph and that x is a regular point.

That is, it will suffice to show the following. There is $L > 0$ such that if I, I' are subintervals of regular orbital graphs and $|I'| \geq L|I|$ then I' contains a copy of I.

Let $\mathcal{P} = \{P, \overline{P}_i \mid 0 \leq i \leq 2\}$ be the set of closures of pieces of fragmentation of A. Let $Y \subset \mathcal{P}^{\mathbb{Z}}$ be the set of such sequences $(Q_j)_{j \in \mathbb{Z}}$ that there is x with $\sigma^j(x) \in Q_{j+1}$, for all $j \in \mathbb{Z}$. If x is a regular point, then there is a unique element of Y that corresponds to it, which we will denote by $\phi(x)$. Note that $\phi(x)$ determines the labels of the orbital graph of x. Indeed, we obtain the labels of Γ_x by inserting b between every letter of $\phi(x)$. It follows that in order to show that G is linearly repetitive it suffices to show that the set Y is linearly repetitive.

It is easy to see that Y is a subshift. Moreover, Y is minimal since X is minimal. Consider now the map $\mathcal{P} \to \mathcal{P}^*$, which we also denote T, given by

$$T(P) = PPP_0P, \quad T(P_i) = P_{i+1}PP_0P$$

and consider the corresponding extension $T : \mathcal{P}^{\mathbb{Z}} \to \mathcal{P}^{\mathbb{Z}}$. We have that $\phi(Tx) = T\phi(x)$.

Indeed, let x be a regular point. We have by Lemma 7.48 that $\sigma T(x) \in P$, $\sigma^2 T(x) \in P_0$ and $\sigma^3 T(x) \in P$. That is the second, third and fourth letters of $\phi(Tx)$ are PP_0P. Is it left to note that if $x \in P$ then $T(x) \in P$, and if $x \in P_i$ then $T(x) \in P_{i+1}$. Since ϕ is shift equivariant, it follows that $\phi(Tx) = T\phi(x)$.

We deduce that $T(Y) \subset Y$. Since Y is minimal, we have by Lemma 7.43 and Theorem 7.42 that Y is linearly repetitive (take $e = P$ and $L = 2$). □

If follows from Theorem 7.41 that $Alt(\langle a', a_0, a_1, a_2, b \rangle)$ is a finitely generated simple periodic group of intermediate growth.

CHAPTER 8

An amenability criterion via actions

In this chapter we present one more amenability criterion, which found a lot of applications to classes of groups defined via actions on certain spaces. Firstly we give a group-theoretical version of the criterion due to Stefaan Vaes, and then we deduce a topological version as a corollary due to Nekrashevych, de la Salle and the author. The topological version will be used to deduce amenability of groups acting on Bratteli diagrams in Chapter 9.

1. Group theoretical version of the criteria

THEOREM 8.1. Let G be finitely generated group generated by a finite symmetric set S. Suppose it acts on two countable sets Y, X and the action of G on X is extensively amenable. Assume that there exists a G-map $\pi : Y \to X$ with a section $t : X \to Y$ which satisfies the following properties:

(1) for every $g \in G$, the set $\{x \in X : t(gx) \neq gt(x)\}$ is finite;
(2) for every $x \in X$, the quotient G_x/N_x is amenable, where

$$N_x = \{g \in G_x : \text{ for all } y \in \pi^{-1}(x) : gy = y\} \trianglelefteq G_x,$$

where G_x is the stabilizer of x;
(3) the group $H = \{g \in G_x : t(gy) = gt(y) \text{ for all } y \in X\}$ is amenable.

Then G is amenable.

PROOF. The aim is to apply Theorem 2.21 to the following space:

$$\mathcal{Z} := \{\phi : X \to Y \mid \phi \text{ is a section map of } \pi,$$
$$\phi(x) = t(x) \text{ for all but finitely many } x \in X\}.$$

Indeed, the group G acts on $\mathcal{Z}$ by $(g\phi)(x) = g\phi(g^{-1}x)$. Since t is almost a G-map we have that $g\phi$ is in $\mathcal{Z}$. The proof will be divided into two parts. Both claims together with Lemma 2.21 imply that G is amenable.

CLAIM 1. The action of G on $\mathcal{Z}$ has amenable stabilizers.

Note that, if G has a non-amenable subgroup K, then for all $x \in X$ we have that $K \cap N_x$ is not amenable. Indeed, by Lemma 5.3 and Theorem 2.21 the action of K on $K.x$ has an invariant mean. Thus by Theorem 2.21 the group $K \cap G_x$ can not be amenable. Then $K \cap N_x$ is not amenable, since it is the kernel of the homomorphism $K \cap G_x \to G_x/N_x$ and G_x/N_x is amenable.

To reach a contradiction, assume that G_ϕ is not amenable for some ϕ. Let $V = \{x_1, \ldots, x_n\}$ be the finite set for which $\phi(x) \neq t(x)$. Then by induction we see that $K = G_\phi \cap N_{x_1} \cap \ldots \cap N_{x_n}$ is not amenable. In order to reach a contradiction it is sufficient to show that K is a subgroup of an amenable group H. To prove the later we need to show that for all $x \in X$ and $g \in K$ we have that $t(gx) = gt(x)$. Note that g fixes all elements of V. Therefore if x is in V we have $gt(x) = t(x) = t(gx)$. Now assume that x is not in V, then gx is not in V. Thus $\phi(x) = t(x)$ and $\phi(gx) = t(gx)$. Moreover, since $g \in G_\phi$ we have $\phi(gx) = g\phi(x)$. All together gives us $t(gx) = \phi(gx) = g\phi(x) = gt(x)$. Therefore K is a subgroup of H which gives a contradiction.

CLAIM 2. The action of G on $\mathcal{Z}$ is amenable.

Firstly we will show that there are probability measures $\nu_{x,n} \in l_1(Y)$ with finite support in $\pi^{-1}(x)$, such that

$$(12) \qquad \lim_n \|\nu_{gx,n} - g\nu_{x,n}\|_1 = 0 \text{ for all } x \in X, g \in G.$$

Let $T \subset X$ be a G-orbit transversal of the action on X, i.e. the set which contains one point from each orbit of G. For every $x \in T$ choose $L_x \subset G$ such that the map from L_x into G_x defined by $g \mapsto gx$ is bijective.

In general, if $H_1 < H_2 < \Gamma$ then taking the push-forward of the map $\Gamma/H_1 \to \Gamma/H_2$, we obtain that amenability of the action of Γ on Γ/H_1 implies amenability of the action of Γ on Γ/H_2. Therefore, since G_x/N_x is amenable and N_y stabilizers all points of $\pi^{-1}(x)$, the action of G_x on $\pi^{-1}(x)$ is amenable. Thus we can find probability measures $\nu_{x,n} \in l_1(\pi^{-1}(x))$ with finite support such that

$$\lim \|\nu_{x,n} - g\nu_{x,n}\|_1 = 0 \text{ for all } x \in T, g \in G_x.$$

Define a probability measure on Y for the G-orbits of x by $\nu_{gx,n} := g\nu_{x,n}$ for $x \in T$ and $g \in L_x$. Fix now $g \in G$ and $x' \in X$. We can express $x' = hx$ for some $x \in T$ and $h \in L_x$. Choose $k \in L_x$ such that $(gh)x = kx$. Then $k^{-1}gh$ belongs to G_x, thus applying the equality above to this element we obtain:

$$0 = \lim_n \|\nu_{x,n} - k^{-1}gh\nu_{x,n}\|_1 = \lim_n \|k\nu_{x,n} - gh\nu_{x,n}\|_1$$
$$= \lim_n \|\nu_{kx,n} - g\nu_{hx,n}\|_1 = \lim_n \|\nu_{gx',n} - g\nu_{x',n}\|_1.$$

Let now X' be a finite subset of X on the complement of which the map t is S-map, i.e. for all $x \in X \backslash X'$ and $s \in S$ we have $t(sx) = st(x)$. By Theorem 2.19 and the remarks following it, for every $\varepsilon > 0$ we can find a finitely supported measure $\mu \in l_1(\mathcal{P}_f(X))$ that satisfies

$$\|s\mu - \mu\|_1 < \varepsilon \text{ for all } s \in S$$

and such that its support is in the the set of all finite subsets of X which contain X'.

Let X_0 be the union of all finite sets in the support of μ. Choose n large enough so that

$$\|\nu_{sx,n} - g\nu_{x,n}\|_1 \le \varepsilon \text{ for all } x \in X_0 \text{ and } s \in S.$$

Consider the following identification

$$\mathcal{Z} = \{(w_x)_{x \in X} \in \prod_{x \in X} \pi^{-1}(x) : w_x = t(x) \text{ for all but finitely many } x \in X\}.$$

For every finite $F \subset X$ define a finitely supported probability measure on $\mathcal{Z}$ by

$$\mu_F = \prod_{x \in F} \nu_{x,n} \times \prod_{x \in X \backslash F} \delta_{t(x)}.$$

Consider a finitely supported probability measure m on $\mathcal{Z}$ which is defined as a convex combination of μ_F:

$$m = \sum_{F \in \mathcal{P}_f(X)} \mu(F)\mu_F.$$

Changing the summation indexes we have

$$m = \sum_{F \in \mathcal{P}_f(X)} \mu(gF)\mu_{gF},$$

thus from the approximation property of μ we obtain that $\|m - m'\|_1 < \varepsilon$, where

$$m' = \sum_{F \in \mathcal{P}_f(X)} \mu(F)\mu_{gF} = \sum_{F \in \mathcal{P}_f(X)} \mu(F)\left(\prod_{x \in F} \nu_{gx,n} \times \prod_{x \in X \backslash F} \delta_{t(gx)}\right)$$

Moreover

$$gm = \sum_{F \in \mathcal{P}_f(X)} \mu(F)\left(\prod_{x \in F} g\nu_{x,n} \times \prod_{x \in X \backslash F} \delta_{gt(x)}\right).$$

Let F be such that $\mu(F) \neq 0$ then $X_0 \subset F$ and $t(sx) = st(x)$ for all $x \in X \backslash F$ and $s \in S$. Thus

$$\left\|\prod_{x \in F} g\nu_{x,n} \times \prod_{x \in X \backslash F} \delta_{gt(x)} - \prod_{x \in F} \nu_{gx,n} \times \prod_{x \in X \backslash F} \delta_{t(gx)}\right\|_1 \leq \sum \|\nu_{gx,n} - g\nu_{x,n}\|_1 < \varepsilon |X'|.$$

Therefore we get

$$\|gm - m\|_1 \leq \|gm - m'\|_1 + \varepsilon < \varepsilon(|X'| + 1),$$

which proves the second claim. $\qquad \square$

2. Actions by homeomorphisms. Preliminary definitions

In this section we recall basic notions of groupoids of actions which will be useful in topological reformulation of Theorem 8.1. Let G act by homeomorphisms on a topological space $\mathcal{X}$.

DEFINITION 8.2. **The topological full group** of the action of G, denoted by $[[G]]$, is the group of all homeomorphisms h on $\mathcal{X}$ such that for any point $x \in \mathcal{X}$ there exists a neighborhood of it where h acts as an element of G.

The notion of the full topological group of an action is defined using a local structure of action. This suggests that we can eventually study a more general notion using instead of the group G a set which is "closed under local multiplication". For this purpose, we introduce a *groupoid structure*, i.e., the structure where the notion of the full topological group will still make sense.

DEFINITION 8.3. **A groupoid** is a set $\mathcal{G}$ such that the following holds. For each $g \in \mathcal{G}$ the inverse of g is defined, i.e., there is a map $^{-1} : \mathcal{G} \to \mathcal{G}$ with $g \mapsto g^{-1}$ and there is a partially defined multiplication $\cdot : \mathcal{G} \times \mathcal{G} \to \mathcal{G}$ which satisfy the following axioms:

- *Associativity.* If both $a \cdot b$ and $b \cdot c$ are defined then $a \cdot (b \cdot c)$ and $(a \cdot b) \cdot c$ are defined and equal;

- *Inverse.* Both $a \cdot a^{-1}$ and $a^{-1} \cdot a$ are defined;
- *Identity.* If $a \cdot b$ is defined, then $a \cdot b \cdot b^{-1} = a$ and $a^{-1} \cdot a \cdot b = b$.

To emphasize the structure of groupoid we will denote all groupoids by calligraphic letters.

We will define a groupoid structure on a set of homeomorphisms between open subsets of $\mathcal{X}$ as follows. A **germ** of a homeomorphism g of $\mathcal{X}$ is an equivalence class of pairs (g, x) where $x \in \mathcal{X}$ and g is a homeomorphism between a neighborhood of x and a neighborhood of $g(x)$. Two germs (g_1, x_1) and (g_2, x_2) are equal if and only if $x_1 = x_2$ and both g_1 and g_2 coincide on a neighborhood of x_1. A composition of two germs $(g_1, x_1)(g_2, x_2)$ is defined to be the germ $(g_1 g_2, x_2)$, if $g_2(x_2) = x_1$. The inverse of a germ (g, x) is the germ $(g, x)^{-1} = (g^{-1}, g(x))$.

A **groupoid of germs** of homeomorphisms on $\mathcal{X}$ is a set of germs of homeomorphisms of $\mathcal{X}$ that is closed under composition (when it is possible to compose two germs) and taking inverses and contains all germs of the form $(Id_{\mathcal{X}}, x)$ for $x \in \mathcal{X}$. In particular, if a group G acts by homeomorphisms on $\mathcal{X}$, the set of all its germs (g, x) for $g \in G$ and $x \in \mathcal{X}$ forms the groupoid of germs, which we will call **the groupoid of germs of the action of G on $\mathcal{X}$.**

The **topological full group of a groupoid of germs** $\mathcal{G}$, denoted by $[[\mathcal{G}]]$, is the set of all homeomorphisms $F : \mathcal{X} \longrightarrow \mathcal{X}$ such that all germs of F belong to $\mathcal{G}$. If $\mathcal{G}$ is a group, then this coincides with usual notion of the full topological group $[[G]]$.

The groupoid of germs has a natural topology defined by the basis of open sets of the form $\{(g, x) : x \in U\}$, where $g \in G$ and $U \subset \mathcal{X}$ is open.

Denote by $\mathsf{o}(g, x) = x$ and $\mathsf{t}(g, x) = g(x)$ the *origin* and the *target* of the germ (g, x). **The isotropy group** or **the group of germs at** $x \in \mathcal{X}$ is the group of all $\gamma \in \mathcal{G}$ such that $\mathsf{o}(\gamma) = \mathsf{t}(\gamma) = x$. In the case, when $\mathcal{G}$ is the groupoid of germs of the action of a group G on $\mathcal{X}$, then the group of germs $\mathcal{G}_x$ is the quotient of the stabilizer G_x of x by the subgroup of all elements of G that act trivially on a neighborhood of x.

3. Topological version of criterion

For $x \in \mathcal{X}$ the *group of germs* of G at x is the quotient of the stabilizer of x by the subgroup of elements acting trivially on a neighborhood of x.

THEOREM 8.4. *Let G be a finitely generated group of homeomorphisms of a topological space $\mathcal{X}$, and $\mathcal{G}$ be its groupoid of germs. Let $\mathcal{H}$ be a groupoid of germs of homeomorphisms of $\mathcal{X}$. Suppose that the following conditions hold.*

(i) *The group $[[\mathcal{H}]]$ is amenable.*
(ii) *For every generator g of G the set of points $x \in \mathcal{X}$ such that $(g, x) \notin \mathcal{H}$ is finite.*
(iii) *For every singular point $x \in \mathcal{X}$, the action of G on the orbit of x is recurrent.*
(iv) *The groups of germs $\mathcal{G}_x$ are amenable.*

Then the group G is amenable. Moreover, if the space $\mathcal{X}$ is compact then the topological full group $[[G]]$ is amenable.

PROOF. We will deduce the theorem from its combinatorial version Theorem 8.1. Let X be the set of all points $x \in \mathcal{X}$ such that there exists $g \in G$ with

$(g, x) \notin \mathcal{H}$. Let Y be the quotient space $\mathcal{G}/\mathcal{H}$, where two germs γ and ν in $\mathcal{G}$ are equivalent modulo $\mathcal{H}$ if there exists $h \in \mathcal{H}$ such that $\nu = \gamma h$.

Define the G-map $\pi : Y \to X$ to be the target map and the section map $t : X \to Y$ defined by $t(x) = (e, x)$ for all $x \in X$. In these settings we have that $\mathcal{G}_x = G_x/N_x$ is amenable and $t(gx) = gt(x)$ if and only if $(g, x) \in \mathcal{H}$. Thus we can take H to be $G \cap [[\mathcal{H}]]$, which is amenable by assumption. Therefore all conditions of Theorem 8.1 are satisfied, and thus the group G is amenable.

Since the conditions of the theorem are local, we have that $[[G]]$ is amenable. $\quad \square$

CHAPTER 9

Groups acting on Bratteli diagrams

A Bratteli diagram is a graph $D = (V, E)$ with set of vertices V and the set of edges E such that it has finite sets positioned on levels and edges that connect only two consecutive level sets. More precisely, we have two sequences of finite sets $\{V_i\}_{i \geq 1}$ and $\{E_i\}_{i \geq 1}$, such that $V = \bigcup_{i \geq 0} V_i$, $E = \bigcup_{i \geq 1} E_i$ and E_i is the set of edges between V_i and V_{i+1}. We also assume that V_0 consist only of one element. Define two maps $o : E \to V$ and $t : E \to V$ which give to each edge its origin and target.

The definition of Bratteli diagrams takes its origins in C^*-algebra theory [31].

In [107], Vershik-Bratteli diagrams are used to describe *aperiodic* homeomorphisms, i.e., homeomorphisms without finite orbits. A *path of length* n, where n is a natural number or ∞, in the diagram D is a sequence of edges $e_i \in E_i$, $1 \leq i \leq n$, such that $t(e_i) = o(e_{i+1})$ for all i. Denote by $\Omega_n(D) = \Omega_n$ the set of paths of length n. We will write Ω instead of Ω_∞.

The set Ω is a closed subset of the direct product $\prod_{i \geq 1} E_i$, and thus is a compact totally disconnected metrizable space. If $w = (a_1, a_2, \ldots, a_n) \in \Omega_n$ is a finite path, then we denote by $w\Omega$ the clopen subset of Ω which consists of all paths beginning with w. Let $w_1 = (a_1, a_2, \ldots, a_n)$ and $w_2 = (b_1, b_2, \ldots, b_n)$ be elements of Ω_n such that $t(a_n) = t(b_n)$. Then for every infinite path $(a_1, a_2, \ldots, a_n, e_{n+1}, \ldots)$, the sequence $(b_1, b_2, \ldots, b_n, e_{n+1}, e_{n+2}, \ldots)$ is also a path. The map

$$(13) \qquad T_{w_1, w_2} : (a_1, a_2, \ldots, a_n, e_{n+1}, \ldots) \mapsto (b_1, b_2, \ldots, b_n, e_{n+1}, e_{n+2}, \ldots)$$

is a homeomorphism $w_1\Omega \longrightarrow w_2\Omega$.

Let $\mathcal{T}$ be the groupoid of germs of the semigroup generated by the transformations of the form T_{w_1, w_2}. It can be identified with the set of all pairs of cofinal paths, i.e., pairs of paths $(e_i)_{i \geq 1}$, $(f_i)_{i \geq 1}$ such that $e_i = f_i$ for all i big enough. The groupoid structure coincides with the groupoid structure of an equivalence relation: the product $(w_1, w_2) \cdot (w_3, w_4)$ is defined if and only if $w_2 = w_3$, and then it is equal to (w_1, w_4).

Let us describe the topological full group $[[\mathcal{T}]]$. By compactness of Ω, for every $g \in [[\mathcal{T}]]$ we can find a finite partition of $\Omega = \bigcup_i \Omega_i$ into clopen sets such that the restriction of g to each Ω_i is equal to T_{w_1, w_2} for some $w_1, w_2 \in \Omega$. In other words, there exists n such that for every $w_1 \in \Omega_n$ there exist a path $w_2 \in \Omega_n$ such that $g(w) = T_{w_1, w_2}(w)$ for all $w \in w_1\Omega$. Then we say that *depth* of g is at most n. Now taking a finite subset of $F \subseteq [[\mathcal{T}]]$ we have that the depth of an element from the group generated by F has depth which is uniformly bounded. Therefore F generates a finite group. This implies that $[[\mathcal{T}]]$ is locally finite and thus it is amenable.

1. Homeomorphisms of Bratteli of bounded type

Let D be a Bratteli diagram. Recall that we denote by Ω_v, where v is a vertex of D, the set of paths of D ending in v (and beginning of a vertex of the first level of D), and by $w\Omega$ we denote the set of paths whose beginning is a given finite path w.

DEFINITION 9.1. Let $F : \Omega \longrightarrow \Omega$ be a homeomorphism. For $v \in V_i$ denote by $\alpha_v(F)$ the number of paths $w \in \Omega_v$ such that $F|_{w\Omega}$ is not equal to a transformation of the form $T_{w,u}$ for some $u \in \Omega_v$.

The homeomorphism F is said to be *of bounded type* if $\alpha_v(F)$ is uniformly bounded and the set of points $w \in \Omega$ such that the germ (F, w) does not belong to $\mathcal{T}$ is finite.

It is easy to see that the set of all homeomorphisms of bounded type form a group.

THEOREM 9.2. Let D be a Bratteli diagram. Let G be a group acting faithfully by homeomorphisms of bounded type on $\Omega(\mathsf{D})$. If the groupoid of germs of G has amenable isotropy groups, then the group G is amenable.

PROOF. It is enough to prove the theorem for finitely generated groups G. Since $[[\mathcal{T}]]$ is locally finite, it is amenable. Therefore, by Theorem 8.4 with $\mathcal{H} = \mathcal{T}$, it is enough to prove that the orbital Schreier graphs of the action of G on Ω are recurrent.

Let $w \in \Omega$, and let S be a finite symmetric generating set of G. Consider the Schreier graph of the orbit Gw of w. For $F \subset Gw$ denote by $\partial_S F$ the set of elements $x \in F$ such that $g(x) \notin F$ for some $g \in S$.

LEMMA 9.3. There exists an increasing sequence of finite subsets $F_n \subset G(w)$ such that $\partial_S F_n$ are disjoint and $|\partial_S F_n|$ is uniformly bounded.

PROOF. Let U be a finite set points in Ω such that at any $v \in \Omega \backslash U$ we have that (s, v) is in $\mathcal{T}$ for all $s \in S$. Since the generating set is symmetric we have that $\Omega \backslash U$ is invariant under the action of G. Therefore the orbit Gw is the union of a finite number of subsets of $\mathcal{T}$-orbits, namely $Gw \subseteq \bigcup_{x \in U} \mathcal{T}x \cup \mathcal{T}w$. Let $P \subset Gw$ be a $\mathcal{T}$-orbit transversal. For $u = (e_i)_{i \geq 1} \in P$ denote by $F_{n,u}$ the set of paths of the form $(a_1, a_2, \ldots, a_n, e_{n+1}, e_{n+2}, \ldots) \in Gw$. It is a finite subset of Gw. Let $F_n = \bigcup_{u \in P} F_{n,u}$. Then $\bigcup_{n \geq 1} F_n = Gw$.

Let $s \in S$. The number of paths $v = (a_1, a_2, \ldots, a_n, e_{n+1}, e_{n+2}, \ldots) \in F_{n,u}$ such that $sv \notin F_{n,u}$ is not greater than $\alpha_{\mathsf{o}(e_{n+1})}(s)$, see Definition 9.1. It follows that $|\partial_S F_n|$ is not greater than $|P| \cdot |S| \cdot \max\{\alpha_v(s) : s \in S, v \in V\}$, which is finite. We can assume that $\partial_S F_n$ are disjoint by taking a subsequence. □

Applying Theorem 5.10, we conclude that the graph $\Gamma(Gw, G, S)$ is recurrent. Thus by Theorem 8.4 we conclude that G is amenable. □

2. Vershik transformations

A *Bratteli-Vershik* diagram is a Bratteli diagram $\mathsf{D} = ((V_n)_{n \geq 1}, (E_n)_{n \geq 1})$ with origin and target maps (o, t) together with a partial order on the edge set E, such that two edges e_1 and e_2 in E are compatible if and only if $\mathsf{t}(e_1) = \mathsf{t}(e_2)$.

Using this order we can define *minimal and maximal paths* of the diagram. This can be done by declaring a path (infinite or not) to be minimal/maximal if it consists only of minimal/maximal edges.

For every vertex of a Bratteli-Vershik diagram there exist unique maximal and minimal paths that end in it. As before, Ω stands for the space of infinite paths in the diagram. Let $(e_1, e_2, \ldots) \in \Omega$ be a non-maximal path in the diagram, i.e., $e_i \in E_i$ with $\mathsf{o}(e_{i+1}) = \mathsf{t}(e_i)$. Let n be the smallest index such that e_n is non-maximal. Let e_n' be the next edge after e_n in $\mathsf{t}^{-1}(\mathsf{t}(e_n))$, and let $(e_1', e_2', \ldots, e_{n-1}')$ be the unique minimal path in $\Omega_{\mathsf{o}(e_n')}$. Define a map:

$$a(e_1, e_2, \ldots, e_n, e_{n+1}, \ldots) = (e_1', e_2', \ldots, e_{n-1}', e_n', e_{n+1}, e_{n+2}, \ldots).$$

The map a is called the *adic transformation* of the Bratteli-Vershik diagram. The adic transformation is a homeomorphism from the set of non-maximal paths to the set of non-minimal paths. The inverse map is the adic transformation defined by the opposite ordering of the diagram. If the diagram has a unique maximal and a unique minimal infinite paths, then a extends to a homeomorphism of Ω by mapping the maximal path to the minimal path.

3. Realization of Cantor minimal systems as homeomorphisms of Bratteli-Vershik diagrams

The following theorem is due to Herman, Putnam and Skau, proved in [**81**].

THEOREM 9.4. *Every minimal homeomorphism of the Cantor space is topologically conjugate to the adic transformation defined as a homeomorphism of the paths space of a Bratteli-Vershik diagram with a single minimal and single maximal path.*

It follows directly from the definition of the adic transformation a that $\alpha_v(a) = 1$ for every vertex v of the diagram, and that germs of a belong to $\mathcal{T}$ for all points $w \in \Omega$ except for the unique maximal path. It is also obvious that the homeomorphisms a has no fixed points, hence the groups of germs of the group generated by a are trivial. Thus we can deduce Theorem 6.4 from Theorem 9.2 and Theorem 9.4:

THEOREM 9.5. *Let (T, C) be a Cantor minimal system. Then the full topological group of the groupoid of germs of the group generated by T is amenable.*

It follows from the results of [**107**] that the same result is true for aperiodic homeomorphisms of the Cantor set which have finite number of maximal and minimal paths.

4. One-dimensional tilings

Adic transformations and subgroups of their topological full groups naturally appear in the study of one-dimensional aperiodic tilings, see [**19**]. In particular, *the Fibonacci tiling* is an example of a Cantor minimal system. Consider the endomorphism ψ of the free monoid $\langle a, b \rangle$ defined by $a \mapsto ab$, $b \mapsto a$. Then $\psi^n(a)$ is the beginning of $\psi^{n+1}(a)$, so that we can pass to the limit, and get a right-infinite sequence

$$\psi^\infty(a) = abaababaabaababaababaabaababaabab\ldots$$

Let $\mathcal{F}$ be the set of bi-infinite sequences $w \in \{a, b\}^{\mathbb{Z}}$ over the alphabet $\{a, b\}$ such that every finite subword of w is a sub-word of $\psi^{\infty}(a)$. The set $\mathcal{F}$ is obviously invariant under the shift, which we will denote by τ. Here the shift acts by the rule

$$\ldots x_{-2}x_{-1}\underline{x_0}x_1 \ldots \mapsto \ldots x_{-1}x_0\underline{x_1}x_2 \ldots,$$

where the the underlining shows the position of 0.

Every letter b in a sequence $w \in \mathcal{F}$ is uniquely grouped with the previous letter a. Replace each group ab by a, and each of the remaining letters a by b. Denote the new sequence by $\sigma(w) = \ldots y_{-2}y_{-1}\underline{y_0}y_1 \ldots$, so that y_0 corresponds to the group that contained x_0. It follows from the definition of $\mathcal{F}$ that $\sigma(w) \in \mathcal{F}$.

The symbol $\alpha(w)$ of a sequence $\ldots x_{-2}x_{-1}\underline{x_0}x_1 \ldots \in \mathcal{F}$ is an element of $\{a_0, a_1, b\}$ defined by the following conditions:

(1) $\alpha(w) = a_0$ if $x_{-1}x_0 = aa$;
(2) $\alpha(w) = a_1$ if $x_{-1}x_0 = ba$;
(3) $\alpha(w) = b$ if $x_0 = b$.

The itinerary of $w \in \mathcal{F}$ is the sequence $\alpha(w)\alpha(\sigma(w))\alpha(\sigma^2(w)) \ldots$. We have the following description of $\mathcal{F}$, which easily follows from the definitions.

PROPOSITION 9.6. A sequence $w \in \mathcal{F}$ is uniquely determined by its itinerary. A sequence $x_1 x_2 \ldots \in \{a_0, a_1, b\}^{\infty}$ is an itinerary of an element of $\mathcal{F}$ if and only if $x_i x_{i+1} \in \{a_0 a_1, a_1 a_0, a_1 b, ba_0, ba_1\}$. The shift τ acts on $\mathcal{F}$ in terms of itineraries by the rules:

$$\tau(a_0 w) = bw, \quad \tau(bw) = a_1 \tau(w)$$

$$\tau(a_1 w) = \begin{cases} b\tau(w) & \text{if } w \text{ starts with } a_0, \\ a_0 \tau(w) & \text{if } w \text{ starts with } b. \end{cases}$$

Restricting τ_{a_0}, τ_{a_1}, τ_b of τ to the cylindrical sets of sequences starting with a_0, a_1, b, respectively, generate a *self-similar inverse semigroup* in the sense of [120]. The range of each of these transformations does not intersect with the domain. Therefore, we may define homeomorphisms $\alpha_0, \alpha_1, \beta$ equal to transformations $\tau_{a_0} \cup \tau_{a_0}^{-1}$, $\tau_{a_1} \cup \tau_{a_1}^{-1}$, $\tau_b \cup \tau_b^{-1}$ extended identically to transformations of the space $\mathcal{F}$.

It is easy to see that the orbital Schreier graphs of the action of the group $\langle \alpha_0, \alpha_1, \beta \rangle$ on $\mathcal{F}$ coincide with the corresponding two-sided sequences. Namely, the Schreier graph of a point $\ldots x_{-1}.x_0 x_1 \ldots$ is isomorphic to a chain of vertices $(\ldots, w_{-1}, w_0, w_1, \ldots)$, where $w_0 = w$, and the edge (w_i, w_{i+1}) corresponds to the generator α_0, α_1, or β if and only if $x_{i-1}x_i$ is equal to aa, ba, or ab, respectively. It follows from Theorem 9.5 that the group $\langle \alpha_0, \alpha_1, \beta \rangle$ is amenable.

CHAPTER 10

Groups acting on rooted trees

In this chapter we will consider automorphisms of rooted trees. This is a particular example of groups acting on a path space of Bratteli diagrams. Indeed, the path space of a Bratteli diagram $\mathsf{D} = (V_i, E_i)$ such that each level set V_i consists only of one point can be identified with the path space of a rooted tree that has $|E_i|$ edges coming from any vertex on the i-th level.

As before will denote the set of paths of length n starting at the root by $\Omega_n = E_1 \times E_2 \times \cdots \times E_n$ and the set of infinite path starting at the root $\Omega = \prod_{i=1}^{\infty} E_i$. The disjoint union $\Omega^* = \bigsqcup_{n \geq 0} \Omega_n$, where Ω_0 is a singleton can be naturally identified with a rooted tree. The sets Ω_n are its levels, i.e., we will also consider them as the sets of vertices on the n-th level of the rooted tree. Two paths $v_1 \in \Omega_n$ and $v_2 \in \Omega_{n+1}$ are connected by an edge if and only if v_2 is a continuation of v_1, namely $v_2 = v_1 e$ for some $e \in E_{n+1}$. The space Ω of infinite paths of the Bratteli diagram is naturally interpreted as the boundary of the tree Ω^*.

Denote by $\mathrm{Aut}(\Omega^*)$ the automorphism group of the rooted tree Ω^*. The group $\mathrm{Aut}(\Omega^*)$ acts transitively on each of the levels Ω_n. Denote by ${}_n\Omega^*$ the tree of finite paths of the "truncated" diagram defined by the sequence

$$_n\Omega = (E_{n+1}, E_{n+2}, \ldots).$$

For every $g \in \mathrm{Aut}(\Omega^*)$ and $v \in \Omega_n$ there exists an automorphism $g|_v \in \mathrm{Aut}({}_n\Omega^*)$ such that

$$g(vw) = g(v)g|_v(w)$$

for all $w \in {}_n\Omega^*$. The automorphism $g|_v$ is called the *section* of g at v.

For more details on the groups acting on rooted trees see [65, Section 6] and [124].

We list obvious properties of sections. For all $g_1, g_2, g \in \mathrm{Aut}(\Omega^*)$, $v \in \Omega^*$, $v_2 \in {}_n\Omega^*$ and $v_1 \in \Omega_n$ we have

$$(g_1 g_2)|_v = g_1|_{g_2(v)} g_2|_v, \qquad g|_{v_1 v_2} = g|_{v_1}|_{v_2}.$$

For the groups acting on rooted trees it is much easier to deduce amenability of the topological full group of the action with amenability of the group itself, which we do the the following proposition.

PROPOSITION 10.1. Let G be a group acting on a locally connected rooted tree Ω^*. Let $\mathcal{G}$ be the groupoid of germs of the corresponding action on the boundary Ω of the tree. Then $[[\mathcal{G}]]$ is amenable if and only if G is amenable.

PROOF. Since $G \leq [[\mathcal{G}]]$, amenability of $[[\mathcal{G}]]$ implies amenability of G. To prove the converse, suppose that G is amenable. It is enough to prove that every finitely generated subgroup of $[[\mathcal{G}]]$ is amenable. Let $S \subset [[\mathcal{G}]]$ be a finite set. There exists a level Ω_n of the tree Ω^* such that for every $v \in \Omega_n$ and $g \in S$ the restriction of the action of g onto $v(_n\Omega^*)$ is equal to the restriction of an element of G. Then every element $g \in S$ permutes the cylindrical sets $v(_n\Omega^*)$ for $v \in \Omega_n$ and acts inside each of these sets as an element of G. It follows that $\langle S \rangle$ contains a subgroup of finite index which can be embedded into the direct product of a finite number of quotients of subgroups of G. Consequently, the amenability of G implies the amenability of $\langle S \rangle$. $\qquad\square$

DEFINITION 10.2. An automorphism $g \in \operatorname{Aut}\Omega^*$ is said to be *finitary* of *depth* at most n if all sections $g|_v$ for $v \in \Omega_n$ are trivial.

It follows from the properties of section maps that the set of finitary automorphisms and the set of finitary automorphisms of depth at most n are groups. The latter group is finite, hence the group of all finitary automorphisms of Ω^* is locally finite. It is also easy to see that the groupoid of germs of the action of the group of finitary automorphisms on Ω coincides with the tail equivalence groupoid $\mathcal{T}$ of the diagram **D**.

DEFINITION 10.3. Let $g \in \operatorname{Aut}\Omega^*$. Denote by $\alpha_n(g)$ the number of paths $v \in \Omega_n$ such that $g|_v$ is non-trivial. We say that $g \in \operatorname{Aut}\Omega^*$ is *bounded* if the sequence $\alpha_n(g)$ is bounded.

If $g \in \operatorname{Aut}\Omega^*$ is bounded, then there exists a finite set $P \subset \Omega$ of infinite paths such that $g|_v$ is non-finitary only if v is a beginning of some element of P. Consequently, bounded automorphisms of Ω^* act on Ω by homeomorphisms of bounded type, see definitionnition 9.1.

The following is proved in [**124**, Theorem 3.3].

THEOREM 10.4. Let G be a group of automorphisms of a locally finite rooted tree T. If G contains a non-abelian free subgroup, then either there exists a free non-abelian subgroup $F \le G$ and a point w of the boundary ∂T of the tree such that the stabilizer of w in F is trivial, or there exists $w \in \partial T$ and a free non-abelian subgroup of the group of germs $\mathcal{G}_w$.

In particular, if the orbits of the action of G on ∂T have sub-exponential growth, and the groups of germs $\mathcal{G}_w$ do not contain free subgroups (e.g., if they are finite), then G does not contain a free subgroup. We get therefore the following corollary of Theorems 9.2 and 10.4. (The proof of the fact that there is no freely acting subgroup of G under conditions of Theorem 10.5 is the same as the proof of [**124**, Theorem 4.4], and also follow from Lemma 9.3.)

THEOREM 10.5. Let G be a subgroup of the group of bounded automorphisms of Ω^*.

(1) If the groups of germs $\mathcal{G}_w$ are amenable, then the group G is amenable.
(2) If the groups of germs $\mathcal{G}_w$ have no free subgroups, then the group G has no free subgroups.

In many cases it is easy to prove that the groups of germs $\mathcal{G}_w$ are finite. Namely, the following proposition is straightforward (see the proof of [**124**, Theorem 4.4]).

PROPOSITION 10.6. Suppose that the sequence $|E_i|$ is bounded. Let G be a group generated by bounded automorphisms of Ω^*. If for every generator g of G there exists a number n such that the depth of every finitary section $g|_v$ is less than n, then the groups of germs $\mathcal{G}_w$ for $w \in \Omega$ are locally finite, and the group G is amenable.

Amenability of groups satisfying the conditions of Proposition 10.6 answers a question posed in [124]. Below we show some concrete examples of groups satisfying the conditions of Proposition 10.6.

1. Finite automata of bounded activity

DEFINITION 10.7. Suppose that the sequence $\Omega = (E_1, E_2, \ldots) = (X, X, \ldots)$ is constant, so that $_n\Omega^*$ does not depend on n. An automorphism $g \in \operatorname{Aut}\Omega^*$ is said to be *finite-state* if the set $\{g|_v \ : \ v \in \Omega^*\} \subset \operatorname{Aut}\Omega^*$ is finite.

The sequence $\alpha_n(g)$ from definition 10.3 for finite-state automorphisms was studied by S. Sidki in [142]. He showed that it is either bounded, or grows either as a polynomial of some degree $d \in \mathbb{N}$, or grows exponentially (in fact, he showed that the series $\sum_{n \geq 0} \alpha_n(g)x^n$ is rational). For each d the set $P_d(\Omega^*)$ of finite-state automorphisms of Ω^* for which $\alpha_n(g)$ grows as a polynomial of degree at most d is a subgroup of $\operatorname{Aut}\Omega^*$. He showed later in [143] that these groups of *automata of polynomial activity growth* do not contain free non-abelian subgroups.

For various examples of subgroups of the groups of bounded finite-state automorphisms, see [12, Section 1.D] and references therein.

It is easy to see that finite-state bounded automorphisms of the tree Ω^* satisfy the conditions of Proposition 10.6. This proves, therefore, the following.

THEOREM 10.8. The group of finite-state bounded automorphisms of Ω^* is amenable for every finite alphabet X.

This theorem is the main result of the paper [12]. It was proved there by embedding all finitely generated groups of finite-state bounded automorphisms into a sequence of self-similar "mother groups" M_d, and then using the self-similarity structure on M_d to show that the asymptotic entropy of the random walk on M_d is equal to zero. Similar technique was applied in [5] to prove that the group of automata with at most linear activity growth is also amenable. We will prove this fact later using Theorem 8.4.

One of the consequences of Theorem 10.8 is an alternative proof of amenability of Grigorchuk's group and the Basilica group, both are finite automata of bounded activity.

2. Groups of Neumann-Segal type

The conditions of Definition 10.7 are very restrictive. In particular, the set of all finite-state automorphisms of X^* is countable, whereas the set of all bounded automorphisms is uncountable. There are many interesting examples of groups generated by bounded but not finite-state automorphisms of X^*. For example, the groups from the uncountable family of Grigorchuk groups [69] are generated by bounded automorphisms of the binary rooted trees. They are of sub-exponential growth.

An uncountable family of groups of non-uniformly exponential growth was constructed in [32]. All groups of the family (if the degrees of the vertices of the tree are bounded) satisfy the conditions of Proposition 10.6, hence are amenable. Amenability of these groups were proved in [32] using the techniques of [13], and then reproved in [33] by exhibiting Følner sequences.

Other examples are given by constructions of P. Neumann [125] and D. Segal in [141].

Let us describe a general version of D. Segal's construction. Let (G_i, X_i), $i = 0$, $1, \ldots$, be a sequence of groups acting transitively on finite sets X_i. Let $a_{i,j} \in G_i$ for $1 \leq j \leq k$ be sequences of elements such that $a_{i,1}, a_{i,2}, \ldots, a_{i,k}$ generate G_i. Choose also points $x_i, y_i \in X_i$. Define then automorphisms $\alpha_{i,j}, \beta_{i,j}$, $i = 0, 1$, $\ldots$, of the tree $\mathsf{X}_{(j)}^*$ for the sequence $\mathsf{X}_{(j)} = (X_i, X_{i+1}, \ldots)$ given by the following recurrent rules:

$$\alpha_{i,j}(xw) = a_{i,j}(x)w, \beta_{i,j}(xw) = \begin{cases} x_i \beta_{i+1,j}(w) & \text{if } x = x_i, \\ y_i \alpha_{i+1,j}(w) & \text{if } x = y_i, \\ xw & \text{otherwise,} \end{cases}$$

where $w \in \mathsf{X}_{(j+1)}^*$ and $x \in X_i$.

PROPOSITION 10.9. The group $G = \langle \alpha_{0,1}, \ldots, \alpha_{0,k}, \beta_{0,1}, \ldots, \beta_{0,k} \rangle$ is amenable if and only if the group generated by the sequences $(a_{1,j}, a_{2,j}, \ldots) \in \prod_{i=1}^{\infty} G_i$, for $j = 1, \ldots, k$, is amenable.

PROOF. The group generated by the sequences $(a_{1,j}, a_{2,j}, \ldots)$ is isomorphic to the group generated by $\beta_{0,1}, \beta_{0,2}, \ldots, \beta_{0,k}$. Consequently, if this group is non-amenable, then G is non-amenable too.

The automorphisms $\alpha_{i,j}$ are finitary. All sections of $\beta_{i,j}$ are finitary except for the sections in finite beginnings of the sequence $x_i x_{i+1} \ldots$. It follows that $\beta_{i,j}$ are bounded, and the groups of germs the action of G on X^ω are either trivial or isomorphic to the group of germs of G at the point $x_0 x_1 \ldots$. It also follows from the description of the sections that the group of germs of G at $x_0 x_1 \ldots$ is a quotient of $\langle \beta_{0,1}, \beta_{0,2}, \ldots, \beta_{0,k} \rangle$. Then Theorem 10.5 finishes the proof. □

The examples considered by P. Neumann in [125] are similar, but they are finite-state, so their amenability follows from Theorem 10.8. The main examples of D. Segal [141] are non-amenable (they are constructed for G_i equal to $PSL(2, p_i)$ for an increasing sequence of primes p_i).

A. Woryna in [157] and E. Fink in [58] consider the case when G_i are cyclic groups (of variable order). A. Woryna uses the corresponding group G to compute the minimal size of a topological generating set of the profinite infinite wreath product of groups G_i. E. Fink shows that if the orders of G_i grow sufficiently fast, then the group G is of exponential growth, but does not contain free subgroups. Proposition 10.9 immediately implies that such groups are amenable (for any sequence of cyclic groups).

I. Bondarenko used in [27] the above construction in the general case to study number of topological generators of the profinite infinite wreath product of permutation groups.

3. Iterated monodromy groups of polynomial iterations

Two uncountable families of groups generated by bounded automorphisms were studied in [121] in relation with holomorphic dynamics. Let us describe one of them. For a sequence $w = x_1 x_2 \ldots$, $x_i \in \{0, 1\}$ define $s(w) = x_2 x_3 \ldots$, and let $\alpha_w, \beta_w, \gamma_w$ be automorphisms of $\{0, 1\}^*$ defined by

$$\alpha_w(0v) = 1v, \qquad \gamma_w(0v) = 0v, \qquad \beta_w(0v) = 0\alpha_{s(w)}(v),$$
$$\alpha_w(1v) = 0\gamma_{s(w)}(v), \quad \gamma_w(1v) = 1\beta_{s(w)}(v), \qquad \beta_w(1v) = 1v,$$

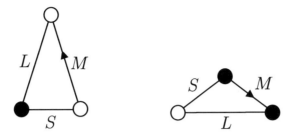

FIGURE 1. Tiles of Penrose tilings

if $x_1 = 0$, and
$$\beta_w(0v) = 0v, \qquad \beta_w(1v) = 1\alpha_{s(w)}(v),$$
if $x_1 = 1$, where $s(w) = x_2x_3\ldots$.

The automorphisms $\alpha_w, \beta_w, \gamma_w$ are obviously bounded. Note that $\alpha_w, \beta_w, \gamma_w$ are finite-state if and only if w is eventually periodic. It is easy to see that the groups of germs of the action of the group $R_w = \langle \alpha_w, \beta_w, \gamma_w \rangle$ on the boundary of the binary tree are trivial. Therefore, it follows from Theorem 10.5 that the groups G_w are amenable.

It is shown in [**121**] that the sets of isomorphism classes of groups R_w, for $w \in \{0, 1\}^{\mathbb{Z}}$ are countable, and that the map $w \mapsto R_w$ is a homeomorphic embedding of the Cantor space of infinite binary sequences into the space of three-generated groups.

The groups R_w are iterated monodromy groups of sequences of polynomials of the form $f_n(z) = 1 - \frac{z^2}{p_n^2}$, where $p_n \in \mathbb{C}$ satisfy $p_n = 1 - \frac{1}{p_{n+1}^2}$, $n = 0, 1, \ldots$.

See more on the iterated monodromy groups of sequences of polynomials in [**123**]. Many of them satisfy the conditions of Proposition 10.6, and hence are amenable.

EXAMPLE 10.10. Consider an arbitrary sequence $f_n(z)$, $n \geq 0$, such that $f_n(z) = z^2$ or $f_n(z) = 1 - z^2$. The iterated monodromy group of such a sequence is generated by automorphisms a_w, b_w, for some sequence $w = x_1x_2\ldots \in \{0, 1\}^{\infty}$, where

$$a_w(0v) = 1v, \quad a_w(1v) = 0b_{s(w)}(v), \quad b_w(0v) = 0v, \quad b_w(1v)1a_{s(w)}(v),$$

if $x_1 = 0$, and

$$a_w(0v) = 1v, \quad a_w(1v) = 0a_{s(w)}(v), \quad b_w(0v) = 0v, \quad b_w(1v)1b_{s(w)}(v),$$

otherwise. All these groups are amenable by Proposition 10.6.

4. Penrose tilings

Consider isosceles triangles formed by two diagonals and a side, and two sides and a diagonal of a regular pentagon. Mark their vertices by white and black dots, and orient one of the sides as it is shown on Figure 1.

A *Penrose tiling* is a tiling of the plane by such triangles obeying the *matching rules*: if two triangles have a common vertex, then this vertex must be marked by dots of the same color; if two triangle have a common side, then either they both are not oriented, or they are both oriented and the orientations match.

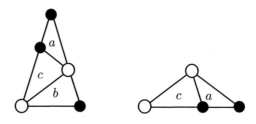

FIGURE 2. Grouping of tiles

One can show, just considering all possible sufficiently big finite patches of Penrose tilings, that tiles of any Penrose tilings can be grouped into blocks as on Figure 2. The blocks are triangles similar to the original tiles (with similarity coefficient $(1 + \sqrt{5})/2$), and the new tiles also form a Penrose tiling, which we call *inflation* of the original tiling.

Given a Penrose tiling with a marked tile, consider the sequence of iterated inflations of the tiling, where in each tiling the tile containing the original marked tile is marked. Let $x_1 x_2 \ldots$ be the corresponding *itinerary*, where $x_i \in \{a, b, c\}$ is the letter describing the position of the marked tile of the $(i-1)$st inflation in the tile of the ith inflation according to the rule shown on Figure 2. A sequence is an itinerary of a marked Penrose tiling if and only if it does not contain a subword ba. More on the inflation and itineraries of the Penrose tilings, see [**78**].

Given a marked Penrose tiling with itinerary $w = x_1 x_2 \ldots$, denote by $L(w)$, $S(w)$, $M(w)$ the itineraries of the same tiling in which a neighboring tile is marked, where the choice of the neighbor is shown on Figure 1.

One can show by considering sufficiently big finite patches of the Penrose tilings (see also [**14**, **118**]) that the transformations L, S, and M on the space of itineraries is given by the rules

$$S(aw) = cw, \quad S(bw) = bM(w), \quad S(cw) = aw,$$

$$L(aw) = \begin{cases} bS(w) & \text{if } w \text{ starts with } a, \\ aM(w) & \text{otherwise,} \end{cases}$$

$$L(bw) = \begin{cases} bS(w) & \text{if } w \text{ starts with } b, \\ aS(w) & \text{if } w \text{ starts with } c, \end{cases} \quad L(cw) = cL(w),$$

$$M(aw) = aL(w), \quad M(bw) = cw, \quad M(cw) = \begin{cases} cM(w) & \text{if } w \text{ starts with } a, \\ bw & \text{otherwise.} \end{cases}$$

The orbital Schreier graphs of the action of the group $\langle L, S, M \rangle$ coincide then with the graphs dual to the Penrose tilings (except in the exceptional cases when the tilings have a non-trivial symmetry group; then the dual graphs are finite coverings of the Schreier graphs). The group generated by the transformations L, S, and M remains to be mysterious, in particular, we do not know if it is amenable (even if it is different from the free product of three groups of order 2).

Let us redefine the transformations L, S, M, trivializing the action on some cylindrical sets, so that in some cases they correspond to moving the marking to a neighboring tile, but sometimes they correspond to doing nothing. Namely, define

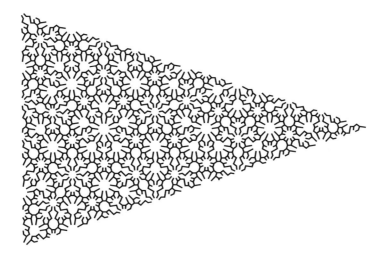

FIGURE 3. A part of the Schreier graph of $\langle L', S', M' \rangle$

new transformations L', S', M' by the rules.

$$S'(aw) = cw, \quad S'(bw) = bM'(w), \quad S'(cw) = aw,$$

$$L'(aw) = \begin{cases} bS'(w) & \text{if } w \text{ starts with } a, \\ aw & \text{otherwise}, \end{cases}$$

$$L'(bw) = \begin{cases} bS'(w) & \text{if } w \text{ starts with } b, \\ aS'(w) & \text{if } w \text{ starts with } c, \end{cases} \quad L'(cw) = cL'(w),$$

$$M'(aw) = aw, \quad M'(bw) = cw, \quad M'(cw) = \begin{cases} cM'(w) & \text{if } w \text{ starts with } a, \\ bw & \text{otherwise}. \end{cases}$$

Then the Schreier graphs of $\langle L', S', M' \rangle$ are subgraphs of the graphs dual to the Penrose tilings. A piece of such Schreier graph is shown on Figure 3.

It is easy to see that M', and hence S' are finitary. It follows that L' is bounded. Further analysis shows that the groups of germs are finite, hence the group $\langle L', S', M' \rangle$ is amenable.

5. Linearly and quadratically growing automata

In the previous section we applied Theorem 8.4 in the case when the topological full group $[[\mathcal{H}]]$ is locally finite. Here we present some other examples of applications of Theorem 8.4.

Recall that $P_d(\mathsf{X})$, for $d = 1, 2, \ldots$, denotes the group of finite-state automorphisms g of X^* such that $\alpha_n(g)$ is bounded by a polynomial of degree d. In particular, $P_1(\mathsf{X})$ is the group of finite-state automorphisms of *linear activity growth*. Here $\alpha_n(g)$, as before, is the number of words v of length n such that $g|_v \neq 1$.

For example, consider the group generated by the following two transformations of $\mathbb{Z}$.

$$a : n \mapsto n + 1, \qquad b : 2^m(2k + 1) \mapsto 2^m(2k + 3), \quad b(0) = 0,$$

where $n, k, m \in \mathbb{Z}$ and $m \geq 0$. It is isomorphic to the group generated by automorphisms of $\{0, 1\}^*$ defined by the relations

$$a(0v) = 1v, \; a(1v) = 0a(v), \qquad b(0v) = 0b(v), \; b(1v) = 1a(v).$$

The orbital Schreier graphs of this group were studied in [**17, 28**].

The following theorem was proved in [**5**]. We present here a proof based on Theorem 8.4.

THEOREM 10.11. *For every finite alphabet X the group $P_1(X)$ is amenable.*

PROOF. Let us investigate the groups of germs of finitely generated subgroups of $P_d(X)$. Let S be a finite subset of $P_d(X)$, and $G = \langle S \rangle$. We may assume that S is *state-closed*, i.e., that $g|_x \in S$ for all $x \in X$ and $g \in S$. Replacing X by X^N for some integer N, we may assume that the elements of S satisfy the following condition. For every element $g \neq 1$ of the form $g = h|_x$, for $h \in S$ and $x \in X$, there exists a unique letter $x_g \in X$ such that $g|_{x_g} = g$, for all other letters $x \in X$ the section $g|_x$ has degree of activity growth lower than that of g (in particular, it is finitary if g is bounded and trivial if g is finitary). This fact follows from the structure of automata of polynomial activity growth [**142**], see also [**12**, proof of Theorem 3.3].

In particular, it follows that for every $g \in P_d(X)$ the set of points $w \in X^\omega$ such that the germ (g, w) is not a germ of an element of $P_{d-1}(X)$ is finite.

Let $w = x_1 x_2 \ldots \in X^\omega$, and consider the group of germs $\mathcal{G}_w$. Denote by Φ the set of all eventually constant sequences. If w does not belong to Φ, our assumptions on S imply that the germ (g, w) of every $g \in S$ (and hence every $g \in G$) belongs to the groupoid of germs of the finitary group. This implies that $\mathcal{G}_w$ is trivial. Assume now that w belongs to Φ, say $x_n = x$ for all n large enough. The sequence $g|_{x_1 x_2 \ldots x_n}$ is eventually constant for every $g \in S$ (and hence in G). In particular if $g \in G$ fixes w, then for all $y \neq x$ the sequence $g|_{x_1 x_2 \ldots x_n y}$ is eventually constant and belongs to $P_{d-1}(X)$. We therefore get a homomorphism from the stabilizer of w in G to the wreath product $P_{d-1}(X) \wr \mathrm{Symm}(X \setminus \{x\})$ with kernel the elements of G that act trivially on a neighborhood of w. This shows that $\mathcal{G}_w$ embeds in $P_{d-1}(X) \wr \mathrm{Symm}(X \setminus \{x\})$.

Now Theorem 8.4 shows that the amenability of G will follow from the amenability of $P_{d-1}(X)$ and recurrence of the orbital Schreier graphs of G. We have proved in Theorem 10.8 that $P_0(X)$ is amenable. Let us prove the amenability of finitely generated subgroups of $P_1(X)$, i.e., the amenability of $P_1(X)$.

If $w_0 \notin \Phi$, then w_0 is not singular in the sense of Theorem 8.4, i.e., the germs of elements of $P_1(X)$ at w_0 are equal to germs of some elements of $P_0(X)$.

We therefore only have to show that the action of G on the orbit of an element w_0 of Φ is recurrent. Let $F_n \subset \Phi$ be the set of all sequences $w = x_1 x_2 \ldots \in X^\omega$ in the G-orbit of w_0 such that $x_i = x_j$ for all $i, j > n$. Suppose that $w \in \partial_S F_n$ for $n > 1$. Then $w = vx^\omega$ for some $|v| = n$ and $x \in X$, and there exists $g \in S$ such that $g(w) \notin F_n$, i.e., $g|_v(x^\omega)$ is not a constant sequence. This implies that $g|_v \neq 1$, and $g|_{vx} \neq g|_v$, hence $g|_{vx}$ is bounded. Then either $g|_v(x^\omega)$ is of the form $y_1 y^\omega$, for $y_1, y \in X$; or $g|_{vxx}$ is finitary, so that $g|_v(x^\omega)$ is of the form $y_1 y_2 y_3 x^\omega$, for $y_i \in X$. It follows that $|\partial_S F_n| \leq |X| \sum_{g \in S} \alpha_n(g)$ and that every element of $g(\partial_S F_n)$ for $g \in S$, belongs to F_{n+3}. Then $\partial_S F_{3n}$ are disjoint, $\cup_n F_n = G(\omega_0)$ and $|\partial_S F_{3n}|$ is bounded from above by a linear function, which implies by Theorem 5.10 that the Schreier graph of G on the orbit of ω_0 is recurrent. □

Note that arguments of the proof of Theorem 10.11 imply the following.

THEOREM 10.12. *If $G \leq P_2(X)$ is a finitely generated group with recurrent Schreier graphs of the action on X^ω, then G is amenable.*

It was announced in [3] that the Schreier graphs of the "mother group" of automata of quadratic activity growth are recurrent. This implies, by Theorem 10.12, that these groups are amenable, which in turn implies amenability of $P_2(X)$ for every finite alphabet X.

On the other hand, it is shown in [3] that the Schreier graphs of some groups generated by automata of growth of activity of degree greater than 2 are transient.

Definitions of amenability and basic facts

Here we provide basic facts and definitions of amenability that we have used through the book. We do not claim that this list of definitions is complete and refer the reader to other sources of expositions for example:

- A survey paper of Day, [**45**], 1969.
- The book of Greenleaf, [**64**], 1969.
- Pier's book on amenability of locally compact groups, [**134**], 1984.
- The book of Paterson, mostly covers general theory of amenability of locally compact groups, [**133**], 1988.
- Wagon's book on Banach-Tarski paradox, [**154**], 1993.
- A survey paper on amenable groups by Ceccherini-Silberstein, Grigorchuk and de la Harpe, [**35**], 1999.
- Lecture notes of Runde, topics on amenable Banach algebras, [**138**], 2002.
- A chapter devoted to amenability of topological groups of the book Bekka, de la Harpe, and Valette, [**15**], 2008.
- A survey paper on amenability of topological groups of Grigorchuk and de la Harpe, [**72**], 2014.

1. Means and measures

In this section we present one-to-one correspondence between means and finitely additive probability measures. This correspondence was proved by Banach in his famous monograph [**7**] as one of the first applications of the Hahn-Banach theorem. It was further used by von Neumann, and became one of the central tools in amenability, transferring the subject from measure theory to functional analysis. More contemporary exposition on means and measures can be found for instance in the book [**51**].

Let X be a set and let $\mathcal{P}(X)$ denote the set of all subsets of X. For $E \in \mathcal{P}(X)$ denote by χ_E the characteristic function of the set E, i.e., $\chi_E(x) = 1$ if $x \in E$ and $\chi_E(x) = 0$ otherwise.

DEFINITION A.1. A map $\mu : \mathcal{P}(X) \to [0, 1]$ is called a finitely additive probability measure if it satisfies:

(i) $\mu(X) = 1$
(ii) $\mu(A \cup B) = \mu(A) + \mu(B)$ whenever $A \cap B = \emptyset$ and $A, B \in \mathcal{P}(X)$.

Denote the set of all finitely additive probability measures on X by $PM(X)$. One of the examples of finitely additive probability measures is the counting measure supported on a finite set, i.e., $\mu_E(F) = |E \cap F|/|F|$ for some finite set F in X. Recall, that the space of all bounded functions on X and it's dual are denoted by $l^\infty(X)$ and $l^\infty(X)^*$ correspondingly.

DEFINITION A.2. A mean on a set X is a functional $m \in l^\infty(X)^*$ which satisfies

(i) $m(\chi_X) = 1$,
(ii) $m(f) \geq 0$ for all $f \geq 0$, $f \in l^\infty(X)$.

For each mean m on X we can associate a finitely additive probability measure on X:

$$\hat{m}(A) = m(\chi_A), \text{ for all } A \in \mathcal{P}(X).$$

Indeed, since $\chi_A \leq \chi_X$ we have that $\hat{m}$ takes its values in $[0, 1]$. Moreover, the linearity of m implies $\hat{m}(A \cup B) = \hat{m}(A) + \hat{m}(B)$ for all $A, B \in \mathcal{P}(X)$ with $A \cap B = \emptyset$. This section is devoted to prove that this correspondence is one-to-one.

Define $M(X)$ to be the set of all means on X, and

$$Prob(X) = \{f : X \to \mathbb{R}_+ : \sum_{x \in X} f(x) = 1\},$$

$$Prob_{fin}(X) = \{f : X \to \mathbb{R}_+ : \sum_{x \in X} f(x) = 1, f \text{ is finitely supported.}\}$$

Then $Prob_{fin}(X) \subseteq Prob(X) \subseteq M(X)$. Indeed, for each $h \in Prob(X)$ we can define a mean $m_h \in M(X)$ by

$$m_h(f) = \sum_{x \in X} h(x)f(x)$$

for all $f \in l^\infty(X)$.

FACT A.3. We list the following classical properties of means:

(i) For each $m \in M(X)$, we have $\|m\| = 1$.
(ii) The set of all means $M(X) \subset l^\infty(X)^*$ is convex and closed in the weak*-topology.
(iii) $Prob_{fin}(X)$ and $Prob(X)$ are convex in $M(X)$.
(iv) The set $Prob_{fin}(X)$, and thus $Prob(X)$, is weak*-dense in $M(X)$.

PROOF. To prove ((i)), observe that $\|m\| \geq 1$, since $m(\chi_X) = 1$. Now, if $f, h \in l^\infty(X)$ and $f \leq h$ then $m(h - f) \geq 0$ and thus $m(f) \leq m(h)$. Applying this to $f \leq \|f\|_\infty \cdot \chi_X$, we obtain $m(f) \leq \|f\|_\infty \cdot m(\chi_X) = \|f\|_\infty$, therefore $\|m\| = 1$.

The properties ((ii)) and ((iii)) are trivial.

To see ((iv)), assume $m \in M(X)$ is not a weak*-limit of means in $Prob_{fin}(X)$. By Hahn-Banach theorem, we can find a function f in $l^\infty(X)$ and $\delta > 0$, such that $m(f) > \delta > \overline{m}(f)$ for all $\overline{m} \in Prob_{fin}(X)$. In particular, this holds for the Dirac measures $\delta_x \in Prob_{fin}(X)$, for which we have $\delta_x(f) = f(x)$. Therefore, $m(f) > \delta > f(x)$ for all $x \in X$. We have $\delta - f > 0$, and $m(\delta - f) = \delta - m(f) < 0$, which is a contradition. $\square$

Recall, that for each mean $m \in M(X)$ we associated a finitely additive measure on X:

$$\hat{m}(A) = m(\chi_A), \text{ for all } A \in \mathcal{P}(X).$$

THEOREM A.4. The map between means and finitely additive probability measures given by $m \mapsto \hat{m}$ is bijective.

PROOF. Let $\mathcal{E}(X)$ be the set of all $\mathbb{R}$-valued functions on X which take only finitely many values. Then $\mathcal{E}(X)$ is dense in $l^\infty(X)$. Indeed, for each positive

function in $h \in l^\infty(X)$, define $\lambda_i = \frac{i}{n}\|h\|_\infty$, $i \in \{\pm 1, \ldots, \pm n\}$, and a function $f : X \to \mathbb{R}$ by setting
$$f_n(x) = \min\{\lambda_i : h(x) \leq \lambda_i\},$$
for all $x \in X$.

Then $f_n \in \mathcal{E}(X)$ and $\|h - f_n\|_\infty \leq \|h\|_\infty/n$. Since every function $h \in l^\infty(X)$ can be decomposed as a difference of two positive functions, we have that $\mathcal{E}(X)$ is dense in $l^\infty(X)$.

For $\mu \in PM(X)$ and $h \in \mathcal{E}(X)$ define
$$\overline{\mu}(h) = \sum_{t \in \mathbb{R}} \mu(h^{-1}(t))t.$$

We have that $\overline{\mu}$ is linear. Indeed, for a number λ,
$$\overline{\mu}(\lambda h) = \sum_{t \in \mathbb{R}} \mu((\lambda h)^{-1}(t))t = \sum_{t \in \mathbb{R}} \mu((h)^{-1}(\lambda^{-1}t))t = \lambda\overline{\mu}(h)$$

For $h, g \in \mathcal{E}(X)$ we have, since $(h+g)^{-1}(t) = \cup_{(x,y):x+y=t} h^{-1}(x) \cap g^{-1}(y)$,
$$\overline{\mu}(h+g) = \sum_{(x,y) \in Image(h) \times Image(g)} \mu(h^{-1}(x) \cap g^{-1}(y))(x+y)$$
$$= \sum_{x \in Image(h)} \mu(h^{-1}(x)) + \sum_{y \in Image(g)} \mu(g^{-1}(y))$$
$$= \mu(h) + \mu(g).$$

Note that $\overline{\mu}(\chi_A) = \mu(A)$, and thus by linearity if $h = \sum_{i \in I} c_i A_i$ for a finite I, then $\overline{\mu}(h) = \sum_{i \in I} c_i \mu(A_i)$.

Since $|\overline{\mu}(h)| \leq \sum_{i \in I} |\lambda_i|\mu(A_i) \leq \|h\|_\infty \cdot \mu(X) = \|h\|_\infty$, we can extend $\overline{\mu}$ to a linear functional m on $l^\infty(X)$ with $\|m\| \leq 1$. Moreover, $m(\chi_X) = \mu(X) = 1$. By construction, if $f \in \mathcal{E}(X)$ is a positive function then $m(f) \geq 0$. As we showed above, each positive function in $l^\infty(X)$ can be approximated by positive functions from $\mathcal{E}(X)$, thus we have $m(f) \geq 0$ for all positive functions $f \in l^\infty(X)$.

Since for every $E \subset X$
$$m(\chi_E) = \mu(E)$$
we have that $\hat{m} = \mu$ and thus the statement of the theorem follows. $\square$

2. Almost invariant vectors of the left regular representation

Let $\lambda : \Gamma \to B(l^2(\Gamma))$ be the left regular representation of Γ:
$$\lambda(t)f = \delta_t * f \text{ for every } f \in l^2(\Gamma).$$
where the convolution of two functions is defined by
$$(f * h)(t) = \sum_{s \in \Gamma} f(s)h(s^{-1}t),$$

assuming that the later sum exists. Equivalently, we have $(\lambda(t)h)(s) = h(t^{-1}s)$. Let H be a Hilbert space and let $\pi : \Gamma \to B(H)$ be a representation of Γ by unitary operators. A vector $\xi \in H$ is an *invariant* vector of π, if $\pi(g)\xi = \xi$ for every $g \in \Gamma$. It is easy to check that the left regular representation admits an invariant vector if and only if Γ is finite. A representation π has *almost invariant vectors* if there exists a sequence of unit vectors ξ_i such that
$$\|\pi(g)\xi_i - \xi_i\| \to 0 \text{ for every } g \in \Gamma.$$

Obviously, it is sufficient to check this convergence on a generating set. The existence of almost invariant vectors characterizes amenability.

THEOREM A.5. A group Γ is amenable if and only if the left regular representation has almost invariant vectors.

PROOF. Assume that Γ is amenable and let F_i be a Følner sequence, i.e. $|gF_i \Delta F_i|/F_i \to 0$ for every $s \in \Gamma$. Define $\xi_i = \frac{1}{\sqrt{|F_i|}} \chi_{F_i}$. Then

$$\|\lambda(g)\xi_i - \xi_i\| = \frac{|gF_i \Delta F_i|}{F_i}.$$

Thus λ has almost invariant vectors.

Assume now that there exist almost invariant vectors, $\xi_i \in l^2(\Gamma)$. By Theorem 2.16, it is sufficient to construct an approximately invariant mean. Define $\mu_i = \xi_i^2 \in l^1(\Gamma)$, then by Cauchy-Schwarz we have

$$\|s\mu_i - \mu_i\|_1 = \left| \sum_{t \in \Gamma} s.\xi_i^2(t) - \xi_i(t) \right|$$

$$= \left| \sum_{t \in \Gamma} \xi_i^2(s^{-1}t) - \xi_i(t) \right|$$

$$= \left| \sum_{t \in \Gamma} (\xi_i(s^{-1}t) - \xi_i(t))(\xi_i(s^{-1}t) - \xi_i(t)) \right|$$

$$\leq 2\|\xi\| \left(\sum_{t \in \Gamma} |\xi_i(s^{-1}t) - \xi_i(t)|^2 \right)^{1/2}$$

$$= \|\lambda(s)\xi_i - \xi_i\| \to 0.$$

Hence μ_i is an approximately invariant mean. □

3. Weakening of the Følner condition

In the section we give one more characterization of amenability due to Følner. We follow the proof of T. Nagnibeda and the author, [87].

THEOREM A.6. A finitely generated group Γ is amenable if and only if there exists a constant $C < 2$ such that for every finite set $S \subset \Gamma$ there exists a finite set $F \subset \Gamma$ such that

$$|sF \Delta F| \leq C|F|, \text{ for every } s \in S.$$

We will need the following well known lemma (see e.g. Proposition 11.5 in [15]).

LEMMA A.7. Let $\pi : \Gamma \to B(H)$ be a unitary representation of a discrete group Γ. Suppose that there exists a unit vector $\xi \in H$ such that $\|\pi(g)\xi - \xi\| \leq C < \sqrt{2}$ for every $g \in \Gamma$. Then π has an invariant vector.

PROOF. Note that

$$Re(\langle \pi(g)\xi, \xi \rangle) = 1 - \frac{1}{2}\|\pi(g)\xi - \xi\|^2$$

$$\geq 1 - \frac{C^2}{2} = C' > 0.$$

Let $V = \overline{conv\{\pi(g)\xi : g \in \Gamma\}}$ then V is $\pi(\Gamma)$-invariant and

$$Re(\langle \theta, \xi \rangle) \geq C' \text{ for every } \theta \in V.$$

Let $\nu \in V$ be the unique element of V that has minimal norm, then $Re(\langle \nu, \xi \rangle) \geq C'$ and $\nu \neq 0$. Since π is a unitary representation, ν is invariant under the action of $\pi(\Gamma)$.   □

Before proving Theorem A.6, let us recall definition of ultraproduct of Banach spaces. Let J be a set equipped with an ultrafilter $\mathcal{U}$. Let $(X_j)_{j \in J}$ be a family of Banach spaces. Let us denote by X the space of all sequences $x = (x_j)_{j \in J}$ with $x_j \in X_j$ and $\sup_{j \in J} \|x_j\| < \infty$. We equip X with norm $\|x\| = \sup_{j \in J} \|x_j\|$. Let $N = \{x : \lim_{\mathcal{U}} \|x_j\| = 0\}$. Then the quotient X/N is a Banach space denoted by $\prod_{j \in J} X_j \backslash \mathcal{U}$ and called the ultraproduct relative to $\mathcal{U}$ of $(X_j)_{j \in J}$. Whenever $(Y_j)_{j \in J}$ is another family of Banach spaces and $u_j : X_j \to Y_j$ are such that $\sup_{j \in J} \|u_j\| < \infty$, we can canonically define $u : \prod_{j \in J} X_j \backslash \mathcal{U} \to \prod_{j \in J} Y_j \backslash \mathcal{U}$ by setting $u((x_j)) = (u(x_j))$. In case $(X_j)_{j \in J}$ is a family of Hilbert spaces, the ultraproduct $\prod_{j \in J} X_j$ has a natural Hilbert space structure, i.e. $\langle (x_j)_{j \in J}, (y_j)_{j \in J} \rangle = \lim_{\mathcal{U}} \langle x_j, y_j \rangle$.

PROOF OF THE THEOREM A.6. The existence of $C \leq 2$ that satisfies the condition of the theorem for an amenable group Γ follows from Følner's criterion.

To prove the converse fix a finite set S and let F be a finite set of Γ such that

$$|sF \Delta F| \leq C|F|, \text{ for every } s \in S.$$

Consider $\xi_F = \frac{1}{\sqrt{|F|}} \chi_F$, we have $\|\lambda(s)\xi_F - \xi_F\| \leq \sqrt{C}$ for every $s \in S$. Let S_i be an increasing sequence of sets in Γ with $\Gamma = \cup S_i$. Let $\mathcal{U}$ be an ultrafilter and let $\lambda_\mathcal{U} : G \to B(\prod l_2(\Gamma)/\mathcal{U})$ be an ultraproduct of the left-regular representation acting on an ultrapower of the Hilbert space $l_2(\Gamma)$. Then for the vector $\xi = (\xi_{F_i})_{i \in \mathbb{N}}$ we have that $\|\lambda_\mathcal{U}(g)\xi - \xi\| \leq \sqrt{C}$ for every $g \in G$. By Lemma A.7 we have that $\lambda_\mathcal{U}$ has an invariant vector. Thus λ has a sequence of almost invariant vectors, therefore Γ is amenable.   □

4. Kesten's criterion

The criterion of Kesten, [97], proved to be useful in many applications and many other reformulations of amenability.

Let Γ be a group generated by a finite symmetric set S and μ be a symmetric measure, i.e., $\mu(g^{-1}) = \mu(g)$ for every $g \in \Gamma$, which is supported on S. Given a symmetric measure μ on Γ define a self-adjoint bounded operator $M(\mu)$ on $l^2(\Gamma)$ by setting

$$[M(\mu)f](x) = \sum_{t \in \Gamma} f(t^{-1}x)\mu(t), \text{ for every } f \in l^2(\Gamma).$$

The operator $M(\mu)$ is called *Markov operator* associated to μ. In terms of the left regular representation we have the following

$$M(\mu) = \sum_{t \in \Gamma} \mu(t)\lambda(t).$$

A direct computation shows that

$$M(\mu)M(\nu) = M(\mu * \nu),$$

for all finitely supported probability measures μ, ν on Γ, where the convolution of the measure is given by

$$\mu * \nu(x) = \sum_{t \in \Gamma} \mu(xt^{-1})\nu(t).$$

It is easy to check that $M(\mu)$ is a contraction, i.e., $\|M(\mu)\| \leq 1$. Recall, a measure μ on Γ is called generating if its support generates the group, it is symmetric if $\mu(t) = \mu(t^{-1})$ for every $t \in \Gamma$.

THEOREM A.8. A group Γ with a generating symmetric measure μ is amenable if and only if

$$\|M(\mu)\|_{B(l^2(\Gamma))} = 1.$$

PROOF. Since amenability is a local property, without loss of generality we can assume that Γ is finitely generated by a set S, which is contained in the support of the measure μ.

If Γ is amenable then, by Theorem A.5 λ has almost invariant vectors, which immediately implies that the norm of the Markov operator is equal to 1.

Conversely, assume that $\| \sum_{t \in \Gamma} \mu(t)\lambda(t)\| = 1$. Since S is symmetric we have that $M(S)$ is a self-adjoint operator. Thus for every $\varepsilon > 0$ we can find a unit vector $\xi \in l^2(\Gamma)$ such that

$$|\langle \sum_{t \in \Gamma} \mu(t)\lambda(t)\xi, \xi \rangle| > 1 - \varepsilon.$$

Denote by $|\xi|$ the pointwise absolute value of ξ, then we have

$$\langle \sum_{t \in \Gamma} \mu(t)\lambda(t)|\xi|, |\xi| \rangle| \geq \langle \sum_{t \in \Gamma} \mu(t)\lambda(t)\xi, \xi \rangle| > 1 - \varepsilon.$$

Taking ε arbitrarily small, for every t in S we have that $\langle \lambda(t)|\xi|, |\xi| \rangle|$ is arbitrarily close to 1. Thus, $|\xi|$ is an almost invariant vector, and by Theorem A.5 the claim follows. $\square$

Random walks and spectral radius. One of the basic tools to study Markov operator is the spectral theorem for self-adjoint operators. Denote by $\sigma(\mu)$ the spectrum of $M(\mu)$ and by $\rho(\mu) = \max(|t| : t \in \sigma(\mu))$ the spectral radius of $M(\mu)$. Since $M(\mu)$ is self-adjoint we have $\|M(\mu)\| = \rho(\mu)$.

Applying the spectral theorem for self-adjoint operators to $M(\mu)$ we obtain a resolution of the identity $E(dt)$, i.e., a measure that takes values in self-adjoint projections, and a probability measure $\nu(dt)$ given by $\langle E(dt)\delta_e, \delta_e \rangle$ on the interval $[-1, 1]$ such that

$$\langle M(\mu)\delta_e, \delta_e \rangle = \int_{[-1,1]} t^n \nu(dt).$$

Let $\mu^{*n} := \mu * \ldots * \mu$ be the n-th convolution of μ with itself. We have the following theorem.

THEOREM A.9. Let Γ be a finitely generated group and μ be a symmetric probability measure supported on a finite generation set of Γ, then

$$\|M(\mu)\| = \lim_n \mu^{*2n}(e)^{1/2n}$$

PROOF. Since $M(\mu^{*n}) = M(\mu)^n$ and $\mu^{*n}(g) = M(\mu)^n \delta_g = \langle M(\mu)^n, \delta_e, \delta_e \rangle$ we have

$$\mu^{*n}(e) \leq \|M(\mu)^n\|.$$

Applying the spectral theorem to $M(\mu)$ we obtain:

$$\mu^{*2n}(e)^{1/2n} = \langle M(\mu)^{2n} \delta_e, \delta_e \rangle^{1/2n} = \left(\int_{[-1,1]} t^{2n} \nu(dt) \right)^{1/2n}.$$

Since $\mathrm{supp}(\nu) = \sigma(\mu)$ we obtain

$$\lim_n \mu^{*2n}(e)^{1/2n} = \lim_n \left(\int_{[-1,1]} t^{2n} \nu(dt) \right)^{1/2n} = \lim \|t\|_{2n} = \|t\|_\infty$$
$$= \max(|t| : t \in \sigma(M(\mu))) = \rho(M(\mu)) = \|M(\mu)\|.$$

$\square$

Now, Theorem A.8 in a combination with Theorem A.9 imply:

COROLLARY A.10. Let Γ be a finitely generated group and μ be a symmetric probability measure with the support generating Γ. Then Γ is amenable if and only if

$$\lim_n \mu^{*2n}(e)^{1/2n} = 1$$

5. Hulanicki's criterion

One of the applications of the Kesten's criteria is Hulanicki's criteria. Given a function $f \in l^1(\Gamma)$, define

$$\lambda(f) = \sum_{t \in \Gamma} f(t) \lambda(t) \in B(l^2(\Gamma)).$$

THEOREM A.11. For a discrete group Γ the following are equivalent:

(i) Γ is amenable;
(ii) There is constant $C > 0$ such that for every positive finitely supported function f on Γ we have

$$\sum_{t \in \Gamma} f(t) \leq C \|\lambda(f)\|_{B(l^2(\Gamma))};$$

(iii) The same as in ((ii)) with constant $C = 1$.

PROOF. Assume that Γ is amenable and let $f \geq 0$ be a finitely supported function. Let $(F_n)_{n \in \mathbb{N}}$ be a Følner sequence that $1/n$-approximates the support of f, i.e.,

$$|g F_n \Delta F_n| \leq 1/n |F_n|, \text{ for every } g \in supp(f).$$

Denote by $\xi_n = \frac{1}{\sqrt{|F_n|}} \chi_{F_n} \in l^2(\Gamma)$. Note that $\|\xi_n\|_2 = 1$. Assume that

$$\|\lambda(f)\| \leq 1.$$

Then we have

$$\langle \sum_{t\in\Gamma} f(t)\lambda(t)\xi_n, \xi_n \rangle = \sum_{t\in\Gamma} f(t)\langle \lambda(t)\xi_n, \xi_n \rangle$$

$$= \sum_{s,t\in\Gamma} f(t)\xi_n(t^{-1}s)\overline{\xi_n(s)}$$

$$\leq 1.$$

But $\|\lambda(t)\xi_n - \xi_n\| = \|\delta_t * \xi_n - \xi_n\| \to 0$, when $n \to \infty$. Thus we have

$$1 \geq \lim_{n\to\infty} \left| \sum_{s,t\in\Gamma} f(t)\xi_n(t^{-1}s)\overline{\xi_n(s)} \right|$$

$$= \lim_{n\to\infty} \left| \sum_{s,t\in\Gamma} f(t)\xi_n(s)\overline{\xi_n(s)} \right|$$

$$= \sum_{t\in\Gamma} f(t).$$

This, by homogeneity of the inequality, implies that

$$\sum_{t\in\Gamma} f(t) \leq \|\lambda(f)\|.$$

Now assume ((ii)), we will deduce ((iii)). Note that

$$\lambda(f * \ldots * f) = \lambda(f) \ldots \lambda(f).$$

Applying ((ii)) to the convolution of f we get

$$\left(\sum_{t\in\Gamma} f(t) \right)^n = \sum_{t\in\Gamma} [f * \ldots * f](t) \leq C\|\lambda(f * \ldots * f)\|$$

$$\leq C\|\lambda(f)\|^n.$$

Thus we obtain

$$\sum f(t) \leq C^{1/n}\|\lambda(t)\|,$$

which implies ((iii)).

Assume now ((iii)). Let E be a finite subset of Γ, then applying ((iii)) to $f = \chi_E$ we obtain

$$\| \sum_{t\in E} \lambda(t) \| = |E|,$$

which by Kesten's criterion implies amenability of Γ.   □

6. Weak containment of representations

Let Γ be a discrete group with two unitary representation $\pi : \Gamma \to B(\mathcal{H})$ and $\rho : \Gamma \to B(\mathcal{K})$ on Hilbert spaces $\mathcal{H}$ and $\mathcal{K}$ respectively. The representation π is **weakly contained** in ρ, denoted by $\pi \prec \rho$, if for every $\xi \in \mathcal{H}$, finite set E of Γ and $\varepsilon > 0$ there are $\eta_1, \ldots, \eta_n \in \mathcal{K}$ such that for all $g \in E$ we have

$$\left| \langle \pi(g)\xi, \xi \rangle - \sum_{i=1}^n \langle \rho(g)\eta_i, \eta_i \rangle \right| < \varepsilon.$$

Denote by $1_\Gamma : \Gamma \to \mathbb{C}$ the trivial representation, i.e., $1_\Gamma(g) = 1$ for every $g \in \Gamma$.

THEOREM A.12. A discrete group Γ is amenable if and only if $1_\Gamma \prec \lambda$.

PROOF. We will show that $1_\Gamma \prec \lambda$ is equivalent to the existence of almost invariant vectors for λ, which by Theorem A.5 is equivalent to amenability of Γ.

Assume that λ admits almost invariant vectors. It is sufficient to show that for every $\varepsilon > 0$ and a finite set E of Γ there are $\eta_1, \ldots, \eta_n \in l^2(\Gamma)$ such that

$$\left|1 - \sum_{i=1}^{n} \langle \lambda(t)\eta_i, \eta_i \rangle\right| < \varepsilon, \text{ for every } t \in E.$$

This follows if we take $n = 1$ and $\eta_1 = \xi$, where ξ is (E, ϵ)-almost invariant vector, i.e., $\|\lambda(g)\xi - \xi\| < \varepsilon$ for every $g \in E$.

Conversely, assume that $1_\Gamma \prec \lambda$, we will deduce that λ has almost invariant vectors. By the definition, for every $\varepsilon > 0$ and a finite subset E of Γ there are $\eta_1, \ldots, \eta_n \in l^2(\Gamma)$, such that

(14) $$\left|1 - \sum_{i=1}^{n} \langle \lambda(t)\eta_i, \eta_i \rangle\right| < \varepsilon, \text{ for every } t \in E.$$

Assuming that E contains the identity element e, we obtain

$$\left|1 - \sum_{i=1}^{n} \|\eta_i\|^2\right| < \varepsilon.$$

Rescaling the norm we may assume that $\sum_{i=1}^{n} \|\eta_i\|^2 = 1$ and (14) is still satisfied.

To reach a contradiction assume λ does not have almost invariant vectors. Then there exists $C > 0$ and a finite set $S \subset \Gamma$ such that for every $\xi \in l^2(\Gamma)$ we have

$$\|\xi\|^2 |S| - \sum_{\gamma \in S} \langle \lambda(\gamma)\xi, \xi \rangle > C\|\xi\|^2.$$

Now applying this to the vectors $\eta_1, \ldots, \eta_n$ and summing up, we obtain

$$|S| - \sum_{\gamma \in S} \sum_{i=1}^{n} \langle \lambda(\gamma)\eta_i, \eta_i \rangle > C.$$

This implies that there exists $\gamma \in S$ such that

$$1 - \sum_{i=1}^{n} \langle \lambda(\gamma)\eta_i, \eta_i \rangle > C/|S| > 0,$$

which contradicts (14). Thus λ admits almost invariant vectors. $\qquad\square$

More on weak containment of representations can be found in the book [15].

7. Day's fixed point theorem

Let Γ be a finitely generated group and X be a locally convex vector space. Let G act on a convex subset $K \subseteq X$. The action is *affine* if for every $x, y \in K$, $t \in [0, 1]$ and $g \in \Gamma$ we have

$$g(tx + (1 - t)y) = tg(x) + (1 - t)g(y).$$

THEOREM A.13. A group Γ is amenable if and only if every affine action on a non-empty compact convex subset of a locally convex vector space has a fixed point.

PROOF. Consider $l^\infty(\Gamma)^*$ equipped with the weak*-topology and the set of means on Γ, $M(\Gamma)$, which is convex and compact in the weak*-topology. Thus the action of Γ has a fixed point on $M(\Gamma)$, which implies that Γ is amenable.

Conversely, let Γ act on a convex, compact subset K of a locally compact vector space X. For a probability measure $m \in C(K)^*$ denote by $b_m \in K$ its barycenter, i.e.,

$$b_m = \int_K x \, dm(x)$$

Using the change of variables $y = g^{-1}x$ and the fact that g acts by affine transformation, thus commutes with integration, we have

$$b_{gm} = \int_K x \, dgm(x) = \int_K gy \, dm(y) = g\left(\int_K y \, dm(y)\right) = g b_m.$$

Now fix a point $p \in X$ and let $t : \Gamma \to K$ be the orbital map: $t(g) = gx$. Let m be a Γ-invariant mean on $l^\infty(\Gamma)$, and define a measure μ on K, the push-forward of m, by setting $\mu(f) = m(f \circ t)$, $f \in C(K)$. Now the barycenter b_μ of μ is a point in K, fixed by the action of Γ. $\qquad\square$

The theorem also holds for locally compact groups with continuous action.

8. Tarski theorem and Tarski numbers

Let Γ be a group acting on a set X. We start with the following basic lemma which will be useful in the later sections. We will follow the exposition of [135].

LEMMA A.14. Let a discrete group Γ act on a set X, then the following are equivalent:

(i) there exist pairwise disjoint subsets $A_1, \ldots, A_n$ and $B_1, \ldots, B_m$ in X and there exist $g_1 \ldots g_n, h_1, \ldots, h_m$ in Γ such that

$$X = \bigcup_{i=1}^n g_i A_i = \bigcup_{j=1}^m h_j B_j.$$

(ii) there exist pairwise disjoint subsets $A_1, \ldots, A_n$ and $B_1, \ldots, B_m$ in X and there exist $g_1 \ldots g_n, h_1, \ldots, h_m$ in Γ such that

$$X = \bigsqcup_{i=1}^n g_i A_i = \bigsqcup_{j=1}^m h_j B_j.$$

(iii) there exist pairwise disjoint subsets $A_1, \ldots, A_n$ and $B_1, \ldots, B_m$ in X and there exist $g_1 \ldots g_n, h_1, \ldots, h_m$ in Γ such that

$$X = \bigsqcup_{i=1}^n A_i \cup \bigsqcup_{j=1}^m B_j = \bigsqcup_{i=1}^n g_i A_i = \bigsqcup_{j=1}^m h_j B_j.$$

PROOF. The trivial implications are (iii) $\Longrightarrow$ (ii) $\Longrightarrow$ (i). Without loss of generality we can assume that $g_1 = h_1 = e$. Assume (i) and define inductively $A_1' = A_1$, $A_k' = A_k \backslash g_k^{-1}(\bigsqcup_{i=1}^{k-1} g_i A_i')$, and $B_1' = B_1$, $B_k' = B_k \backslash h_k^{-1}(\bigsqcup_{i=1}^{k-1} h_j B_j')$. It is easy to check that these sets satisfy (ii).

Assume (ii) and let $A = \bigcup_{1 \le i \le n} A_i$, $B = \bigcup_{1 \le j \le m} B_j$. Note that $A \cap B = \emptyset$. Define a map $f : X \to B$ by $f(x) = b_x$, where $b_x \in B_j$ is the unique element such that $x = h_j b_x$.

Put $D = \bigcup_{k=0}^{\infty} f^k(A)$, with $f^0(A) = A$, and $T = (X \backslash A) \backslash f(D)$. Then $A \cap f(D) = \emptyset$ and $A \cup f(D) = D$. Let $D_j = B_j \cap h_j^{-1} D$. Then we have

$$X = A \cup T \cup (\bigcup_{1 \leq j \leq m} D_j)$$

and

$$X = \bigsqcup_{i=1}^{n} g_i A_i = eT \cup \bigsqcup_{i=1}^{m} h_j D_j.$$

Since $h_1 = e$, we can gather eT and D_1 together in order to keep m and n as in (ii) unchanged. Thus (iii) follows. $\qquad \square$

The action is **paradoxical** if it satisfies one of the conditions of the lemma.

THEOREM A.15 (Tarski). Let Γ be a discrete group. The following are equivalent:

(i) Γ is amenable;
(ii) The action of Γ on itself by left multiplication is not paradoxical;
(iii) Γ does not admit a paradoxical action.

We start by proving a graph theoretical lemma, which will be also useful for the proof of Tarski's theorem.

THEOREM A.16 (Hall's (1-1)-matching). Let $G = (A, B, E)$ be a bipartite graph with the set of edges E between the sets A and B. Assume that the degree of every vertex in A is finite and for every finite set $D \subseteq A$ we have

$$|N(D)| \geq |D|,$$

where $N(D)$ is the set of all vertices in B connected with a vertex in D. Then there exists an injective map $i : A \to B$, such that

$$(a, i(a)) \in E \text{ for every } a \in A.$$

PROOF. It is sufficient to prove the lemma for finite graphs. Indeed, assume that the statement is true for all finite subsets of A. Let A_n be an increasing to A sequence of finite subset of A and i_n be corresponding maps. Since these maps correspond to finite subgraphs of G, we can take a cluster point in the topology of $\{0, 1\}^E$. Then this cluster point satisfies all required properties.

We will prove the theorem by induction of the size of the set A. For $|A| = 1$ the statement is trivial, assume that it holds for all sets with size less or equal to n. Let then $|A| = n + 1$. Take $v \in A$, then there exists at least one edge going out of v.

Assume that for all $X \subset A \backslash \{v\}$, we have $|N(X)| \geq |X| + 1$, then we can connect v with any edge and apply induction to $A \backslash \{v\}$. Thus the only case we need to treat is when there exists a subset $X \subseteq A \backslash \{v\}$ with $|N(X)| = |X|$. Choose a minimal set X with this property. By induction and minimality of X we have that X can be matched to $N(X)$. Consider now the complement of X, we will show that it can be matched with the complement of $N(X)$. Let $Y \subseteq A \backslash X$, then it is easy to check that Y must have $|Y|$ neighbors outside $N(X)$. Therefore, by induction, we can match these points with $N(Y) \backslash N(X)$. Combining both matchings we obtain a matching of the whole set A. $\qquad \square$

COROLLARY A.17 (Hall's (k,1)-matching). Let $G = (A, B, E)$ be a bipartite graph with the set of edges E between the sets A and B, and let k be a natural number. Assume that the degree of every vertex is A is finite and for every finite set $D \subseteq A$ we have
$$|N(D)| \geq k|D|,$$
where $N(D)$ is the set of all vertices in B connected with a vertex in D. Then there are injective maps $i_1, \ldots, i_k : A \to B$ with pairwise disjoint images such that
$$(a, i_t(a)) \in E \text{ for every } a \in A \text{ and } 1 \leq t \leq k.$$

PROOF. Let G satisfy the statement then taking a disjoint union of k copies of A and adding edges between each copy and B in the case there was an edge between A and B, we obtain a graph bipartite graph (A', B), which satisfies the conditions of Hall's $(1, 1)$. Thus we can match the disjoint union of k copies of A with B, which defines us the maps i_t, $1 \leq t \leq k$. $\square$

Now we are ready to prove Theorem A.15.

PROOF OF THE THEOREM A.15. Assume that Γ is not amenable. Then there are a finite set $S \subset \Gamma$ and $\varepsilon > 0$ such that for every $E \subset \Gamma$ there is $g \in S$ such that
$$|gE \backslash E| \geq \varepsilon|E|.$$
Without loss of generality we can assume that S contains e. Thus $E \subset SE$ and we have
$$|SE| \geq (1 + \varepsilon)|E|$$
Applying this inequality to the set $S^{k-1}E$ we obtain
$$|S^k E| \geq (1 + \varepsilon)|S^{k-1}E| \geq \ldots \geq (1 + \varepsilon)^k|E|$$
Choose k such that $(1 + \varepsilon)^k \geq 2$ and denote S^k again by S. Thus we obtain
$$|SE| \geq 2|E|$$
Consider a bipartite graph $G = (\Gamma, \Gamma, E)$ with edges between two copies of Γ defined by $(g, h) \in E$ if and only if $h = sg$ for some $s \in S$. Then for every finite set F we automatically have $|N(F)| \geq 2|F|$. Thus by Hall's $(1,2)$-matching theorem there are injective on Γ maps i and j with disjoint images such that for each $g \in \Gamma$ there exists $s, t \in S$ with $i(g) = sg$ and $j(g) = tg$. For $s, t \in S$, define
$$A_s = s\{g \in \Gamma : i(g) = sg\},$$
$$B_t = t\{g \in \Gamma : j(g) = tg\}.$$
Then it is trivial to check that these sets are pairwise disjoint and we have the following paradoxical decomposition:
$$\Gamma = \bigcup_{s \in S} s^{-1} A_s = \bigcup_{t \in S} t^{-1} B_t.$$
Conversely, if Γ is amenable then for every action of Γ on a set X, there exists a Γ-invariant finitely additive probability measure μ on X. To reach a contradiction assume that the action has a paradoxical decomposition, i.e., there are pairwise disjoint sets $A_1, \ldots, A_n, B_1, \ldots, B_m$ in X and $g_1, \ldots, g_n, h_1, \ldots, h_m$ in Γ such that
$$X = \bigcup_{i=1}^{n} g_i A_i = \bigcup_{j=1}^{m} h_j B_j.$$

Applying μ to this equality we obtain

$$1 = \mu(X) \geq \sum_{i=1}^{n} \mu(A_i) + \sum_{j=1}^{m} \mu(B_j)$$
$$= \sum_{i=1}^{n} \mu(g_i A_i) + \sum_{j=1}^{m} \mu(h_j B_j)$$
$$\geq 2\mu(X) = 2,$$

which is a contradiction. Thus the action is not paradoxical. □

Sometimes non-amenable groups are also called *paradoxical*. By Tarski's Theorem, each non-amenable group admits a paradoxical decomposition. The minimal number of sets required in this decomposition, i.e., the number $n + m$, is called **Tarski number** of the group. By Tarski's Theorem, each non-amenable group admits a paradoxical decomposition. The minimal number of sets required in this decomposition, i.e., the number $n + m$, is called **Tarski number** of the group. We will show that $\mathcal{T}(\Gamma) = 4$ if and only if Γ contains a free non-abelian group. In order to identify free subgroups in a group we will use the following classical lemma.

LEMMA A.18 (Ping-Pong). Let a group Γ act on a set X and $a, b \in \Gamma$. Suppose that there are pairwise disjoint sets $A^{\pm}$ and $B^{\pm}$ such that

$$a(X \backslash A^-) \subseteq A^+, \quad a^{-1}(X \backslash A^+) \subseteq A^-,$$
$$b(X \backslash B^-) \subseteq B^+, \quad b^{-1}(X \backslash B^+) \subseteq B^-,$$

then the group generated by a and b is the free group $\mathbb{F}_2$.

PROOF. To reach a contradiction assume that there exists a reduced word w in a and b which is equal to identity. Assume in addition that w is not of the form gvg^{-1} for some g, v in Γ, since if it is we can take the word v instead. Without loss of generality we can assume that w ends on the letter a and, thus, bringing all a's from the beginning of the word to the end we have that w has the form:

$$w = b^{k_1} a^{k_2} \ldots b^{k_2} a^{k_1},$$

where $k_1 > 0$ and $k_2, \ldots, k_n \in \mathbb{Z}$. Pick a point $p \in A^+$, now we play the ping-pong:

$$a^{k_1}(p) \in A^+,$$
$$b^{k_2} a^{k_1}(p) \in B^{\pm}$$
$$a^{k_3} b^{k_2} a^{k_1}(p) \in A^{\pm}$$
$$\cdot \quad \cdot \quad \cdot$$
$$b^{k_1} a^{k_2} \ldots b^{k_2} a^{k_1}(p) \in B^{\pm},$$

which is a contradiction, thus a and b generate $\mathbb{F}_2$. □

We observe that for $\Gamma' < \Gamma$ and a normal subgroup $H \trianglelefteq \Gamma$ we have

$$\mathcal{T}(\Gamma) \leq \mathcal{T}(\Gamma'), \qquad \mathcal{T}(\Gamma) \leq \mathcal{T}(H).$$

THEOREM A.19. For a group Γ we have $\mathcal{T}(\Gamma) = 4$ if and only if Γ contains a free non-abelian group.

PROOF. Assume, firstly, that $\mathbb{F}_2 < \Gamma$. Since $\mathcal{T}(\mathbb{F}_2) = 4$ and $\mathcal{T}(\Gamma)$ is always greater or equal to 4, we have $\mathcal{T}(\Gamma) = 4$.

Now assume that $\mathcal{T}(\Gamma) = 4$. Thus there are sets X_1, X_2, Y_1, Y_2 in Γ and g_1, g_2, h_1, h_2 in Γ such that

$$\Gamma = X_1 \sqcup X_2 \sqcup Y_1 \sqcup Y_2 = g_1 X_1 \sqcup g_2 X_2 = h_1 Y_1 \sqcup h_2 Y_2.$$

Let $g = g_1^{-1} g_2$, $h = h_1^{-1} h_2$. Then

$$g^{-1} X_1 = \Gamma \backslash X_2, \qquad h^{-1} Y_1 = \Gamma \backslash Y_1,$$
$$g X_2 = \Gamma \backslash X_1, \qquad h Y_2 = \Gamma \backslash Y_2.$$

Hence, by ping-pong lemma we have that g and h generate the free group $\mathbb{F}_2$. □

In [**56**], Ershov, Golan and Sapir show that Tarski's number can be arbitrarily large.

9. Gromov's doubling condition. Grasshopper criteria

Through this section we assume that Γ is generated by a finite set S. Denote by $d : \Gamma \times \Gamma \in \mathbb{N}$ the distance in the Cayley graph of Γ with respect to S.

Assume that Γ acts on a set X and let Y be a subset of X. A injective map $\tau : Y \to X$ is called *wobbling* if there exists a finite set $E \subset \Gamma$ such that for each $y \in Y$ we have that $\tau(y) = gy$ for some $g \in E$. The set E will be called the set that defines the wobbling τ.

The proof of the following equivalences is very similar to the proof of Tarski's theorem. The name "Grasshopper criteria" came from the following visual explanation. We put one grasshopper in each vertex of the Cayley graph and let them jump by connecting edges. Then, if grasshoppers will be smart enough, after finite number of jumps each of them will find itself at a vertex with one mate.

THEOREM A.20. *The following are equivalent*

  (i) Γ is not amenable;
 (ii) **Gromov's doubling condition.** There exists a finite set S, for every finite set $E \subset \Gamma$

$$|N(E)| \geq 2|E|,$$

   where $N(E) = \{g \in \Gamma : g = sf \text{ for some } f \in E \text{ and } s \in S\}$.
(iii) **Grasshopper criteria.** There exists a map $\phi : \Gamma \to \Gamma$ such that

$$\sup(d(g, \phi(g)) : g \in \Gamma) < \infty$$

   and for every $g \in \Gamma$ we have $|\phi^{-1}(g)| = 2$;
 (iv) There are two wobbling maps $i, j : \Gamma \to \Gamma$ with $i(\Gamma) \cap j(\Gamma) = \emptyset$ and $i(\Gamma) \cup j(\Gamma) = \Gamma$;

PROOF. Because of the Følner condition, amenable group can not satisfy the inequality from ((ii)). Thus ((i)) $\implies$ ((ii)).

Let us prove that ((ii)) implies ((i)), assume that for every finite set $E \subset \Gamma$

$$|N_S(E)| \geq 2|E|.$$

Consider a bipartite graph $G = (\Gamma, \Gamma, E)$ with edges between two copies of Γ defined by $(g, h) \in E$ if and only if $h = sg$ for some $s \in S$. Then for every finite set F we have $|N(F)| \geq 2|F|$. Thus by Hall's (1,2)-matching theorem there are injective on

Γ maps i and j, $i(\Gamma) \cap j(\Gamma)$ and for each $g \in \Gamma$ there exists $s, t \in S$ with $i(g) = sg$ and $j(g) = tg$.

For $s, t \in E$, define

$$A_s = s\{g \in \Gamma : i(g) = sg\}, \quad B_t = t\{g \in \Gamma : j(g) = tg\}.$$

It is trivial to check that these sets are pairwise disjoint and we have the following paradoxical decomposition:

$$\Gamma = \bigcup_{s \in E} s^{-1} A_s = \bigcup_{t \in E} t^{-1} B_t,$$

which implies that Γ is not amenable.

The equivalence of ((iii)) and ((iv)) with ((i)) follows from the Lemma A.14 and Theorem A.15 □

Related open problems

We have discussed multiple examples of finitely generated simple amenable groups through the book. However, the following conjecture is still open.

CONJECTURE B.1. There exist a finitely presented simple amenable group.

The main candidate for this conjecture is Penrose tiling group. In [36], it was proved that the commutator of this group is simple and finitely generated. The main reason to believe that this group is amenable is because it admits extensively amenable actions. The finite presentation should be arranged using the fact that it is defined using a subshift of finite type. None of these statements have been worked through so far and have technical difficulties.

Similarly to Penrose tiling group one can define a group of polygon rearrangements. The amenability of it is also an open problem.

The following set of conjectures is naturally a next step of the development of discussed in Chapter 7.

CONJECTURE B.2. There exist a finitely presented group of intermediate growth. Is there a finitely presented amenable group that surjects onto a group of intermediate growth?

PROBLEM B.3. Does there exist amenable finitely generated Burnside groups of bounded periods?

PROBLEM B.4. Does there exist amenable finitely generated simple Burnside groups of bounded periods?

PROBLEM B.5. Is there a finitely presented simple group that is not 2-generated? Is there a 2-generated infinite simple amenable group?

The following questions were posed by Rostislav Grigorchuk.

PROBLEM B.6. Does there exists finitely generated amenable group with uniformly bounded periods? Does there exists finitely generated simple amenable group with uniformly bounded periods

The following problem were asked by Vitaliy Bergelson, see also [20] for more problems in amenability.

PROBLEM B.7. Is it true that any infinite amenable group contains an infinite abelian subgroup?

PROBLEM B.8 (Olshanskiy, Grigorchuk, Kravchenko). Does there exist finitely generated torsion free simple amenable group?

PROBLEM B.9 (Grigorchuk). A finitely presented group is either virtually nilpotent, or contains a free subsemigroup of order 2.

A group G is *supramenable* if for every action of G on X and any non-empty subset $E \subseteq X$ there is an invariant finitely additive measure normalized on E. It is known that the groups of subexponential growth are superamenable.

PROBLEM B.10 (Rosenblatt '74). Is there a supramenable group of exponential growth? Is the direct product of 2 supramenable groups also supramenable?

In a relation with what have been discussed about branch groups we have the following problem.

PROBLEM B.11. Is there a finitely presented branch group? Is there amenable finitely presented branch group?

A group G is *hereditary just-infinite* group if it is residually finite and such that every finite index subgroup of it is just-infinite. Hereditary just-infinite groups are closely related to groups acting on trees, it is natural to ask the following problem.

PROBLEM B.12. Is there an amenable hereditary just-infinite group that is not elementary amenable? Is there a finitely presented one?

The following conjecture of Grigorchuk would be interesting to answer in the framework of the Chapter 7.

CONJECTURE B.13. If the Følner function of a group is sub-exponential, then the group is virtually nilpotent.

Is this group amenable?

Here we list groups amenability of which is an open problem. All these groups are known to be not in the class of elementary amenable groups. The approach to attack amenability of some of these groups have been outlined in the Chapter 10, we also add additional explanations to some of the approaches.

PROBLEM B.14. Are contracting groups amenable? See definition of contracting groups in [**119**].

PROBLEM B.15. Are polynomial activity automata groups amenable?

PROBLEM B.16. Are the Hanoi tower groups H_n, $n \geq 4$ amenable?

Thompson's group F. Let F be the Thompson group F, i.e., the groups of piece-wise linear homeomorphisms of $[0, 1]$ with slopes in integer powers of 2 and with points of discontinuity of the derivative in the dyadic integers. The action of F on $X = \mathbb{Z}[\frac{1}{2}] \cap [0, 1]$ is transitive. Consider a semidirect product $F \ltimes \bigoplus_X \mathbb{Z}/2\mathbb{Z}$ and its action on $\bigoplus_X \mathbb{Z}/2\mathbb{Z}$ given by $(g, \omega)(\overline{\omega}) = g(\overline{\omega}) + \omega$.

THEOREM B.17. The Thomson group F is amenable if and only if its action on X is extensively amenable.

PROOF. Let A be the group of the integer powers of 2. Denote by g'_- and g'_+ left and right derivative of g. The following embedding of the Thompson group F into $F \ltimes \bigoplus_X A$ has trivial stabilizers when it acts on $\bigoplus_X A$:

$$g \mapsto (g, \{g'_-(x)/g'_+(x) : x \in X\})$$

Thus, the Lemma 5.5 (see also Example 5.24) implies the statement. $\square$

The cocycle, that we use, was also used by V. Kaimanovich to prove that the Thompson group F does not have Liouville property, [**91**].

CONJECTURE B.18 (Brin, Sapir). A subgroup of F is elementary amenable if and only if it does not contain a copy of F.

Interval exchange transformation group. We refer to the Chapter 6 for the definitions and partial solutions to the listed in this section problems. The following basic questions remain open.

CONJECTURE B.19 (Katok). Interval exchange transformation group contains the free group on two generators.

PROBLEM B.20 (de Cornulier). Is interval exchange transformation group amenable?

Topological full groups

As we saw in Chapter 6, the topological full group $[[T]]$ of Cantor minimal system is amenable. In [**105**], it was shown that if T is homeomorphism of linear complexity the $[[T]]$ is amenable. While linear complexity homeomorphisms can act minimally they don't always do so. It seems interesting to classify amenable systems $[[T]]$ in terms of dynamics of T, and ask the following.

QUESTION B.21. What are other the conditions on a homeomorphism T of the Cantor set so that the topological full group $[[T]]$ is amenable?

PROBLEM B.22. Are there any examples of a $\mathbb{Z}^2$-action on a Cantor set such that the commutator subgroup of the topological full group of this action is finitely presented and amenable?

PROBLEM B.23. Is non-amenability of a topological full group preserved under taking restrictions? To be more precise: let a non-amenable group G act on a Cantor space C minimally. Assume $G = [[G]]$. Let U be a clopen subset of the Cantor set C, and let G_U be the group of all homeomorphisms in G that keep U invariant and act as identity outside U. Is G_U non-amenable?

Path entropy. Let Γ be a group generated by a finite symmetric set S. Assume Γ acts on a set X faithfully. Define

$$H(n) = |\{(g_1, \ldots, g_n) \in S^n : \text{there exists } x \in X \text{ with property that all}$$
$$g_1 x, g_2 g_1 x, \ldots, g_n g_{n-1} .. g_1 x \text{ are all distinct }\}|$$

Then *the path entropy of the action* is defined to be

$$h(\Gamma, X) := \lim_{n \to \infty} \frac{\log[H(n)]}{n}.$$

CONJECTURE B.24. Let a finitely generated group Γ faithfully act on X. Assume in addition that the Schreier graph of this action has polynomial growth and $h(\Gamma, X) = 0$. Then Γ does not contain non-abelian free groups.

A weaker version of this conjecture also seems to be open:

CONJECTURE B.25. Let a finitely generated group Γ faithfully act on X with $h(\Gamma, X) = 0$. Then Γ does not contain non-abelian free groups.

We suspect that the weaker form has negative solution. Both conjectures imply that the interval exchange transformation group does not contain non-abelian free group. We recall that Katok conjectured that the interval exchange transformation group contains a non-abelian free group.

Growth of Følner sets. Let Γ be group generated by a finite symmetric set S with $e \in S$. Define for every natural number n the following constant, called Følner function:

$$\text{Føl}(n) = \inf(|E| : |SE\backslash E| \leq |E|/n)$$

Let T be a minimal homeomorphism of the Cantor space.

QUESTION B.26. What is the exact growth of the Følner function of $[[T]]$?

Let d be a natural number and $W(\mathbb{Z}^d)$ be the wobbling group of $\mathbb{Z}^d$.

PROBLEM B.27. Let $W(\mathbb{Z}^d)$ and the wobbling group of integers. Is the action of $W(\mathbb{Z}^d)$ on $\mathbb{Z}^d$ extensively amenable?

As we know from Theorem 5.10 and Theorem 5.12, that for $d \leq 2$ the action of $W(\mathbb{Z}^d)$ on $\mathbb{Z}^d$ is extensively amenable. Now let T_1 and T_2 be minimal homeomorphisms of the Cantor space $\mathbf{C}$. Consider the full topological group of the action of $\mathbb{Z}^2 = \langle T_1 \times Id, Id \times T_2 \rangle$ on $\mathbf{C} \times \mathbf{C}$.

QUESTION B.28. Is the full topological group of the action of $\mathbb{Z}^2$ described above amenable?

A more general question can be asked.

QUESTION B.29. Let $T_1, \ldots, T_d$ be minimal homeomorphisms of the Cantor space. Consider the action of $\mathbb{Z}^d$ on $\mathbf{C} \times \ldots \times \mathbf{C}$ by homeomorphisms $T_1 \times Id \times \ldots \times Id$, $Id \times T_2 \times \ldots \times Id$, $\ldots$, $\times Id \times \ldots \times T_d$. Is the full topological group $[[\mathbb{Z}^d]]$ of this action amenable? Does it contain the free group on two generators?

This question is motivated by the work of Matui, who showed that under the assumptions of the question above the commutator subgroup of $[[\mathbb{Z}^d]]$ is simple and finitely generated. Moreover, if $d_1 \neq d_2$, then $[[\mathbb{Z}^{d_1}]]'$ and $[[\mathbb{Z}^{d_2}]]'$ are non-isomorphic.

Recall that $\mathcal{P}_f(\mathbb{Z}^2) \rtimes W(\mathbb{Z}^2)$ is acting on $\mathcal{P}_f(\mathbb{Z}^2)$. Under assumptions of the Question B.28, one can still arrange $[[\mathbb{Z}^2]]$ to be a subgroup of $W(\mathbb{Z}^2)$. The difficulty arises when one embeds $[[\mathbb{Z}^2]]$ into

$$\mathcal{P}_f(\mathbb{Z}^2) \rtimes W(\mathbb{Z}^2).$$

Namely, it is not clear how to make a good enough embedding, so that the action of it on $\mathcal{P}_f(\mathbb{Z}^2)$ would have amenable stabilizers.

The question about existence of free non-abelian subgroups for different actions of $\mathbb{Z}^d$ is quite appealing. So far we don't know any direct proof that would imply that $[[T]]$ is free group free.

Bibliography

[1] S. I. Adyan, *Random walks on free periodic groups* (Russian), Izv. Akad. Nauk SSSR Ser. Mat. **46** (1982), no. 6, 1139–1149, 1343. MR682486

[2] S. V. Alešin, *Finite automata and the Burnside problem for periodic groups* (Russian), Mat. Zametki **11** (1972), 319–328. MR301107

[3] Gideon Amir and Bálint Virág, *Positive speed for high-degree automaton groups*, Groups Geom. Dyn. **8** (2014), no. 1, 23–38, DOI 10.4171/GGD/215. MR3209701

[4] Gideon Amir and Bálint Virág, *Speed exponents of random walks on groups*, Int. Math. Res. Not. IMRN **9** (2017), 2567–2598, DOI 10.1093/imrn/rnv378. MR3658209

[5] Gideon Amir, Omer Angel, and Bálint Virág, *Amenability of linear-activity automaton groups*, J. Eur. Math. Soc. (JEMS) **15** (2013), no. 3, 705–730, DOI 10.4171/JEMS/373. MR3085088

[6] S. Banach, *Théorie des opérations linéaires*, Instytut Matematyczny Polskiej Akademi Nauk, 1932.

[7] Stefan Banach, *Théorie des opérations linéaires* (French), Chelsea Publishing Co., New York, 1955. MR0071726

[8] S. Banach, *Sur le probléme de la mesure*, Fund. Math. 4, 7–33 (1923).

[9] S. Banach and A. Tarski, *Sur la décomposition des ensembles de points en parties respectivement congruents*, Fund. Math., 14 (1929), 127–131.

[10] Laurent Bartholdi and Anna Erschler, *Growth of permutational extensions*, Invent. Math. **189** (2012), no. 2, 431–455, DOI 10.1007/s00222-011-0368-x. MR2947548

[11] Laurent Bartholdi and Anna Erschler, *Poisson-Furstenberg boundary and growth of groups*, Probab. Theory Related Fields **168** (2017), no. 1-2, 347–372, DOI 10.1007/s00440-016-0712-6. MR3651055

[12] Laurent Bartholdi, Vadim A. Kaimanovich, and Volodymyr V. Nekrashevych, *On amenability of automata groups*, Duke Math. J. **154** (2010), no. 3, 575–598, DOI 10.1215/00127094-2010-046. MR2730578

[13] Laurent Bartholdi and Bálint Virág, *Amenability via random walks*, Duke Math. J. **130** (2005), no. 1, 39–56, DOI 10.1215/S0012-7094-05-13012-5. MR2176547

[14] Laurent Bartholdi, Rostislav Grigorchuk, and Volodymyr Nekrashevych, *From fractal groups to fractal sets*, Fractals in Graz 2001, Trends Math., Birkhäuser, Basel, 2003, pp. 25–118. MR2091700

[15] Bachir Bekka, Pierre de la Harpe, and Alain Valette, *Kazhdan's property (T)*, New Mathematical Monographs, vol. 11, Cambridge University Press, Cambridge, 2008, DOI 10.1017/CBO9780511542749. MR2415834

[16] G. Bell and A. Dranishnikov, *Asymptotic dimension*, Topology Appl. **155** (2008), no. 12, 1265–1296, DOI 10.1016/j.topol.2008.02.011. MR2423966

[17] Itai Benjamini and Christopher Hoffman, *ω-periodic graphs*, Electron. J. Combin. **12** (2005), Research Paper 46, 12. MR2176522

[18] I. Benjamini and O. Schramm, *Every graph with a positive Cheeger constant contains a tree with a positive Cheeger constant*, Geom. Funct. Anal. **7** (1997), no. 3, 403–419, DOI 10.1007/PL00001625. MR1466332

[19] Jean Bellissard, Antoine Julien, and Jean Savinien, *Tiling groupoids and Bratteli diagrams*, Ann. Henri Poincaré **11** (2010), no. 1-2, 69–99, DOI 10.1007/s00023-010-0034-7. MR2658985

[20] V. Bergelson, *Questions on amenability*, L'Enseignement Mathématique 2.54 (2008): 28–30.

[21] S. Bezuglyi and K. Medynets, *Full groups, flip conjugacy, and orbit equivalence of Cantor minimal systems*, Colloq. Math. **110** (2008), no. 2, 409–429, DOI 10.4064/cm110-2-6. MR2353913

[22] Bruce Blackadar, *K-theory for operator algebras*, 2nd ed., Mathematical Sciences Research Institute Publications, vol. 5, Cambridge University Press, Cambridge, 1998. MR1656031

[23] C. Bleak and K. Juschenko, *Ideal structure of the C*-algebra of Thompson group T*, arXiv preprint arXiv:1409.8099, 2014.

[24] N. Bogolyubov, *On some ergodic properties of continuous groups of transformations*, 1939. Published first in Ukrainian (in Sci- entific Notes of Kiev State University of T.G. Shevchenko, Physics - Mathematics zbirnyk, 4, N. 5 (1939), 45–52), and then in Russian (In "Selected works", Vol. 1, Kiev 1969, pp. 561–569).

[25] Nicolas Kryloff and Nicolas Bogoliouboff, *La théorie générale de la mesure dans son application à l'étude des systèmes dynamiques de la mécanique non linéaire* (French), Ann. of Math. (2) **38** (1937), no. 1, 65–113, DOI 10.2307/1968511. MR1503326

[26] Ievgen Bondarenko, *Groups generated by bounded automata and their Schreier graphs*, ProQuest LLC, Ann Arbor, MI, 2007. Thesis (Ph.D.)–Texas A&M University. MR2711289

[27] Ievgen V. Bondarenko, *Finite generation of iterated wreath products*, Arch. Math. (Basel) **95** (2010), no. 4, 301–308, DOI 10.1007/s00013-010-0169-2. MR2727305

[28] Ievgen Bondarenko, Tullio Ceccherini-Silberstein, Alfredo Donno, and Volodymyr Nekrashevych, *On a family of Schreier graphs of intermediate growth associated with a self-similar group*, European J. Combin. **33** (2012), no. 7, 1408–1421, DOI 10.1016/j.ejc.2012.03.006. MR2923458

[29] Ievgen V. Bondarenko and Dmytro M. Savchuk, *On Sushchansky p-groups*, Algebra Discrete Math. **2** (2007), 22–42. MR2364061

[30] Mike Boyle and Jun Tomiyama, *Bounded topological orbit equivalence and C*-algebras*, J. Math. Soc. Japan **50** (1998), no. 2, 317–329, DOI 10.2969/jmsj/05020317. MR1613140

[31] Ola Bratteli, *Inductive limits of finite dimensional C*-algebras*, Trans. Amer. Math. Soc. **171** (1972), 195–234, DOI 10.2307/1996380. MR312282

[32] Jérémie Brieussel, *Amenability and non-uniform growth of some directed automorphism groups of a rooted tree*, Math. Z. **263** (2009), no. 2, 265–293, DOI 10.1007/s00209-008-0417-3. MR2534118

[33] Jérémie Brieussel, *Folner sets of alternate directed groups* (English, with English and French summaries), Ann. Inst. Fourier (Grenoble) **64** (2014), no. 3, 1109–1130. MR3330165

[34] Tullio Ceccherini-Silberstein and Michel Coornaert, *Cellular automata and groups*, Computational complexity. Vols. 1–6, Springer, New York, 2012, pp. 336–349, DOI 10.1007/978-1-4614-1800-9_23. MR3074498

[35] P. de lya Arp, R. I. Grigorchuk, and T. Chekerini-Sil′berstaĭn, *Amenability and paradoxical decompositions for pseudogroups and discrete metric spaces* (Russian, with Russian summary), Tr. Mat. Inst. Steklova **224** (1999), no. Algebra. Topol. Differ. Uravn. i ikh Prilozh., 68–111; English transl., Proc. Steklov Inst. Math. **1(224)** (1999), 57–97. MR1721355

[36] Maksym Chornyi, Kate Juschenko, and Volodymyr Nekrashevych, *On topological full groups of $\mathbb{Z}^d$-actions*, Groups Geom. Dyn. **14** (2020), no. 1, 61–79, DOI 10.4171/ggd/534. MR4077654

[37] Ching Chou, *Elementary amenable groups*, Illinois J. Math. **24** (1980), no. 3, 396–407. MR573475

[38] A. Connes, *Classification of injective factors. Cases II_1, II_∞, III_λ, $\lambda \neq 1$*, Ann. of Math. (2) **104** (1976), no. 1, 73–115, DOI 10.2307/1971057. MR454659

[39] A. Connes, J. Feldman, and B. Weiss, *An amenable equivalence relation is generated by a single transformation*, Ergodic Theory Dynam. Systems **1** (1981), no. 4, 431–450 (1982), DOI 10.1017/s014338570000136x. MR662736

[40] I. P. Cornfeld, S. V. Fomin, and Ya. G. Sinaĭ, *Ergodic theory*, Grundlehren der mathematischen Wissenschaften [Fundamental Principles of Mathematical Sciences], vol. 245, Springer-Verlag, New York, 1982. Translated from the Russian by A. B. Sosinskiĭ, DOI 10.1007/978-1-4615-6927-5. MR832433

[41] Yves de Cornulier, *Groupes pleins-topologiques (d'après Matui, Juschenko, Monod, ...)* (French, with French summary), Astérisque **361** (2014), Exp. No. 1064, viii, 183–223. MR3289281

[42] Yves Cornulier and Pierre de la Harpe, *Metric geometry of locally compact groups*, EMS Tracts in Mathematics, vol. 25, European Mathematical Society (EMS), Zürich, 2016. Winner of the 2016 EMS Monograph Award, DOI 10.4171/166. MR3561300

[43] François Dahmani, Koji Fujiwara, and Vincent Guirardel, *Free groups of interval exchange transformations are rare*, Groups Geom. Dyn. **7** (2013), no. 4, 883–910, DOI 10.4171/GGD/209. MR3134029

[44] Mahlon M. Day, *Amenable semigroups*, Illinois J. Math. **1** (1957), 509–544. MR92128

[45] Mahlon M. Day, *Semigroups and amenability*, Semigroups (Proc. Sympos., Wayne State Univ., Detroit, Mich., 1968), Academic Press, New York, 1969, pp. 5–53. MR0265502

[46] W. A. Deuber, M. Simonovits, and V. T. Sós, *A note on paradoxical metric spaces*, Studia Sci. Math. Hungar. **30** (1995), no. 1-2, 17–23. MR1341564

[47] Jacques Dixmier, *Les C*-algèbres et leurs représentations* (French), Les Grands Classiques Gauthier-Villars. [Gauthier-Villars Great Classics], Éditions Jacques Gabay, Paris, 1996. Reprint of the second (1969) edition. MR1452364

[48] Jacques Dixmier, *Les algèbres d'opérateurs dans l'espace hilbertien (Algèbres de von Neumann)* (French), Cahiers Scientifiques, Fasc. XXV, Gauthier-Villars, Paris, 1957. MR0094722

[49] Eric K. van Douwen, *Measures invariant under actions of F_2*, Topology Appl. **34** (1990), no. 1, 53–68, DOI 10.1016/0166-8641(90)90089-K. MR1035460

[50] David Damanik and Daniel Lenz, *Substitution dynamical systems: characterization of linear repetitivity and applications*, J. Math. Anal. Appl. **321** (2006), no. 2, 766–780, DOI 10.1016/j.jmaa.2005.09.004. MR2241154

[51] Nelson Dunford and Jacob T. Schwartz, *Linear Operators. I. General Theory*, Pure and Applied Mathematics, Vol. 7, Interscience Publishers, Inc., New York; Interscience Publishers Ltd., London, 1958. With the assistance of W. G. Bade and R. G. Bartle. MR0117523

[52] Gábor Elek and Nicolas Monod, *On the topological full group of a minimal Cantor $\mathbf{Z}^2$-system*, Proc. Amer. Math. Soc. **141** (2013), no. 10, 3549–3552, DOI 10.1090/S0002-9939-2013-11654-0. MR3080176

[53] R. Exel and J. Renault, *AF-algebras and the tail-equivalence relation on Bratteli diagrams*, Proc. Amer. Math. Soc. **134** (2006), no. 1, 193–206, DOI 10.1090/S0002-9939-05-08129-3. MR2170559

[54] Mikhail Ershov, *Golod-Shafarevich groups with property (T) and Kac-Moody groups*, Duke Math. J. **145** (2008), no. 2, 309–339, DOI 10.1215/00127094-2008-053. MR2449949

[55] Mikhail Ershov, *Golod-Shafarevich groups: a survey*, Internat. J. Algebra Comput. **22** (2012), no. 5, 1230001, 68, DOI 10.1142/S0218196712300010. MR2949205

[56] Mikhail Ershov, Gili Golan, and Mark Sapir, *The Tarski numbers of groups*, Adv. Math. **284** (2015), 21–53, DOI 10.1016/j.aim.2015.07.010. MR3391070

[57] Jacob Feldman and Calvin C. Moore, *Ergodic equivalence relations, cohomology, and von Neumann algebras. I*, Trans. Amer. Math. Soc. **234** (1977), no. 2, 289–324, DOI 10.2307/1997924. MR578656

[58] Elisabeth Fink, *A finitely generated branch group of exponential growth without free subgroups*, J. Algebra **397** (2014), 625–642, DOI 10.1016/j.jalgebra.2013.06.030. MR3119242

[59] T. Gelander, *Lecture notes: analytic group theory*, https://www.weizmann.ac.il/math/Gelander/sites/math.Gelander/files/uploads/AGT.pdf.

[60] Étienne Ghys and Yves Carrière, *Relations d'équivalence moyennables sur les groupes de Lie* (French, with English summary), C. R. Acad. Sci. Paris Sér. I Math. **300** (1985), no. 19, 677–680. MR802650

[61] Thierry Giordano, Ian F. Putnam, and Christian F. Skau, *Full groups of Cantor minimal systems*, Israel J. Math. **111** (1999), 285–320, DOI 10.1007/BF02810689. MR1710743

[62] Eli Glasner and Benjamin Weiss, *Weak orbit equivalence of Cantor minimal systems*, Internat. J. Math. **6** (1995), no. 4, 559–579, DOI 10.1142/S0129167X95000213. MR1339645

[63] E. S. Golod and I. R. Šafarevič, *On the class field tower* (Russian), Izv. Akad. Nauk SSSR Ser. Mat. **28** (1964), 261–272. MR0161852

[64] F. P. Greenleaf, *Amenable actions of locally compact groups*, J. Functional Analysis **4** (1969), 295–315, DOI 10.1016/0022-1236(69)90016-0. MR0246999

[65] R. I. Grigorchuk, V. V. Nekrashevich, and V. I. Sushchanskiĭ, *Automata, dynamical systems, and groups* (Russian, with Russian summary), Tr. Mat. Inst. Steklova **231** (2000), no. Din. Sist., Avtom. i Beskon. Gruppy, 134–214; English transl., Proc. Steklov Inst. Math. **4(231)** (2000), 128–203. MR1841755

[66] R. I. Grigorčuk, *On Burnside's problem on periodic groups* (Russian), Funktsional. Anal. i Prilozhen. **14** (1980), no. 1, 53–54. MR565099

[67] R. I. Grigorchuk, *Symmetrical random walks on discrete groups*, Multicomponent random systems, Adv. Probab. Related Topics, vol. 6, Dekker, New York, 1980, pp. 285–325. MR599539

[68] R. Grigorchuk, *Milnor's problem on the growth of groups*, Sov. Math., Dokl, 28 (1983), 23–26.

[69] R. I. Grigorchuk, *Degrees of growth of finitely generated groups and the theory of invariant means* (Russian), Izv. Akad. Nauk SSSR Ser. Mat. **48** (1984), no. 5, 939–985. MR764305

[70] R. I. Grigorchuk, *An example of a finitely presented amenable group that does not belong to the class EG* (Russian, with Russian summary), Mat. Sb. **189** (1998), no. 1, 79–100, DOI 10.1070/SM1998v189n01ABEH000293; English transl., Sb. Math. **189** (1998), no. 1-2, 75–95. MR1616436

[71] R. I. Grigorchuk, *Superamenability and the occurrence problem of free semigroups* (Russian), Funktsional. Anal. i Prilozhen. **21** (1987), no. 1, 74–75. MR888020

[72] Rostislav Grigorchuk and Pierre de la Harpe, *Amenability and ergodic properties of topological groups: from Bogolyubov onwards*, Groups, graphs and random walks, London Math. Soc. Lecture Note Ser., vol. 436, Cambridge Univ. Press, Cambridge, 2017, pp. 215–249. MR3644011

[73] R. Grigorchuk and K. Medynets, *Topological full groups are locally embeddable into finite groups*, Preprint, `arXiv:1105.0719v3`, 2012.

[74] Rostislav I. Grigorchuk and Andrzej Żuk, *On a torsion-free weakly branch group defined by a three state automaton*, Internat. J. Algebra Comput. **12** (2002), no. 1-2, 223–246, DOI 10.1142/S0218196702001000. International Conference on Geometric and Combinatorial Methods in Group Theory and Semigroup Theory (Lincoln, NE, 2000). MR1902367

[75] M. Gromov, *Asymptotic invariants of infinite groups*, Geometric group theory, Vol. 2 (Sussex, 1991), London Math. Soc. Lecture Note Ser., vol. 182, Cambridge Univ. Press, Cambridge, 1993, pp. 1–295. MR1253544

[76] M. Gromov, *Hyperbolic groups*, Essays in group theory, Math. Sci. Res. Inst. Publ., vol. 8, Springer, New York, 1987, pp. 75–263, DOI 10.1007/978-1-4613-9586-7_3. MR919829

[77] Mikhael Gromov, *Groups of polynomial growth and expanding maps*, Inst. Hautes Études Sci. Publ. Math. **53** (1981), 53–73. MR623534

[78] Branko Grünbaum and G. C. Shephard, *Tilings and patterns*, W. H. Freeman and Company, New York, 1987. MR857454

[79] Pierre de la Harpe, *Topics in geometric group theory*, Chicago Lectures in Mathematics, University of Chicago Press, Chicago, IL, 2000. MR1786869

[80] F. Hausdorff, *Bemerkung über den Inhalt von Punktmengen* (German), Math. Ann. **75** (1914), no. 3, 428–433, DOI 10.1007/BF01563735. MR1511802

[81] Richard H. Herman, Ian F. Putnam, and Christian F. Skau, *Ordered Bratteli diagrams, dimension groups and topological dynamics*, Internat. J. Math. **3** (1992), no. 6, 827–864, DOI 10.1142/S0129167X92000382. MR1194074

[82] Yutaka Ishii, *Hyperbolic polynomial diffeomorphisms of $\mathbb{C}^2$. I. A non-planar map*, Adv. Math. **218** (2008), no. 2, 417–464, DOI 10.1016/j.aim.2007.11.025. MR2407941

[83] Yutaka Ishii, *Hyperbolic polynomial diffeomorphisms of $\mathbb{C}^2$. II. Hubbard trees*, Adv. Math. **220** (2009), no. 4, 985–1022, DOI 10.1016/j.aim.2008.09.015. MR2483714

[84] Yutaka Ishii, *Hyperbolic polynomial diffeomorphisms of $\mathbb{C}^2$. III: Iterated monodromy groups*, Adv. Math. **255** (2014), 242–304, DOI 10.1016/j.aim.2013.12.031. MR3167483

[85] K. Juschenko, *Non-elementary amenable subgroups of automata groups*, arXiv preprint `arXiv:1504.00610`, 2015.

[86] Kate Juschenko and Nicolas Monod, *Cantor systems, piecewise translations and simple amenable groups*, Ann. of Math. (2) **178** (2013), no. 2, 775–787, DOI 10.4007/annals.2013.178.2.7. MR3071509

[87] Kate Juschenko and Tatiana Nagnibeda, *Small spectral radius and percolation constants on non-amenable Cayley graphs*, Proc. Amer. Math. Soc. **143** (2015), no. 4, 1449–1458, DOI 10.1090/S0002-9939-2014-12578-0. MR3314060

[88] Kate Juschenko, Volodymyr Nekrashevych, and Mikael de la Salle, *Extensions of amenable groups by recurrent groupoids*, Invent. Math. **206** (2016), no. 3, 837–867, DOI 10.1007/s00222-016-0664-6. MR3573974

[89] Kate Juschenko and Mikael de la Salle, *Invariant means for the wobbling group*, Bull. Belg. Math. Soc. Simon Stevin **22** (2015), no. 2, 281–290. MR3351042

[90] Kate Juschenko, Nicolás Matte Bon, Nicolas Monod, and Mikael de la Salle, *Extensive amenability and an application to interval exchanges*, Ergodic Theory Dynam. Systems **38** (2018), no. 1, 195–219, DOI 10.1017/etds.2016.32. MR3742543

[91] V. Kaimanovich, *Boundary behaviour of Thompson's group*, Preprint.

[92] V. A. Kaĭmanovich and A. M. Vershik, *Random walks on discrete groups: boundary and entropy*, Ann. Probab. **11** (1983), no. 3, 457–490. MR704539

[93] Martin Kassabov and Igor Pak, *Groups of oscillating intermediate growth*, Ann. of Math. (2) **177** (2013), no. 3, 1113–1145, DOI 10.4007/annals.2013.177.3.7. MR3034295

[94] Anatole Katok and Boris Hasselblatt, *Introduction to the modern theory of dynamical systems*, Encyclopedia of Mathematics and its Applications, vol. 54, Cambridge University Press, Cambridge, 1995. With a supplementary chapter by Katok and Leonardo Mendoza, DOI 10.1017/CBO9780511809187. MR1326374

[95] A. B. Katok and A. M. Stepin, *Approximations in ergodic theory* (Russian), Uspehi Mat. Nauk **22** (1967), no. 5 (137), 81–106. MR0219697

[96] Michael Keane, *Interval exchange transformations*, Math. Z. **141** (1975), 25–31, DOI 10.1007/BF01236981. MR357739

[97] Harry Kesten, *Symmetric random walks on groups*, Trans. Amer. Math. Soc. **92** (1959), 336–354, DOI 10.2307/1993160. MR109367

[98] Y. Lavrenyuk and V. Nekrashevych, *On classification of inductive limits of direct products of alternating groups*, J. Lond. Math. Soc. (2) **75** (2007), no. 1, 146–162, DOI 10.1112/jlms/jdl009. MR2302735

[99] M. Laczkovich, *Equidecomposability and discrepancy; a solution of Tarski's circle-squaring problem*, J. Reine Angew. Math. **404** (1990), 77–117, DOI 10.1515/crll.1990.404.77. MR1037431

[100] Henri Leon Lebesgue, *Leçons sur l'intégration et la recherche des fonctions primitives professées au Collège de France* (French), Cambridge Library Collection, Cambridge University Press, Cambridge, 2009. Reprint of the 1904 original, DOI 10.1017/CBO9780511701825. MR2857993

[101] Felix Leinen and Orazio Puglisi, *Some results concerning simple locally finite groups of 1-type*, J. Algebra **287** (2005), no. 1, 32–51, DOI 10.1016/j.jalgebra.2004.12.021. MR2134257

[102] Yash Lodha and Justin Tatch Moore, *A nonamenable finitely presented group of piecewise projective homeomorphisms*, Groups Geom. Dyn. **10** (2016), no. 1, 177–200, DOI 10.4171/GGD/347. MR3460335

[103] Alexander Lubotzky, *Group presentation, p-adic analytic groups and lattices in* $SL_2(\mathbf{C})$, Ann. of Math. (2) **118** (1983), no. 1, 115–130, DOI 10.2307/2006956. MR707163

[104] Russell Lyons and Yuval Peres, *Probability on trees and networks*, Cambridge Series in Statistical and Probabilistic Mathematics, vol. 42, Cambridge University Press, New York, 2016, DOI 10.1017/9781316672815. MR3616205

[105] Nicolás Matte Bon, *Subshifts with slow complexity and simple groups with the Liouville property*, Geom. Funct. Anal. **24** (2014), no. 5, 1637–1659, DOI 10.1007/s00039-014-0293-4. MR3261637

[106] Hiroki Matui, *Some remarks on topological full groups of Cantor minimal systems*, Internat. J. Math. **17** (2006), no. 2, 231–251, DOI 10.1142/S0129167X06003448. MR2205435

[107] Konstantin Medynets, *Cantor aperiodic systems and Bratteli diagrams* (English, with English and French summaries), C. R. Math. Acad. Sci. Paris **342** (2006), no. 1, 43–46, DOI 10.1016/j.crma.2005.10.024. MR2193394

[108] Yu. I. Merzlyakov, *Infinite finitely generated periodic groups* (Russian), Dokl. Akad. Nauk SSSR **268** (1983), no. 4, 803–805. MR693210

[109] John Milnor, *Pasting together Julia sets: a worked out example of mating*, Experiment. Math. **13** (2004), no. 1, 55–92. MR2065568

[110] J. Milnor, *A note on curvature and fundamental group*, J. Differential Geometry **2** (1968), 1–7. MR232311

[111] John Milnor, *Growth of finitely generated solvable groups*, J. Differential Geometry **2** (1968), 447–449. MR244899

[112] MILNOR, J., *Problem 5603*, Amer. Math. Monthly, 75 (1968), 685–686.

[113] Bojan Mohar, *Isoperimetric inequalities, growth, and the spectrum of graphs*, Linear Algebra Appl. **103** (1988), 119–131, DOI 10.1016/0024-3795(88)90224-8. MR943998

[114] Nicolas Monod, *Groups of piecewise projective homeomorphisms*, Proc. Natl. Acad. Sci. USA **110** (2013), no. 12, 4524–4527, DOI 10.1073/pnas.1218426110. MR3047655

[115] F. J. Murray and J. Von Neumann, *On rings of operators*, Ann. of Math. (2) **37** (1936), no. 1, 116–229, DOI 10.2307/1968693. MR1503275

[116] I. Namioka, *Følner's conditions for amenable semi-groups*, Math. Scand. **15** (1964), 18–28, DOI 10.7146/math.scand.a-10723. MR180832

[117] Volodymyr Nekrashevych, *Palindromic subshifts and simple periodic groups of intermediate growth*, Ann. of Math. (2) **187** (2018), no. 3, 667–719, DOI 10.4007/annals.2018.187.3.2. MR3779956

[118] V. V. Nekrashevych, *Self-similar inverse semigroups and groupoids*, Ukrainian Mathematics Congress—2001 (Ukrainian), Natsīonal. Akad. Nauk Ukraïni, Īnst. Mat., Kiev, 2002, pp. 176–192. MR2228863

[119] Volodymyr Nekrashevych, *Self-similar groups*, Mathematical Surveys and Monographs, vol. 117, American Mathematical Society, Providence, RI, 2005, DOI 10.1090/surv/117. MR2162164

[120] Volodymyr Nekrashevych, *Self-similar inverse semigroups and Smale spaces*, Internat. J. Algebra Comput. **16** (2006), no. 5, 849–874, DOI 10.1142/S0218196706003153. MR2274718

[121] Volodymyr Nekrashevych, *A minimal Cantor set in the space of 3-generated groups*, Geom. Dedicata **124** (2007), 153–190, DOI 10.1007/s10711-006-9118-4. MR2318543

[122] Volodymyr Nekrashevych, *Symbolic dynamics and self-similar groups*, Holomorphic dynamics and renormalization, Fields Inst. Commun., vol. 53, Amer. Math. Soc., Providence, RI, 2008, pp. 25–73. MR2477417

[123] Volodymyr Nekrashevych, *Combinatorics of polynomial iterations*, Complex dynamics, A K Peters, Wellesley, MA, 2009, pp. 169–214, DOI 10.1201/b10617-5. MR2508257

[124] Volodymyr Nekrashevych, *Free subgroups in groups acting on rooted trees*, Groups Geom. Dyn. **4** (2010), no. 4, 847–862, DOI 10.4171/GGD/110. MR2727668

[125] Peter M. Neumann, *Some questions of Edjvet and Pride about infinite groups*, Illinois J. Math. **30** (1986), no. 2, 301–316. MR840129

[126] J. von Neumann, *Zur allgemeinen Theorie des Masses*, Fund. Math., vol 13 (1929), 73–116.

[127] C. St. J. A. Nash-Williams, *Random walk and electric currents in networks*, Proc. Cambridge Philos. Soc. **55** (1959), 181–194, DOI 10.1017/s0305004100033879. MR124932

[128] Ricardo Antonio Oliva, *On the combinatorics of external rays in the dynamics of the complex Henon map*, ProQuest LLC, Ann Arbor, MI, 1998. Thesis (Ph.D.)–Cornell University. MR2697417

[129] A. Ju. Olʹšanskiĭ, *On the question of the existence of an invariant mean on a group* (Russian), Uspekhi Mat. Nauk **35** (1980), no. 4(214), 199–200. MR586204

[130] Alexander Yu. Olʹshanskii and Mark V. Sapir, *Non-amenable finitely presented torsion-by-cyclic groups*, Publ. Math. Inst. Hautes Études Sci. **96** (2002), 43–169 (2003). MR1985031

[131] D. V. Osin, *Elementary classes of groups* (Russian, with Russian summary), Mat. Zametki **72** (2002), no. 1, 84–93, DOI 10.1023/A:1019869105364; English transl., Math. Notes **72** (2002), no. 1-2, 75–82. MR1942584

[132] Denis V. Osin, L^2-*Betti numbers and non-unitarizable groups without free subgroups*, Int. Math. Res. Not. IMRN **22** (2009), 4220–4231, DOI 10.1093/imrn/rnp085. MR2552302

[133] Alan L. T. Paterson, *Amenability*, Mathematical Surveys and Monographs, vol. 29, American Mathematical Society, Providence, RI, 1988, DOI 10.1090/surv/029. MR961261

[134] Jean-Paul Pier, *Amenable locally compact groups*, Pure and Applied Mathematics (New York), John Wiley & Sons, Inc., New York, 1984. A Wiley-Interscience Publication. MR767264

[135] A. Rejali and A. Yousofzadeh, *Configuration of groups and paradoxical decompositions*, Bull. Belg. Math. Soc. Simon Stevin **18** (2011), no. 1, 157–172. MR2809910

[136] Joseph Max Rosenblatt, *A generalization of Følner's condition*, Math. Scand. **33** (1973), 153–170, DOI 10.7146/math.scand.a-11481. MR333068

[137] Walter Rudin, *Functional analysis*, McGraw-Hill Series in Higher Mathematics, McGraw-Hill Book Co., New York-Düsseldorf-Johannesburg, 1973. MR0365062

[138] Volker Runde, *Lectures on amenability*, Lecture Notes in Mathematics, vol. 1774, Springer-Verlag, Berlin, 2002, DOI 10.1007/b82937. MR1874893

[139] Shôichirô Sakai, C^*-*algebras and W^*-algebras*, Ergebnisse der Mathematik und ihrer Grenzgebiete, Band 60, Springer-Verlag, New York-Heidelberg, 1971. MR0442701

[140] Jan-Christoph Schlage-Puchta, *A p-group with positive rank gradient*, J. Group Theory **15** (2012), no. 2, 261–270, DOI 10.1515/jgt.2011.101. MR2900227

[141] Dan Segal, *The finite images of finitely generated groups*, Proc. London Math. Soc. (3) **82** (2001), no. 3, 597–613, DOI 10.1112/plms/82.3.597. MR1816690

[142] Said Sidki, *Automorphisms of one-rooted trees: growth, circuit structure, and acyclicity*, J. Math. Sci. (New York) **100** (2000), no. 1, 1925–1943, DOI 10.1007/BF02677504. Algebra, 12. MR1774362

[143] Said Sidki, *Finite automata of polynomial growth do not generate a free group*, Geom. Dedicata **108** (2004), 193–204, DOI 10.1007/s10711-004-2368-0. MR2112674

[144] Otto Schreier, *Die Untergruppen der freien Gruppen* (German), Abh. Math. Sem. Univ. Hamburg **5** (1927), no. 1, 161–183, DOI 10.1007/BF02952517. MR3069472

[145] V. Sushchansky, *Periodic permutation p-groups and the unrestricted Burnside problem*, DAN SSSR., 247(3):557–562, 1979 (Russian).

[146] S. Świerczkowski, *On a free group of rotations of the Euclidean space*, Nederl. Akad. Wetensch. Proc. Ser. A 61 = Indag. Math. **20** (1958), 376–378. MR0096732

[147] A. Tarski, *Algebraische Fassung de Massproblems*, Fund. Math. 31 (1938), 47–66.

[148] Masamichi Takesaki, *Theory of operator algebras. I*, Springer-Verlag, New York-Heidelberg, 1979. MR548728

[149] M. Takesaki, *Theory of operator algebras. II*, Encyclopaedia of Mathematical Sciences, vol. 125, Springer-Verlag, Berlin, 2003. Operator Algebras and Non-commutative Geometry, 6, DOI 10.1007/978-3-662-10451-4. MR1943006

[150] M. Takesaki, *Theory of operator algebras. III*, Encyclopaedia of Mathematical Sciences, vol. 127, Springer-Verlag, Berlin, 2003. Operator Algebras and Non-commutative Geometry, 8, DOI 10.1007/978-3-662-10453-8. MR1943007

[151] Mikhael Gromov, *Groups of polynomial growth and expanding maps*, Inst. Hautes Études Sci. Publ. Math. **53** (1981), 53–73. MR623534

[152] Marcelo Viana, *Ergodic theory of interval exchange maps*, Rev. Mat. Complut. **19** (2006), no. 1, 7–100, DOI 10.5209/rev_REMA.2006.v19.n1.16621. MR2219821

[153] G. Vitali, *Sul problema della misura dei gruppi di punti di una retta*, Bologna, Tip. Camberini e Parmeggiani (1905).

[154] Stan Wagon, *The Banach-Tarski paradox*, Cambridge University Press, Cambridge, 1993. With a foreword by Jan Mycielski; Corrected reprint of the 1985 original. MR1251963

[155] Wolfgang Woess, *Random walks on infinite graphs and groups*, Cambridge Tracts in Mathematics, vol. 138, Cambridge University Press, Cambridge, 2000, DOI 10.1017/CBO9780511470967. MR1743100

[156] Joseph A. Wolf, *Growth of finitely generated solvable groups and curvature of Riemannian manifolds*, J. Differential Geometry **2** (1968), 421–446. MR248688

[157] Adam Woryna, *The rank and generating set for iterated wreath products of cyclic groups*, Comm. Algebra **39** (2011), no. 7, 2622–2631, DOI 10.1080/00927872.2010.544697. MR2821737

[158] Robert J. Zimmer, *Ergodic theory and semisimple groups*, Monographs in Mathematics, vol. 81, Birkhäuser Verlag, Basel, 1984, DOI 10.1007/978-1-4684-9488-4. MR776417

Subject Index

action on rooted trees, 33
adic transformation, 122
almost invariant vector, 137
amenable action, 17
amenable group, 2, 6, 12, 13
aperiodic homeomorphism, 45

Banach-Schröder-Bernstein, 11
Banach-Tarski paradox, 5
Banah-Tarski paradox, 10
Bartholdi-Erschler group, 33
barycenter of a measure, 18
bounded type (automorphism), 34
bounded type (homeomorphism),
    121
bounded type automata, 126
Boyle's flip conjugation theorem, 57
branch group, 39
Bratteli diagrams, 121
Bratteli-Vershik transformation, 122

Cantor dynamical system, 42
Chou-Milnor-Wolf's dichotomy, 3
construction rank, 27
contracting group, 152
cylinder sets, 52

Day's fixed point theorem, 143
dichotomy of growth, 29
dynamical system of a rotation, 58

elementary amenable group, 25
elementary classes of groups, 28
elementary operation, 25
equidecomposibility, 9
extensive amenability, 63, 64

Følner's condition, 13
Fibonacci tiling, 123

finitary depth, 34, 126
finite state, 127
finite state (automorphism), 34
flip conjugate, 57

germs, 118
Giordano-Putnam-Skau theorem, 53
Glasner-Weiss theorem, 46
Golod-Shafarevich's group, 3
Grasshopper's criteria, 148
Grigorchuk group, 3
Grigorchuk's group, 36
Gromov's doubling condition, 148
group of germs, 118
groupoid, 117
groupoid of germs, 118
growth function, 26

Hall's matching lemma, 145
Hausdorff paradox, 5, 8
hereditary just infinite, 152
homogeneous sequence, 43
Hulanicki's criteria, 141

interated monodromy groups, 128
intermediate growth, 3, 26, 32
interval exchange transformation, 85
inverted orbit of random walk, 77
isotropy group, 118

Kakutani-Rokhlin partition, 44
Kakutani-Rokhlin refinement, 44
Kassabov-Pak group, 33
Kesten's criteron, 139
Krylov-Bogolyubov theorem, 46

lamplighter, 63
Lebesgue's conjecture, 1

meßbar group, 6

Notation Index

SELECTED PUBLISHED TITLES IN THIS SERIES

For a complete list of titles in this series, visit the
AMS Bookstore at **www.ams.org/bookstore/survseries/**.